KU-337-102

The Family Quiz Book

THIS IS A CARLTON BOOK

Text and design copyright © Carlton Books Limited 1999
This Edition published 1999 by Carlton Books Limited

All rights reserved.

This book is sold subject to the condition that is shall not,
by way of trade or otherwise, be lent, resold, hired out or
otherwise circulated without the publisher's prior written
consent in any form of cover or binding other than that in
which it is published and without a similar condition,
including this condition, being imposed upon the subse-
quent purchaser.

ISBN 1 85868 843 4

A CIP Catalogue for this book is available from the British
Library

Executive Editor: Tim Dedopulos
Editorial Assistant: Liam Wickham
Senior Art Editor: Tim Brown
Design: Jessica Hughes
Production: Garry Lewis

Printed and bound in England

The Family QUIZ Book

CARLTON

CONTENTS

Quiz 1 | History

FOR ANSWERS SEE QUIZ NO 2

EASY - LEVEL ONE

1 Henry VIII had how many wives?

2 Who was the first US president?

3 The invasion of which country led to the outbreak of World War II?

4 Which French heroine was burned at the stake?

5 Cleopatra ruled which country?

6 What led to the sinking of the Titanic in 1912?

7 Which French statesman crowned himself emperor in 1804?

8 Which English admiral won the battle of Trafalgar?

9 Who was Spain's dictator until his death in 1975?

10 Which admiral organized the German navy of World War I?

11 Which African–American civil rights leader was shot dead in Memphis in 1968?

12 In which army was Moshe Dayan an important figure?

13 What were Russian heads of state called before the 1917 Revolution?

14 Who was American president at the start of World War II?

15 Who succeeded Bloody Mary as queen of England?

16 When Columbus discovered America in 1492, where did he think he had landed?

17 The Battle of the Somme took place during which war?

18 Which American president was famous for abolishing slavery?

19 Who was leader of Germany during the Third Reich?

20 Which judge presided over the Bloody Assizes?

21 Where did the Incas originate?

22 In which battle did Sitting Bull defeat General Custer?

23 Which aviator made the first non-stop flight across the Atlantic?

24 What started in Pudding Lane on September 2, 1666?

25 Which city was divided into four sectors at the end of World War II?

26 Who was responsible for the assassination of Julius Caesar?

27 In which city was Archduke Franz Ferdinand assassinated, causing the start of World War I?

28 The Battle of Bosworth Field took place during which war?

29 What was Baron Manfred von Richthofen popularly known as?

30 What was Ferdinand, Graf von Zeppelin famous for?

31 Which civilization did the Norsemen belong to?

32 What was discovered in California in 1848?

33 When was the American Declaration of Independence?

34 Which state succeeded the Roman Empire?

35 The Hundred Years' War was between which two countries?

36 In which American state did the

English first settle in 1607?

37 From which French town were more than 330,000 Allied Troops evacuated in 1940?

38 In which country did the Industrial Revolution start?

39 Which World War was called the Great War?

40 What, in the 16th century, were the conquistadores?

41 Who was the Russian monk who reputedly could treat the czarevich's haemophilia?

42 Which event triggered the Great Depression?

43 Which army were known for their black-shirted uniforms?

44 Which American gangster was also known as Scarface?

45 Which treaty ended World War I?

46 What was the Japanese warrior class that rose to power in the 11th century?

47 What is the town of Auschwitz associated with?

48 The tomb of which king was found almost completely intact?

49 Which war were tanks first used in?

50 William the Conqueror was duke of which French province?

A nswers to Quiz 67, POT LUCK

1. Thou shalt not commit adultery. 2. Cycling. 3. Mars. 4. Lulu. 5. Beethoven. 6. Cribbage. 7. 66. 8. Junior Wimbledon. 9. Okra. 10. Davy Jones. 11. Black. 12. Holes. 13. Dennis Potter. 14. Look-In. 15. Steeplechase. 16. Track 29. 17 Yellow. 18 German. 19 Peter Adamson. 20. Beginning. 21. West Ham. 22. West Point. 23. Eggs. 24. Tchaikovsky. 25. Arthur. 26. After Henry. 27. Side saddle. 28. Tommy Cooper. 29. In a wall. 30. The B.B.C.. 31. Magic. 32. 50 pence piece. 33. Birmingham City. 34. Guys and Dolls. 35. Bowler. 36. Aquarius. 37. Golf. 38. Smallpox. 39. J B Priestley. 40. Wonderwoman. 41. Wet Wet Wet. 42. Horoscope. 43. Violin. 44. Buckingham Palace. 45. June. 46. Clannad. 47. The river Fleet. 48. David Hasselhoff. 49. Oliver McCall. 50. A French stew.

QUIZ 2 Pot Luck

EASY - LEVEL ONE

1 What is another name for the constellation known as the Big Dipper?
2 What was the name of Robin Hood's girlfriend?
3 Who owned a sword called Excalibur?
4 How many grams are there in a kilogram?
5 What colors would you mix to make purple?
6 Is a north wind coming from or going to the north?
7 What drink is Brazil famous for?
8 Of which country is Stockholm the capital?
9 Which native American tribe has the same name as a US helicopter?
10 Mohammed was the founder of which religion?
11 Which city is the capital of France?
12 Is titanium animal, vegetable or mineral?
13 What, according to the proverb, do birds of a feather do?
14 What forms the main diet of the heron?
15 What is a Colt .45?
16 For what purpose were dachshunds originally bred?
17 Which famous outlaw partnered Butch Cassidy?
18 In which criminal act did Bonnie and Clyde specialize?
19 Which planet is so large it could contain all the others?
20 Theoretically, how many bodies the size of the Earth could fit into the Sun?
21 What is the name of the imaginary line of latitude around the middle of Earth?
22 In which story would you find the Lost Boys?
23 Which famous book is divided into two testaments?
24 Who wrote the play Romeo and Juliet?
25 What is measured on the Beaufort scale?
26 Who was the infamous captain of The Bounty?
27 What spare-time career did the Hardy Boys follow?
28 Which country did Ivan the Terrible rule?
29 In which country would you find Mandalay?
30 Name Charlie Brown's dog in the "Peanuts" cartoons.
31 Who lives at 10 Downing Street?
32 Who occupies the Oval Office?
33 What sort of plane was a Spitfire?
34 With which festival do you associate Good Friday?
35 To which domestic animal is the tiger related?
36 For what purpose is the husky used?
37 Venison is the meat of which animal?
38 Maco, tiger, and hammer head are

8

all varieties of which creature?

39 In which story does the ghost of Jacob Marley appear?

40 What is an aubergine?

41 Can you eat green tomatoes?

42 According to tradition, what happens to people who pick dandelions?

43 Which American hero was noted for his coonskin cap?

44 Who had a horse called Black Bess?

45 What ancient monuments, all looking similar, is Egypt famous for?

46 What sort of person would live in an igloo?

47 From what was paper traditionally made?

48 From what is glass made?

48 What is Big Ben?

50 What unit is used for measuring the height of horses?

A nswers to Quiz 1, HISTORY

1. Six. 2. George Washington. 3. (b) Poland. 4. Joan of Arc. 5. Egypt. 6. The ship struck an iceberg. 7. Napoleon. 8. Horatio Nelson. 9. General Francisco Franco. 10. Admiral Turpitz 11. Martin Luther King, Jr. 12. The Israeli army 13. Czars. 14. Franklin D Roosevelt. 15. Elizabeth I. 16. India. 17. World War I. 18. Abraham Lincoln. 19. Adolf Hitler. 20. Judge Jeffries. 21. Peru. 22. Battle of the Little Bighorn. 23. Charles Lindbergh. 24. The Great Fire of London. 25. Berlin. 26. Brutus. 27. Sarajevo. 28. Wars of the Roses. 29. The Red Baron. 30. His invention of the rigid airship. 31. Vikings. 32. Gold. 33. 1776. 34. the Byzantine Empire. 35. England and France. 36. Virginia, in Jamestown. 37. Dunkirk. 38. England. 39. World War I. 40. Spanish military leaders conquering the New World. 41. Rasputin. 42. The Wall Street Crash. 43. The Italian Fascists in the 1920s and 1930s. 44. Al Capone. 45. Treaty of Versailles. 46. Samurai. 47. It was the site of the largest concentration camp. 48. Tutankhamen. 49. World War I. 50. Normandy.

Q UIZ 3 Transport

EASY - LEVEL ONE

1 What is a one-wheeled bicycle called?

2 What is a bicycle for two called?

3 What was the full name for what we now call a bus?

4 What type of vehicle floats on a cushion of air?

5 What is a catamaran?

6 How would a galleon be powered?

7 On which type of vehicle would you have found a cow-catcher?

8 Where would you find the caboose located on a freight train?

9 What three forms of power have been used to drive trains?

10 What sort of car was the Sinclair C5?

11 What is known as 'the ship of the desert'?

12 What are the toothed cogs called that transmit the power of a car's engine to the wheels?

13 What are in-line skates more popularly called?

14 What name is given to a group of camels used for transport?

15 What was a trireme?

16 What sort of vehicles would you have met on the Oregon Trail?

17 What command is given to make a ship go forward as fast as possible?

18 In nautical language what does it mean if you are told to 'belay' something?

19 In the last century which vessel is was popularly associated with the Mississippi river?

20 Why is avoiding work known as 'swinging the lead'?

21 Why was a stage coach so called?

22 What was a landau?

23 What name was given to Viking ships?

24 What make of car did Janis Joplin sing about?

25 What connection is there between the county of Surrey, England, and horse-drawn transport?

26 What is the pillion on a motorcycle?

27 What sort of vehicles did William Harley and Arthur Davidson produce?

28 Which car contains the German word for Bavaria in its name?

29 In which sport would you come across the expression 'Formula 1'?

30 What name, other than BMX, is given to a bicycle intended for off-road use?

31 What was a prairie schooner?

32 What was a Zeppelin?

33 What sort of vehicle was the Flying Scot?

34 What was strange about the ship known as the Flying Dutchman?

35 What was odd about the ship named the Mary Celeste?

36 Under what name is the US rail

passenger service known?

37 What was a sedan chair?

38 What was the business of Wells, Fargo & Co?

39 What sort of boat is a punt?

40 What sort of vehicle was a penny-farthing?

41 What does the expression BMX stand for?

42 What name is given to a light weight motorized bicycle that can be pedalled as well as driven by a small engine?

43 What is a wheelie?

44 Which sort of naval vessel fires torpedoes?

45 What is different about the way in which a Harrier jump jet takes off?

46 What name is given to a boat that carries passengers, vehicles, or goods back and forth across the same route?

47 What name would you give to a wheeled or flying vehicle that carries passengers, vehicles, or goods back and forth across the same route?

48 Henry Ford made the world's first mass-produced car. What was it called?

49 You could buy the Model T in only one color. What was it?

50 What happened to the German airship Hindenburg in New Jersey in 1937?

A nswers to Quiz 2, Pot Luck

1. The Plough. 2. Maid Marian. 3. King Arthur. 4. 1,000. 5. Red and blue. 6. It comes from the north. 7. Coffee. 8. Sweden 9. Apache. 10. Islam. 11. Paris. 12. Mineral 13. Flock together. 14. Fish and sometimes frogs. 15. A revolver. 16. Badger hunting. 17. The Sundance Kid. 18. Armed robbery. 19. Jupiter. 20. A million. 21. The equator. 22. Peter Pan. 23. The Bible. 24. William Shakespeare. 25. Wind speed. 26. Captain Bligh. 27. They were detectives. 28. Russia. 29. Burma 30. Snoopy. 31. The British Prime Minister. 32. The President of the USA. 33. A World War II fighter plane. 34. Easter. 35. The cat. 36. Pulling sleds. 37. Deer. 38. Shark. 39. A Christmas Carol. 40. Egg plant. 41. Yes – when cooked they are considered a delicacy. 42. They wet their beds. 43. Davy Crockett. 44. Dick Turpin. 45. The pyramids. 46. An Inuit. 47. Wood. 48. Melted sand. 49. It is the bell found in the clock tower of the Palace of Westminster in London, although the name is often used to refer to the whole tower. 50. Hands.

Q^{UIZ}_4 Pot Luck

EASY - LEVEL ONE

1 Which is the world's most valuable type of gem stone?

2 Is papyrus animal, vegetable or mineral?

3 What is a coracle?

4 What is the approximate distance in miles from the Earth to the Sun?

5 What do we call trees that lose their leaves in winter?

6 Which continent, according to legend, mysteriously sank beneath the waves?

7 What was Cambodia called between 1970 and 1975?

8 What fate befell Icarus?

9 Which is the only country in South America where Portuguese is spoken?

10 Which of the following would you not find in Africa: lions, crocodiles or tigers?

11 Name the four gospels of the New Testament.

12 What is a wat?

13 In which town was William Shakespeare born?

14 Which fictional hero shot an apple from his son's head with a crossbow?

15 What is the name which describes all the species of pine tree?

16 Whose nose grew longer every time he told a lie?

17 What path did Dorothy have to follow in "The Wizard of Oz"?

18 Who, according to the Bible, was swallowed by a whale?

19 Which Dickens character was beaten for asking for more gruel?

20 Which city, according to the well-known proverb, was not built in a day?

21 What is unusual about the way an owl can turn its head?

22 What do we call animals that carry their young in a pouch?

23 What is lace?

24 Who used the code name 007?

25 What do we call it when animals go to sleep during the winter months?

26 Who was Sherlock Holmes' faithful companion?

27 Snoopy, in the Peanuts cartoons, fantasized about fighting a German World War I flying ace. Who was he?

28 What, originally, did the word POG stand for?

29 A statue of which fairy-tale character guards Copenhagen harbor?

30 Water is a mixture of which two gases?

31 Which gas do spiders breathe?

32 When are nocturnal animals most active?

33 Which mythical creature is used to represent the constellation of Sagittarius?

34 Which mythological creature, half

man and half bull, lived in a labyrinth?

35 Which people fought a famous war against the Trojans?

36 In which continent would you find Zulus?

37 What is the name for a long journey made by Australian Aboriginals?

38 In which city would you find the Louvre?

39 Which country is known for growing tulips?

40 Size for size, spider silk is stronger than steel. True or false?

41 What drink is flavored with hops?

42 What is produced from fermented grape juice?

43 In the northern hemisphere which is the shortest day?

44 What are the two tropics called?

45 What sport does Magic Johnson play?

46 What role does the Mikado play in Japanese life?

47 What is ikebana?

48 Who are the paparazzi?

49 Does tea contain caffeine?

50 How many is a gross?

Answers to Quiz 3, Transport

1. A unicycle. 2. A tandem. 3. An omnibus. 4. A hovercraft. 5. A boat with two hulls. 6. By sail. 7. Trains. 8. As the last car. 9. Steam, diesel, and electricity. 10. A single-passenger electric car. 11. The camel. 12. Gears. 13. Roller blades. 14. A caravan. 15. One powered by three banks of oars. 16. Covered wagons. 17. Full speed ahead. 18. Stop doing it. 19. The paddle steamer. 20. On ships, using a plumb line to check the depth of water under the ship was regarded as an easy job. 21. Because it had to make its journey in stages, stopping frequently for fresh horses. 22. A type of horse-drawn carriage. 23. Long ships. 24. Mercedes. 25. A surrey was a horse-drawn pleasure carriage with two or four seats. 26. The passenger seat. 27. Motorcycles. 28. BMW. 29. Motor racing. 30. A mountain bike. 31. A covered wagon. 32. A rigid airship. 33. A steam train. 34. It was a ghost ship. 35. The crew disappeared without trace. 36. Amtrak. 37. A portable enclosed chair for one person, having poles in the front and rear, and carried by two other people. 38. To provide a swift transcontinental express coach service. 39. An open, flat-bottomed boat with squared ends, propeled by a long pole and used in shallow waters. 40. An early bicycle with one large and one small wheel. 41. Bicycle moto-cross. 42. A moped. 43. A trick performed while riding a bicycle or motorcycle which involves balancing the vehicle on its rear wheel. 44. A submarine. 45. It can take off vertically. 46. A ferry. 47. A shuttle. 48. The Model T Ford. 49. Black. 50. It burst into flames at its moorings.

QUIZ 5 Films

EASY - LEVEL ONE

1 Walt Disney made a cartoon featuring dalmatians. How many were there in the title?

2 In "Aladdin", what was the name of the Sultan's evil adviser?

3 Complete the title, "Lady and the ..."

4 Who played Tinkerbell in the film "Hook"?

5 Who played Captain Hook in the film "Hook"?

6 What object had the name Chitty Chitty Bang Bang?

7 Supercalifragilisticexpialidotious is from which film?

8 In which Disney film does a lion cub called Simba sing, 'I just can't wait to be king'?

9 Who was the villain of "The Lion King"?

10 Name the warthog and meercat in The Lion King.

11 What was the name of the princess in Disney's "Aladdin"?

12 Which story by E. Nesbitt became a film in 1970?

13 What was the name of the Sea Lord in "The Little Mermaid"?

14 Which prince does the little mermaid rescue from the sea?

15 Name the seawitch from "The Little Mermaid".

16 What was the name of Jodie Foster's son in "Little Man Tate"?

17 What nickname did Fred Tate call his mother by in "Little Man Tate"?

18 Who was the baby elephant with big ears who could fly?

19 Which Disney featured a puppet which came to life?

20 Name Dorothy's dog in "The Wizard of Oz".

21 Who played the role of Mary Poppins?

22 What was the song from "The Wizard of Oz" that made Judy Garland famous?

23 Who were the rival gang leaders in Bugsy Malone?

24 Who was Bugsy Malone's girl friend?

25 What was Macaulay Culkin's character called in "Home Alone"?

26 In "Home Alone", where have Kevin's family gone?

27 In "Home Alone", why can't Kevin's family phone him?

28 What are the names of the villains in "Home Alone"?

29 What was the subtitle of "Home Alone 2"?

30 Where have Kevin's family gone in "Home Alone 2"?

31 In "Home Alone 2", how does Kevin manage to check into an expensive hotel?

32 In the film "Benji", what type of creature was the main character?

33 What type of dog was Beethoven in the film of that name?

34 What was the profession of the main villain in "Beethoven"?

35 What was the name of Macaulay Culkin's screen girlfriend in "My Girl"?

36 Which Olympic champion portrayed Tarzan the 1930s?

37 "My Girl" was actually filmed in Florida, but where was the action supposed to take place?

38 In which country did the film "Buster's World" take place?

39 In "Buster's World", what is Buster's hobby?

40 In "Buster's World", how does Buster earn pocket money?

41 Who were Donald Duck's nephews?

42 Name the puppies in "Beethoven 2".

43 In "Beethoven 2", who is Beethoven's girlfiend?

44 What was the name of the car which starred in "The Lovebug"?

45 In "The Sound of Music", what was Maria's occupation before she became a governess?

46 What was the name of the family for which Maria worked in "The Sound of Music"?

47 Which prehistoric cartoon family made their own movie?

48 In the film "Babe", how does he heard the sheep?

49 Complete the title, "Honey, I Shrunk the ..."

50 In which film would you find a giant that eats rocks, a boy who hunts purple buffalo, and a child-like empress?

A nswers to Quiz 4, Pot Luck

1. Diamond. 2. Vegetable 3. A small, round boat for one occupant. 4. 93,000,000. 5. Deciduous. 6. Atlantis. 7. The Khmer Republic. 8. He flew too near the sun and the wax of his artificial wings melted, causing him to fall to his death. 9. Brazil. 10. Tigers. 11. Matthew, Mark, Luke, John. 12. A Buddhist temple found in SE Asia. 13. Stratford on Avon. 14. William Tell. 15. Coniferous. 16. Pinnochio's. 17. The yellow brick road. 18. Jonah. 19. Oliver Twist. 20. Rome. 21. It can turn it completely round and look backwards. 22. Marsupials. 23. Openwork fabric made by plaiting, knotting, looping or twisting threads. 24. James Bond. 25. Hibernation. 26. Dr Watson. 27. The Red Baron. 28. Passion fruit, orange, and guava. 29. The little mermaid. 30. Oxygen and hydrogen. 31. Oxygen. 32. At night. 33. The centaur. 34. The Minotaur. 35. The Greeks. 36. Africa. 37. Walkabout. 38. Paris. 39. The Netherlands. 40. True. 41. Beer. 42. Wine. 43. December 21. 44. Cancer and Capricorn. 45. Basketball. 46. He is the emperor. 47. A Japanese style of flower-arranging. 48. Paparazzi: they are newspaper photographers. 49. Yes. 50. 144.

QUIZ 6 — Pot Luck

EASY - LEVEL ONE

1 Which knockabout Kops were created by Mack Sennett?

2 In which TV programme did the staff of Grace Brothers appear?

3 What is another name for the creature the axolotl?

4 What is the name of the Irish Parliament?

5 Which band features the lyrics of Michael Stipe?

6 What city is the capital of Kuwait?

7 Who wrote the poem "Sea Fever"?

8 Which Max recorded sing-a-long records?

9 Where is the fictional Bayview Retirement Home?

10 In the children's party game, what is passed around and unwrapped?

11 In which month is Halloween?

12 Who recorded the album "Watermark"?

13 What word taken from the French describes an afternoon show?

14 What are the initials of Irish poet Yeats?

15 Which moorland shrub is said to bring good luck?

16 Which comic Ken says, "How tickled I am"?

17 Which instrument is traditionally held between the knees?

18 What name is given to barristers collectively?

19 What are Hank Marvin, Brian Bennett and Bruce Welch better known as?

20 On what part of your body would you wear a homburg?

21 Which cartoon villain exclaimed, "Drat and double drat!"?

22 In the classic comedy, Kenneth Horne and Richard Murdoch brought which village to radio?

23 In which city did the hamburger originate?

24 What is a young mare called?

25 Which rock group's name is the Latin for the existing state of things?

26 In the song, the House Of The Rising Sun is in which city?

27 Which Conservative politician William spoke of a "short, sharp, shock"?

28 What is the surname of the decidedly anti-social TV characters Wayne and Waynetta?

29 The village of Anatevka appears in which musical?

30 Who played Ned Kelly in the 1970 film of the same name?

31 What is another name for the rowan tree?

32 How many hours in four days?

33 Which country is a car from if it has the international registration letter J?

34 Who provided the voice of The Book in "The Hitch-Hiker's

Guide To The Galaxy"?

35 Which Oscar said, "I have nothing to declare except my genius."

36 In darts, what is the lowest score from three different trebles?

37 Au is the symbol of which chemical element?

38 Which soap features The Woolpack pub?

39 What subject does Geoff Hamilton deal with?

40 What name is given to the vast grassy plains of Russia?

41 Who has been married to Gemma Craven and Liz Hobbs?

42 Who recorded the album "Steam"?

43 Bovine relates to which kind of animals?

44 What is the chief ingredient in the production of glass?

45 Which creatures sang, "We All Stand Together"?

46 Which composer had the Christian names Johann Sebastian

47 Which monster of the horror genre was created by Mary Shelley?

48 Who forms a trio with Clegg and Foggy?

49 How many sides in three rectangles?

50 On which river does Stoke stand?

Answers to Quiz 5, FILMS

1. 101. 2. Jafar. 3. Tramp. 4. Julia Roberts. 5. Dustin Hoffman. 6. A car. 7. Mary Poppins. 8. The Lion King. 9. Scar. 10. Pumbaa and Timon. 11. Jasmine. 12. The Railway Children. 13. Triton. 14. Sebastian. 15. Ursula. 16. Fred. 17 Dede. 18. Dumbo. 19. Pinoccio. 20. Toto. 21. Julie Andrews. 22. 'Over the Rainbow. 23. Fat Sam and Dandy Dan. 24. Blousey Brown. 25. Kevin. 26. Paris. 27. The phones have been knocked out by a storm. 28. Harry and Marv. 29. Lost in New York. 30. Florida. 31. He uses his dad's credit card. 32. A dog. 33. A St Bernard. 34. He is a vet. 35. Vada. 36. Johnny Weissmuller. 37. Pennsylvania. 38. Denmark. 39. Magic. 40. By delivering groceries.. 41. Huey, Dewey and Louis. 42. Tchaikovsky, Chubby, Dolly and Mo. 43. Herbie. 44. Regina. 45. A novice nun. 46. Von Trapp. 47. The Flinstones. 48. He asks the nicely to do what he wants. 49. Kids. 50. The Never-ending Story.

Q UIZ 7 People

EASY - LEVEL ONE

1 Who was the wizard at King Arthur's court?

2 Name Robin Hood's fat friend.

3 Who was the boy who vowed he would never grow up?

4 Name the boy who befriended Pooh, Piglet, and Eeyore.

5 Which American president supposedly chopped down his father's cherry tree?

6 Which mythical Greek hero performed 12 labors?

7 Which lady guards Upper New York Bay?

8 Name an Italian lady, painted by da Vinci, who is famous for her enigmatic smile.

9 Which king supposedly ordered the waves to turn back?

10 Which English king was executed on the orders of Oliver Cromwell?

11 The three graces are Faith, and who else?

12 Name the hero of "The Hobbit".

13 Who was principally responsible for the rise of National Socialism in Germany?

14 Name the medical man involved in the Gunfight at the OK Corral.

15 Name the British king who supposedly lost his jewels in The Wash.

16 Roald Dahl wrote of a man who owned a fantastic chocolate factory. What was his name?

17 Name the communist leader of Cuba.

18 Who was the first man in space?

19 Who was the first human being to walk on the moon?

20 Which crusading king was known as The Lionheart?

21 What profession did Dick Turpin follow?

22 Who, according to the Bible, was the brother of Cain?

23 Name an Egyptian queen who was the lover of Mark Antony.

24 Who was king of the Greek gods?

25 Name the queen who tells the stories of One Thousand and One Nights.

26 Name a legendary Arabian sailor.

27 For what was Dr Crippen hanged?

28 Against which Iraqi dictator was the Gulf War fought?

29 Who was shot at the playhouse by John Wilkes Booth?

30 Which fictional character is famous for the line: 'Frankly, my dear, I don't give a damn'?

31 Name the Chinese leader of the Communist Revolution.

32 Which Frenchman crowned him self Emperor?

33 Which complex character in Greek legend killed his father and married his mother?

34 To what sticky end did Anne Boleyn come?

35 Who, according to Shakespeare, is

supposed to have cried: 'A horse, a horse, my kingdom for a horse!'?

36 What was Richard III's nickname?

37 Which boy, whose adventures were created by Mark Twain, later starred as a detective in another novel?

38 What nationality was Goethe?

39 Who was Calamity Jane?

40 What sport is played by Steffi Graf?

41 In which revolution was Emiliano Zapata an important figure?

42 Which British saint is famous for slaying a dragon?

43 Which President is famous for the line: 'Ich bin ein Berliner'?

44 Which inventor produced the Kodak camera?

45 Who, according to the fairy tale, had problems with a wolf whilst visiting a sick relative?

46 What was unusual about Gog and Magog?

47 To which king's court did Sir Lancelot belong?

48 Who was the heroine of The Wizard of Oz?

49 Who, according to the Bible, was the brother of Jacob?

50 Which Roman emperor is supposed to have said, 'I came, I saw, I conquered'?

Answers to Quiz 6, POT LUCK

1. Keystone. 2. Are You Being Served? 3. Salamander. 4. The Dail. 5. REM. 6. Kuwait City. 7. John Masefield. 8. Bygraves. 9. Bournemouth. 10. Parcel. 11. October. 12. Enya. 13. Matinee. 14. W.B. 15. Heather. 16. Dodd. 17. Bongos. 18. The Bar. 19. Shadows. 20. Head. 21. Dick Dastardly. 22. Much Binding in the Marsh. 23. Hamburg. 24. Filly. 25. Status Quo. 26. New Orleans. 27. Whitelaw. 28. Slob. 29. Fiddler on the Roof. 30. Mick Jagger. 31. Mountain ash. 32. 96. 33. Japan. 34. Peter Jones. 35. Wilde. 36. 18. 37. Gold. 38. Emmerdale. 39. Gardening. 40. Steppes. 41. Frazer Hines. 42. East 17. 43.Oxen. 44. Sand. 45. Frogs. 46. Bach. 47. Frankenstein. 48. Compo. 49. 12. 50. Trent.

19

QUIZ 8 | Pot Luck

EASY - LEVEL ONE

1 Who invented the ball-point pen?

2 Is a gorilla a monkey?

3 Would a sculptor be most likely to work in marble, granite or chalk?

4 Which people wrote on sheets of papyrus?

5 Do people in Thailand normally eat with chopsticks?

6 Brittany is part of which country?

7 The expression 'alternating current' refers to which form of energy?

8 What is coal?

9 Cox, Granny Smith, and Golden Delicious are all varieties of which fruit?

10 Which bird is known for laying its eggs in other birds' nests?

11 What did Sir Alexander Fleming discover?

12 From which country would a Magyar come?

13 Which of these snakes is not venomous: rattlesnake, boa constrictor or viper?

14 Which plant, used as a Christmas decoration, was regarded as sacred by the Druids?

15 What is a rickshaw powered by?

16 What purpose is Stonehenge thought to have served?

17 In which country would you pay in baht?

18 How long does it take light to reach Earth from the Sun?

19 'Adios' means 'goodbye' in which language?

20 What is the difference between a meteor and a meteorite?

21 In badminton, what do you use instead of a ball?

22 What is the highest number that has a name?

23 Which comes first, thunder or lightning?

24 What character fault is known as the green-eyed monster?

25 What is unusual about sandalwood?

26 A grasshopper has its ears in its legs. True or false?

27 According to the Bible who were the sons of Adam and Eve?

28 In which tale is Morgan le Fay a wicked sorceress?

29 What is a zombie?

30 In which country would you be most likely to eat sauerkraut?

31 Which whip-wielding film hero is named after a US state?

32 In modern terms, what nationality were the Spartans?

33 Who was the Maid of Orleans?

34 The word 'shalom' means 'peace' in which language?

35 Which of these airports would you find in Japan: O'Hare, Haneda or Ben Gurion?

36 Which German car is named after a bug?

37 What is the name for an elephant's long tooth?

20

38 Who was the fairy who accompanied Peter Pan?

39 Which are the two major political parties of the USA?

40 What was the coin called a sovereign made of?

41 In SE Asia, what is a stupa?

42 What is brine?

43 The ostrich sticks its head in the sand to avoid danger. True or false?

44 What function did Mercury perform in Greek legend?

45 Where did Norse warriors hope to go when they died?

46 What is a dromedary?

47 We say 'as blind as a bat', but is a bat really blind?

48 How would you get a hen's egg into a bottle without breaking the shell?

48 Who was assassinated on the Ides of March?

50 How many are there in a score?

A nswers to Quiz 7, PEOPLE

1. Merlin. 2. Friar Tuck. 3. Peter Pan. 4. Christopher Robin. 5. George Washington. 6. Hercules. 7. The Statue of Liberty. 8. Mona Lisa. 9. Canute. 10. Charles I. 11. Hope and Charity. 12. Bilbo Baggins. 13. Adolph Hitler. 14. Doc Holliday. 15. King John. 16. Willy Wonka. 17. Fidel Castro. 18. Yuri Gagarin. 19. Neil Armstrong. 20. Richard I. 21. He was a highwayman. 22. Abel. 23. Cleopatra. 24. Zeus. 25. Scheherezade. 26. Sinbad. 27. Murdering his wife. 28. Saddam Hussein. 29. President Lincoln. 30. Rhett Butler in Gone With the Wind. 31. Mao Zedong. 32. Napoleon Bonaparte. 33. Oedipus. 34. She was beheaded. 35. Richard III. 36. Crookback Dick. 37. Tom Sawyer. 38. German 39. An American frontier character 40. Tennis 41. The Mexican Revolution 42. St George. 43. John F. Kennedy. 44. George Eastman. 45. Little Red Riding Hood. 46. They were giants. 47. King Arthur's. 48. Dorothy. 49. Esau. 50. Julius Caesar.

Q^{UIZ}_{9} The Earth

EASY - LEVEL ONE

1 What is the name given to the Earth's hard outer shell?

2 Which science studies the history, structure, and composition of the Earth?

3 Images of ancient living creatures are sometimes found trapped in rock. What are these called?

4 What is the study of the Earth's surface called?

5 Is the Earth a perfect sphere?

6 What do we call the metallic center of the Earth?

7 How much of the Earth's surface is covered by water?

8 What is the name of the continent which contains the South Pole?

9 What do we call a gap in the Earth's crust through which molten rock escapes onto the Earth's surface?

10 What do we call a shallow depression at the top of a volcanic cone?

11 What is a geyser?

12 What name is given to the sudden emergence of hot material from the Earth's interior?

13 What does the Richter scale measure?

14 What name is sometimes given to the tidal wave set off by an under sea earthquake?

15 What do we call a hill over 2,000 ft (600 m) high?

16 What do we call the imaginary lines that divide the Earth from north to south?

17 What do we call the imaginary lines that divide the Earth from east to west?

18 What is the process by which rock is worn down by weather?

19 What is the name given to the heaps of rock debris formed by frost shattering?

20 Does a stalagmite grow up or down?

21 What is the name for a place where a stream disappears under ground in limestone scenery?

22 What is glaciation?

23 What is a glacier?

24 What is an ice age?

25 What is the Norwegian word for a long, deep sea inlet gouged out by a glacier?

26 What is a moraine?

27 What is permafrost?

28 What is a peninsula?

29 What do we call a band of sand, shingle, or pebbles at the edge of the sea?

30 What is strange about the Mediterranean Sea?

31 What is the name for an underwater ridge created by the coral polyp?

32 What is the name for an area of land surrounded by water?

33 What do we call the twice daily rise and fall of the oceans?

34 What is a spring tide?

35 What do we call the thin layer of gases surrounding the Earth?

36 What is the commonest gas in the atmosphere?

37 What is the greenhouse effect?

38 What is a barometer?

39 What is a thermometer?

40 What do we call a stream of air moving from one place to another?

41 Complete the following sentence: An isobar is a line on a map that links points of equal atmospheric...

42 What do we call a dense cloud of water droplets close to the ground?

43 What is humidity?

44 The Beaufort scale describes the effects of various wind speeds. What is the highest speed called?

45 According to the Beaufort scale, is a storm stronger than a gale?

46 What is oil?

47 What is coal?

48 What is so-called 'natural gas' mainly made of?

49 What color are emeralds?

50 Which are the three rare metals often used in jewellery?

Answers to Quiz 8, POT LUCK

1. Ladislao Biro. 2. No, it's an ape. 3. Marble. 4. The ancient Egyptians. 5. No. 6. France. 7. Electricity. 8. Fossilized wood. 9. Apple. 10. The cuckoo. 11. Penicillin. 12. Hungary 13. Boa constrictor. 14. Mistletoe. 15. A person. 16. It was a sacred site and also acted as a calendar. 17. Thailand 18. Eight minutes. 19. Spanish. 20. A meteor remains in space, whereas a meteorite survives contact with our atmosphere and strikes the ground. 21. A shuttlecock. 22. A googol. 23. Lightning. 24. Jealousy. 25. Its sweet smell. 26. True. 27. Cain and Abel. 28. King Arthur. 29. A corpse that has been reanimated by sorcery. 30. Germany. 31. Indiana Jones. 32. Greek. 33. Joan of Arc. 34. Hebrew. 35. Haneda. 36. The VW Beetle. 37. A tusk. 38. Tinkerbell. 39. The Republicans and the Democrats. 40. Gold. 41. A mound containing relics. 42. Salt water. 43. It's false, though commonly believed. 44. He was the messenger of the gods. 45. Valhalla. 46. A one-humped camel. 47. No, but it has poor sight. 48. Soak it in vinegar to soften the shell. 49. Julius Caesar. 50. Twenty.

QUIZ 10 Pot Luck

EASY - LEVEL ONE

1 Is there more or less water now than when the seas were first formed?

2 Spider, horseshoe, and hermit are all varieties of which sea creature?

3 Which of the following is not a sign of the zodiac: Libra, Aquarius, Ceres or Capricorn?

4 What name is given to a white animal with pink eyes (eg, mouse or rabbit)?

5 What sort of game is Yahtzee?

6 Which of the following is not a gambling game: poker, roulette, backgammon or patience?

7 The leaves of which water plant are called pads?

8 What was John Constable's profession?

9 Is Carmen an opera, a car or a game of chance?

10 Which large aircraft has a name that reminds you of an elephant?

11 Which of the following is not a make of car: Rolls Royce, Boeing, Chevrolet or Peugeot?

12 Would a ship called a brigantine be equipped with sails or an engine?

13 Who was the King of Rock 'n' Roll?

14 In the northern hemisphere, which wind would you expect to be colder– the north or the south?

15 Which is further north, Turkey or Switzerland?

16 Which city is smaller, São Paulo or Washington DC?

17 In which country would you not drive on the left: Thailand, UK or Sweden?

18 What game do the Chicago Bulls play?

19 What do children have in common with young goats?

20 What are young swans called?

21 What are young geese called?

22 What is Esperanto?

23 By what other name is the Religious Society of Friends sometimes known?

24 Which animals are thought to commit mass suicide by hurling themselves into the sea?

25 Which of the following is not a citrus fruit: lemon, rhubarb, orange, or grapefruit.

26 Bats' wings are really modified hands. True or false?

27 Is a Portugese Man o' War: a ship, a warrior, a jellyfish or a car?

28 In which country was golf invented?

29 What sort of creature is a Bombay duck?

30 Where would you find the Everglades?

31 By what name did Westerners formerly know Beijing?

32 In which of these places is Chinese not the native language: Taiwan, Hong Kong or Korea?

33 Which religious leader lives in the

24

Vatican?

34 Where in a house would you expect to find the eaves?

35 What is a ravine?

36 Why can't you see around corners?

37 If you flip a coin, what are the chances of it coming down heads?

38 In which country would you find the Sinai Desert?

39 How many years is three score and ten?

40 What is Blue John?

41 What causes hay fever?

42 Which country sent rhubarb to the West?

43 According to the Bible, what was used to feed the five thousand?

44 Which country is the home of the classical guitar?

45 What sort of creature could be described as a Thoroughbred, a Shetland, an Arab, or a Mustang?

46 What name is given to ancient Egyptian writing?

47 What is azure?

48 What is serendipity?

49 What is the difference between astrology and astronomy?

50 What other name is given to the constellation of Ursa Major?

A nswers to Quiz 9, THE EARTH

1. The crust. 2. Geology. 3. Fossils. 4. Geography. 5. No. 6. The core. 7. 70% 8. Antarctica. 9. A volcano. 10. A crater. 11. A hole in the Earth's crust spouting fountains of boiling water. 12. An eruption. 13. The magnitude of an earthquake. 14. Tsunami. 15. A mountain. 16. Lines of latitude. 17. Lines of longitude. 18. Erosion. 19. Scree. 20. Up. 21. A swallow-hole. 22. The covering of the land by ice during an ice age. 23. A large 'river' of slowly moving ice. 24. A cold period in the Earth's history when the ice sheets are much larger than today. 25. A fjord. 26. A pile of debris left by moving ice. 27. Permanently frozen ground. 28. A narrow neck of land projecting into the sea. 29. A beach. 30. It has no tides. 31. A coral reef. 32. An island. 33. Tide. 34. An especially high or low tide. 35. The atmosphere. 36. Nitrogen. 37. The trapping of heat by gases in the atmosphere. 38. An instrument for measuring atmospheric pressure. 39. An instrument for measuring temperature. 40. Wind. 41. Pressure. 42. Fog (or mist). 43. The amount of water vapor in the air. 44. Hurricane. 45. No. 46. A dark, liquid fossil fuel formed from tiny plants and animals. 47. A solid fossil fuel made from the remains of plants. 48. Methane. 49. Green. 50. Gold, silver, and platinum.

Celebrities

QUIZ 11

EASY - LEVEL ONE

1 What is the first name of supermodel Evangelista?

2 Which veteran Scottish rock star is married to Rachel Hunter?

3 Princess Caroline is a member of which royal family?

4 What was the surname of Jackie Onassis's first husband?

5 What is the first name of actress Ms de Cadenet?

6 Lady Helen, daughter of the Duke and Duchess of Kent, named her son after which famous explorer?

7 What was the first name of tycoon Donald Trump's former wife?

8 What is the first name of actress and model Miss Hurley?

9 Who is the magician partner of model Claudia Schiffer?

10 Which Texan model married Mick Jagger?

11 Which Swedish actress was a former wife of the late Peter Sellers?

12 What is the surname of eight-times married actress Zsa Zsa?

13 What is the first name of celebrity photographer Bailey?

14 Which LA Hills are the home of many of the rich and famous?

15 What is the first name of kilt-wearing designer Gaultier?

16 How is skinny 1960s model Lesley Hornby better known?

17 What is the surname of celebrity sisters Joan and Jackie?

18 What is the first name of actress/model Miss Seymour?

19 Who is the head of the Virgin group?

20 What is the first name of gossip columnist Dempster?

21 Which ski resort is a favourite for Prince Charles at Xmas?

22 What nationality is Sophia Loren?

23 Which TV show made Pamela Anderson famous?

24 Which princess is known by her husband's first name?

25 Which Royal has a home on the island of Mustique?

26 What is the first name of fashion designer Westwood?

27 Of which country is Juan Carlos king?

28 What is the profession of the Queen's cousin Lord Lichfield ?

29 Which Pakistani cricketer married heiress Jemima Goldsmith?

30 Which fuel did the Getty family make their fortune from?

31 Michael Hutchence dated which model Helena before Paula Yates?

32 What name did Pamela Anderson add to her own when she wed rock star Tommy?

33 Which Johnny's name was once linked to the model Kate Moss?

34 Which Mrs Carling publicly

criticized the Princess of Wales?

35 Which former Pakistan cricket captain married Jemima Goldsmith?

36 Mandy Allwood's expectation of how many babies made the news in 1996?

37 Which Gareth's summer miss of 1996 made him a household name?

38 What is the first name of the TV presenter Ms Frostrup?

39 What is Mrs Michael Jackson II's first name?

40 In '97 David Beckham was dating one of which pop band?

41 What is the profession of Claudia Shiffer's ex, David Copperfield?

42 Which actress married Richard Burton twice?

43 Which star of "Evita" married the actress Melanie Griffith?

44 Which Royal Prince's name was linked with Koo Stark?

45 Which former son-in-law of the Queen remarried in 1997?

46 Which tenor left his wife for a Miss Mantovani?

47 Although a top model, Jerry Hall is also famous as which star's wife?

48 Which comedian Paul split with wife Caroline Quentin in 1997?

49 Which singer was the second Mrs Andrew Lloyd Webber?

50 What is the first name of David Emanuel's fashion designer ex-wife?

A nswers to Quiz 10, POT LUCK

1. Exactly the same amount. 2. Crab. 3. Ceres. 4. Albino. 5. A dice game. 6. patience. 7. The water lily. 8. A painter. 9. An opera. 10. The jumbo jet. 11. Boeing. 12. Sails. 13. Elvis Presley. 14. The north wind. 15. Switzerland. 16. Washington DC. 17. Sweden. 18. Basketball. 19. The are both called kids. 20. Cygnets. 21. Goslings. 22. An artificial language. 23. The Quakers. 24. Lemmings. 25. Rhubarb. 26. True. 27.A jellyfish. 28. Scotland. 29. A fish. 30. Florida. 31. Peking. 32. Korea. 33. The Pope. 34. In the roof. 35. A deep, narrow valley or gorge worn by .running water. 36. Because light travels in straight lines. 37. Evens. 38. Egypt. 39. Seventy. 40. A semi-precious stone. 41. An allergic reaction to pollen. 42. China. 43. Five loaves and three fish. 44. Spain. 45. A horse. 46. Hieroglyphs. 47. A shade of blue. 48. A lucky accident. 49. Astrology is an attempt to predict events by observation of the stars. Astronomy is the scientific observation of all cosmic phenomena. 50. The Great Bear.

Q UIZ 12 Pot Luck

FOR ANSWERS SEE QUIZ NO 13

EASY - LEVEL ONE

1 Which film studio made Lady and the Tramp, Dumbo, and Pocahontas?

2 Which family group did Michael Jackson sing with when he was a boy?

3 Of which country is Warsaw the capital city?

4 Which is referred to as the 'near side' of a car?

5 Which famous black South African leader spent many years in prison before becoming president of his country?

6 Which group featured Merrill, Jay, Wayne, Alan, and Donny?

7 Which sign of the Zodiac is represented by a crab?

8 What are Tarot cards used for?

9 What is the first letter of the Greek alphabet?

10 What type of shellfish produce pearls?

11 Is it true that a singer can shatter a wine glass simply by hitting a high note?

12 By what name were the National Socialist Party better known?

13 What have Auschwitz, Dachau, and Treblinka in common?

14 Which US national organization is devoted to fighting crime?

15 Under what name is the USA's intelligence gathering organization known?

16 Which country has a security organization called MI5?

17 What do pilgrims expect to receive at Lourdes?

18 In which country did the Khmer Rouge carry out mass murder?

19 What sport is Andre Agassi famous for?

20 What is NASA known for?

21 Which country is the home of the game of boules?

22 What is a so-called fairy ring?

23 To which country does the island of Crete belong?

24 Which two countries dispute ownership of Cyprus?

25 How much of the human body is composed of oxygen?

26 What was Rip van Winkle noted for?

27 In which country did the film "You Only Live Twice" mainly take place?

28 Who won the first ever Super Bowl in 1967?

29 In "The Lion, the Witch and the Wardrobe", what was the first thing Lucy found in Narnia?

30 How many feet make one fathom?

31 Which of the Walton children ran his own newspaper?

32 In The Cosby Show, what is Mrs Huxtable's profession?

33 Which is the first book of the Bible?

34 Which is the odd one out: (a) Daisy, (b) Poppy,

(c) Geranium, (d) Althea?

35 Julius Caesar's horse was supposed to have unusual feet. What was strange about them?

36 Why were some Romans called Postumus?

37 Who would have used wampum?

38 Apart from the animal of that name, what is a white elephant?

39 What does a squirrel live in?

40 Who lives in an igloo?

41 In Thailand, houses were traditionally built on stilts. Why?

42 What name is given to Estonia, Latvia and Lithuania?

43 Where did Robin Hood live?

44 On which coast would you find Oregon?

45 What other name is given to a harmonica?

46 Which boy's name, made popular by a great conqueror, means 'defender of men'?

47 How do you judge the age of a tree which has been felled?

48 On the internet, what is a URL?

49 By what name is Southern Rhodesia now known?

50 Lucifer, Beelzebub, and Baphomet are all names for what?

Answers to Quiz 11, CELEBRITIES

1. Linda. 2. Rod Stewart. 3. Monaco. 4. Kennedy. 5. Amanda. 6. Columbus. 7. Ivana. 8. Elizabeth. 9. David Copperfield. 10. Jerry Hall. 11. Britt Ekland. 12. Gabor. 13. David. 14. Beverly Hills. 15. Jean-Paul. 16. Twiggy. 17. Collins. 18. Jane. 19. Richard Branson. 20. Nigel. 21. Klosters. 22. Italian. 23. Baywatch. 24. Michael. 25. Princess Margaret. 26. Vivienne. 27. Spain. 28. Photographer. 29. Imran Khan. 30. Oil. 31. Christiansen. 32. Lee. 33. Depp. 34. Julia. 35. Imran Khan. 36. Eight. 37. Southgate. 38. Mariella. 39. Debbie. 40. Spice Girls. 41. Magician. 42. Elizabeth Taylor. 43. Antonio Banderas. 44. Andrew. 45. Mark Phillips. 46. Pavarotti. 47. Mick Jagger's. 48. Merton. 49. Sarah Brightman. 50. Elizabeth.

QUIZ 13 Nature

EASY - LEVEL ONE

1 What is the difference between a moth and a butterfly?
2 What is the difference between a frog and a toad?
3 To what family do lions, tigers, and cheetahs belong?
4 What domestic animal is the closest relative of the wolf?
5 Where are penguins found?
6 Where are polar bears found?
7 Which common vegetable did Sir Walter Raleigh introduce to Europe?
8 Which birds are collectively known as a 'murder'?
9 What is the largest species of shark?
10 What is taxonomy?
11 What is the difference between frog spawn and toad spawn?
12 Which bird is notorious for laying its eggs in another bird's nest?
13 What is a dingo?
14 What is a feral animal?
15 What is the name for the Australian bird rather like an ostrich?
16 What domestic animal did the Egyptians worship as a god?
17 Do birds sing for pleasure?
18 Does a fish normally have lungs?
19 Is the cheetah the world's fastest running animal?
20 Is a sponge a plant?
21 Is a lizard warm or cold blooded?
22 Is it true that some birds can use tools?
23 To what family do spiders and scorpions belong?
24 To what family do crabs and lobsters belong?
25 What is the purpose of a rattlesnake's rattle?
26 Do male or female lions do the hunting?
27 What sort of creature is a koi?
28 Which blackbird is not black?
29 Which two animals were responsible for the spread of the Black Death?
30 Is a tomato a fruit or a vegetable?
31 In northern latitudes what are swallows famous for doing in autumn?
32 Is it true that the sight of seagulls inland means there are storms at sea?
33 Is the owl really wise?
34 Which animal defends itself by spraying enemies with an evil-smelling fluid?
35 Which creature is known as a glutton?
36 What do satsumas, clementines, and mandarins have in common?
37 What is another name for a Daddy Longlegs?
38 From which flower is opium produced?
39 What is lichen?
40 Which scavenging animal is famous for its laugh?
41 Where would you find alligators?

42 Are giant pandas herbivores?

43 What is a young swan called?

44 What is a young eel called?

45 What is another name for a dung beetle?

46 Does a frog have ears?

47 Oxeye is a variety of which common wild flower?

48 Girls called Erica are named after which wild flower?

49 What sort of creature is a stickleback?

50 What is the common name for fishes of the family Diodontidae, which have strong, sharp spines on the body and are capable of inflating themselves when attacked?

Answers to Quiz 12, Pot Luck

1. Disney. 2. The Jackson Five. 3. Poland. 4. The one nearest the kerb. 5. Nelson Mandela. 6. The Osmonds. 7. Cancer. 8. Telling fortunes. 9. Alpha. 10. Oysters. 11. Yes – it's difficult but possible. 12. The Nazis. 13. They were all Nazi concentration camps during World War II. 14. The FBI. 15. The CIA. 16. Great Britain. 17. Divine healing. 18. Cambodia. 19. Tennis. 20. Space travel. 21. France. 22. A circle of grass that grows longer than the surrounding grass. 23. Greece. 24. Greece and Turkey. 25. Approximately two thirds. 26. Sleeping for 20 years. 27. Japan. 28. Green Bay Packers. 29. A lamp post. 30. Six. 31. John-Boy. 32. She is a lawyer. 33. Genesis. 34. Geranium. All the others are girls' names. 35. It is said that they had toes instead of hooves. 36. They were born from a mother who died in childbirth. 37. Native Americans. 38. Something of no use. 39. A drey. 40. An Inuit. 41. To keep them dry in the rainy season. 42. The Baltic States. 43. In Sherwood Forest. 44. The west coast. 45. A mouth organ. 46. Alexander. 47. By how many concentric rings it has. 48. A World-Wide Web site address (URL stands for Unique Resource Locator). 49. Zimbabwe. 50. Demons.

Q^{UIZ}_{14} Pot Luck

FOR ANSWERS SEE QUIZ NO 15

EASY - LEVEL ONE

1   Which season does the word vernal relate to?

2   What is the zodiac sign of the Balance?

3   On which island are most lemurs found?

4   Who had a No 1 hit with the song "(I Can't Get No) Satisfaction"?

5   What type of horse racing does not include fences and obstacles?

6   Who created Mickey Mouse?

7   In nursery rhyme, what did Little Jack Horner pull out of a pie?

8   Which device produces the mix of air and petrol in internal combustion engines?

9   What is a butterfly's proboscis?

10 According to proverb, what is a change as good as?

11 What does GMT stand for?

12 What name is shared by athlete Roger and TV presenter Cilla?

13 Called a vest in America, what's the name of this garment in the UK?

14 Hawthorn traditionally blooms in which month?

15 Which game is played with rackets and shuttlecocks?

16 Which part of his anatomy did Van Gogh cut off?

17 What word describes someone mean with money, like Scrooge?

18 What is the first name of John Major's wife?

19 Which George wrote "Animal Farm"?

20 What type of food is Demerara?

21 What name is given to a female donkey?

22 Who says, "Yabbadabba Doo!"?

23 Which month is named after the god Janus?

24 Who recorded the album "Rumours"?

25 Which city of central England gave its name to a shade of green?

26 Was Clement Attlee a Conservative or Labour politician?

27 What was the profession or calling of Tuck in Sherwood Forest?

28 Where is the New York Stock Exchange?

29 In which country would you see wild wombats?

30 Who was Ronnie Barker's comic partner?

31 Which country does the airline Iberia come from?

32 What is the currency of South Africa?

33 What was seemingly fearless "A-Team" member B. A. Baracus very frightened of?

34 Who wrote the Aldwych farces, including "Rookery Nook"?

35 What year is included in the name of the group who recorded

32

"Simon Says"?

36 Which school did Queen Elizabeth II attend as a youngster?

37 In rhyming slang what is dog and bone?

38 What was Frederick Bulsara better known as?

39 On TV, Danny Kane is co-owner of which club?

40 In the Bible, whick book follows Matthew?

41 What famous first did Edward White achieve for America?

42 In which country is the Matterhorn?

43 Who was the first female DJ on Radio I?

44 What colour is associated with an Oxford or Cambridge sports award?

45 Which rock forms the greater part of the White Cliffs of Dover?

46 Which food was advertised to the tune of "I Can't Let Maggie Go"?

47 In tennis, what name is given to a serve which cannot be returned?

48 Who recorded the album "Bad"?

49 Which major river flows through Gloucester?

50 Who created "Dalziel and Pascoe"?

Answers to Quiz 13, NATURE

1. Moths move around at night, have hair-like or feathery antennae, stout bodies, and a frenulum that holds the front and back wings together. 2. Toads are more terrestrial and have a broader body and rougher, drier skin. 3. The cat family. 4. The dog. 5. In the Antarctic. 6. In the Arctic. 7. The potato. 8. Crows. 9. The Great White. 10. The science of classification. 11. Frog spawn is laid in a jelly-like mass, toad spawn is laid in strips like tape. 12. The cuckoo. 13. An Australian wild dog. 14. A domestic animal that has returned to the wild. 15. The emu. 16. The cat. 17. No. They are usually warning other birds to keep out of their territory or trying to attract a mate. 18. No. Fish extract oxygen from the water by the use of gills. 19. Yes, but only over short distances. 20. No. It's an animal. 21. Cold blooded. 22. Yes. Some species can, for example, use a thorn to pick grubs out of cracks. 23. They are arachnids. 24. They are crustaceans. 25. To warn other creatures to keep away. 26. The female. 27. A fish 28. The female. 29. Rats and the fleas which lived on them. 30. A fruit. 31. Flying south for the winter. 32. No. Seagulls have become skilled scavengers and many live inland almost permanently. 33. No. Its brain is actually very small. 34. The skunk. 35. Wolverine 36. They are all types of miniature orange. 37. A crane fly. 38. The poppy. 39. A fungus that grows symbiotically with algae. 40. The hyena. 41. In the USA or China. 42. Mainly, but they eat meat when they can get it. 43. A cygnet. 44. An elver. 45. Scarab 46. Yes. 47. Daisy. 48. Heather. 49. A small freshwater fish with spines along its back. 50. Porcupine fish.

Q UIZ 15 Classical Music

EASY - LEVEL ONE

1 Which composer wrote the opera The Magic Flute?

2 How many symphonies did Beethoven write?

3 In which opera can you find the "Triumphal March"?

4 What nationality was Antonín Dvorák?

5 Who wrote the "Royal Fireworks Music"?

6 In which tempo should a piece of music annotated with the term presto be played?

7 How many movements does a classical symphony usually have?

8 Herbert von Karajan was the conductor of which orchestra?

9 Who wrote the '1812 Overture"?

10 How many operas did Beethoven write?

11 What type of instrument is a clarinet?

12 What kind of musical work is Swan Lake?

13 Who wrote the Peer Gynt suites?

14 In which country was Frédéric Chopin born?

15 How should music described as adagio be played?

16 Of which major work is Götterdämmerung a part?

17 What is the text of an opera correctly termed?

18 In which voice does Luciano Pavarotti sing?

19 Who wrote The Barber of Seville?

20 What does the term pizzicato mean?

21 What type of instrument is a trombone?

22 What is the name of Prokofiev's symphonic fairy tale?

23 Who wrote the Brandenburg Concertos?

24 What is peculiar about Schubert's Symphony No. 8?

25 Mstislav Rostropovich is an artist on which instrument?

26 What nationality was Jean Sibelius?

27 Who wrote the "Moonlight Sonata"?

28 By what other name is a cembalo also known?

29 During which musical era was Bach's music written?

30 Who is a concerto usually written for?

31 What type of musical work is Die schöne Mullerin?

32 Who wrote the opera Carmen?

33 What type of instrument is a saxophone?

34 Who was the leading English composer of the Baroque era?

35 Which instrument was Pictures at an Exhibition written for?

36 Which opera contains the aria 'La ci darem la mano'?

37 Who wrote Bolero?

38 Who lived earlier – Haydn or Schubert?

39 What did Beethoven suffer from in

his later years?

40 What is the name of Mozart's last symphony?

41 Pinchas Zukerman was an artist on which instrument?

42 Who wrote The Four Seasons?

43 What type of music is a minuet?

44 Which nationality was composer Gustav Mahler?

45 How many strings does a guitar usually have?

46 What does the term crescendo mean?

47 In which suite can you find the 'Dance of the Sugar Plum Fairy'?

48 Daniel Barenboim is an artist on which instrument?

49 Who wrote From the New World?

50 In which tempo should a move ment described as largo be played?

A nswers to Quiz 14, Pot Luck

1. Spring. 2. Libra. 3. Madagascar. 4. Rolling Stones. 5. Flat. 6. Walt Disney. 7. Plum. 8. Carburettor. 9. Tongue. 10. A rest. 11. Greenwich Mean Time. 12. Black. 13. Waistcoat. 14. May. 15. Badminton. 16. An ear. 17. Miser. 18. Norma. 19. Orwell. 20. Sugar. 21. Jenny. 22. Fred Flintstone. 23. January. 24. Fleetwood Mac. 25. Lincoln. 26. Labour. 27. Friar. 28. Wall Street. 29. Australia. 30. Ronnie Corbett. 31. Spain. 32. Rand. 33. Flying. 34. Ben Travers. 35. 1910 (Fruitgum Co.) 36. None at all. 37. Phone. 38. Freddie Mercury. 39. The Paradise Club. 40. Mark. 41. First to walk in space. 42. Switzerland. 43. Annie Nightingale. 44. Blue. 45. Chalk. 46. Bread (Brand was Nimble). 47. Ace. 48. Michael Jackson. 49. Severn. 50. Reginald Hill.

Q Quiz 16 Pot Luck

FOR ANSWERS SEE QUIZ NO 17

EASY - LEVEL ONE

1 Which female detective partners Fox Mulder in "The X-Files"?

2 Which detective did Clint Eastwood play?

3 Which fictional 19th-century detective was killed by his creator but resurrected by popular demand?

4 Where is Dixie?

5 What is a pecan?

6 Which nut is named after a South American country?

7 Which popular children's entertainment features a crocodile, a baby, a policeman, and a string of sausages?

8 In which country is a country home called a dacha?

9 What would you do with a glockenspiel?

10 What are timpani?

11 With which sport do you associate the NBA?

12 What does UCLA stand for?

13 What sort of illness does a paediatrician treat?

14 What does a taxidermist do?

15 Which language very nearly became the official language of the USA?

16 Is the Suez Canal longer than the Panama Canal?

17 Which metal provides fuel for nuclear power stations?

18 Hum the opening bars of Beethoven's Fifth Symphony.

19 What caused the Titanic to sink?

20 In which long-running TV show did Lisa Bonet appear as a teenage daughter?

21 Which American actress played the part of a gangster's girlfriend when she was only 12 years old?

22 Which American sitcom is named after a flower?

23 Which of Charlie Brown's friends plays Beethoven on a toy piano?

24 Name the dirty child in the Peanuts cartoons.

25 Who was the Native American princess in "Peter Pan"?

26 What American plant sends horses mad if they eat it?

27 What does the Spanish phrase Hasta la vista mean?

28 What do German and Jewish people say when you sneeze?

29 What is a bagel?

30 Which country is the home of sukiyaki?

31 What have currants, raisins, and sultanas got in common?

32 What does the Spanish word corrida mean?

33 In which country would you find the Dordogne?

34 Who played the film role of Mary Poppins?

35 Who played the male lead in "Mary Poppins"?

36 What is the connection between LaToya, Janet and Michael?

37 Which country is the home of tacos?

38 What is tequila?

39 What is a chihuahua?

40 What would you do with a stethoscope?

41 Name the giant tortoise in The Never-ending Story?

42 What do the stripes on the American flag represent?

43 What is supposed to happen in the Bermuda Triangle?

44 What do the Australians call the uncultivated parts of their country?

45 What are grissini?

46 In which country is Tangiers?

47 What is the main constituent of risotto?

48 Shinto is the national religion of which country?

49 Which country uses roubles as currency?

50 Where would you pay in shekels?

Answers to
Quiz 15, CLASSICAL MUSIC

1. Wolfgang Amadeus Mozart. 2. Nine. 3. Aida. 4. Czech. 5. Georg Friedrich Handel. 6. Very fast. 7. Four. 8. The Berlin Philharmonic. 9. Peter Tchaikovsky. 10. One. 11. A woodwind instrument. 12. A ballet. 13. Edvard Grieg. 14. Poland. 15. In a slow tempo. 16. Der Ring des Nibelungen. 17. The libretto. 18. Tenor. 19. Gioacchino Rossini. 20. The strings should be plucked. 21. A brass instrument. 22. Peter and the Wolf. 23. Johann Sebastian Bach. 24. It is unfinished. 25. The cello. 26. Finnish. 27. Ludwig van Beethoven. 28. A harpsichord. 29. Baroque. 30. An orchestra and one or more solo instruments. 31. A cycle of lyrical songs. 32. Georges Bizet. 33. A woodwind instrument. 34. Henry Purcell. 35. The piano. 36. Don Giovanni. 37. Maurice Ravel. 38. Haydn. 39. Deafness. 40. 'Jupiter' Symphony. 41. The violin. 42. Antonio Vivaldi. 43. A dance. 44. Austrian. 45. Six. 46. Increasing volume gradually. 47. The Nutcracker Suite. 48. The piano. 49. Antonín Dvořák. 50. Very slowly.

Q^{UIZ}_{17} Nature

1 A mule is a cross between which two animals?

2 Which position does a hedgehog take on to protect himself?

3 Which animal is known for being able to change his color?

4 Why are the tusks of elephants so much valued?

5 What makes the larch different from other pine trees?

6 On which continent do koalas live?

7 What is the most obvious difference between a female lion and a male one?

8 Which is the tallest animal?

9 How many humps does a llama have?

10 What do bees gather in order to make honey?

11 Which limb of a tadpole disappears when it turns into a frog?

12 What is the name given to a young horse?

13 What do you call the fruit of an oak tree?

14 What type of animal is a squirrel?

15 How many legs are there on a spider?

16 Which organ do fish breathe with?

17 Which is the largest mammal?

18 What do you call the larva of a butterfly?

19 Which organ do snakes hear with?

20 In what way does the appearance of the fur of a leopard differ from that of a tiger?

21 What does a kangaroo carry in its pouch?

22 The cry of which animal resembles laughter?

23 What color are the flowers of the gorse shrub?

24 Is the guinea pig related to the pig?

25 What do you call dogs of mixed race?

26 What sort of animal is a terrapin?

27 What distinguishes the bat from other mammals?

28 What do you call a male non-working bee?

29 What do you call a female fox?

30 What do vultures mainly feed on?

31 Why do woodpeckers peck holes in trees?

32 What substance can octopuses eject when disturbed?

33 Where do badgers make their homes?

34 What type of animal is a lizard?

35 What sort of plant is a death cap?

36 What is a cobra able to do to its neck?

37 What do female mosquitos feed on?

38 What do you call an adult male chicken?

39 Which is the largest bird?

40 What does the giant panda mainly feed on?

41 What do you call a group of

wolves?

42 What is the most obvious differ ence between a slug and a snail?

43 What animal class does a spider belong to?

44 Where do beavers make their habitat?

45 Where are kippers caught?

46 What do you call a female dog?

47 How do hippopotamuses spend most of their day?

48 How does a hedgehog spend the winter?

49 What is a piranha?

50 What type of animal is a frog?

1. Dana Scully. 2. Dirty Harry. 3. Sherlock Holmes. 4. It is the name sometimes given to the southern states of the USA. 5. A type of nut. 6. A Brazil. 7. Punch and Judy. 8. Russia. 9. Play it; it is a musical instrument. 10. Drums. 11. University of California at Los Angeles. 12. Cricket. 13. Children's diseases. 14. Stuff dead animals. 15. German. 16. Yes; it's twice as long. 17. Uranium. 18. Da da da daah! Da da da daah! 19. It struck an iceberg. 20. The Cosby Show. 21. Jodie Foster. 22. Blossom. 23. Schroeder. 24. Pigpen. 25. Tiger Lily. 26. Loco weed. 27. Until we meet again. 28. Gesundheit. 29. A savory roll. 30. Japan. 31. They are all types of dried grape. 32. A bullfight. 33. France. 34. Julie Andrews. 35. Dick van Dyke. 36. They are members of the Jackson family. 37. Mexico. 38. A Mexican spirit brewed from cactus. 39. A small dog. 40. Listen to the internal workings of someone's body. 41. Morla the Aged. 42. The original 13 colonies. 43. Strange disappearances of ships and aircraft. 44. The Outback. 45. Italian bread sticks. 46. Morocco. 47. Rice. 48. Japan. 49. Russia. 50. Israel.

QUIZ 18 Geography

EASY - LEVEL ONE

1 Which country can you easily walk to from Gibraltar?

2 Urdu is an important language in which two Asian countries?

3 Which is England's most northerly county?

4 What did Bejing used to be called?

5 Which is the Queen's London home?

6 In which European country is Salzburg?

7 Which county divides Cornwall from Somerset?

8 What 'colour' is the Sea between Egypt and Saudi Arabia?

9 In which county is the Peak District?

10 In which country is the resort of Rimini?

11 Madagascar is to the east of which continent?

12 Is California on the east or west coast of the USA?

13 Which is the nearest country to the Falkland Islands?

14 Near which French city is the Disney Theme Park?

15 In which country is the Algarve?

16 Which is further west Algeria or Ethiopia?

17 Which country used to be called Siam?

18 In which country is the county of Tayside?

19 Which Scandinavian capital begins and ends with the same letter?

20 Chad is in which continent?

21 What is Holland also known as?

22 In which US holiday state is Miami?

23 Which country is divided from Spain by the Pyrenees?

24 What is the largest city in the West Midlands?

25 Which town of Tyne and Wear shares its name with the US capital?

26 The Philippines are in which Ocean?

27 What is the largest country of South America?

28 In which continent is Slovenia?

29 Which country originally produced Volvo cars?

30 In which country do most Flemish speakers live?

31 The capital of Western Australia shares its name with which Scottish city?

32 How is Peking now more commonly known?

33 In which country would you see an emu fly?

34 Is French Provence nearer the Channel or the Mediterranean?

35 In which country do people speak Afrikaans?

36 Which bay to the west of France is notorious for its rough seas?

37 What is the principal language of Bulgaria?

38 If you were visiting the home of Parmesan cheese, in which country would you be?

39 Which country used to be called the DDR?

40 In which city is the Wailing Wall?

41 Is the Orinoco in North or South America?

42 How many consonants are there in Mississippi?

43 Which country has the international vehicle registration letter I?

44 Which major town of Morocco shares its name with a famous film?

45 In which country is Bavaria?

46 Which drug is Colombia's chief export?

47 On which long African river is the Aswan Dam?

48 Which Spanish city hosted the 1992 Olympics?

49 In which city is the University of Essex?

50 An Indian city gave its name to which style of riding breeches?

A nswers to Quiz 17, NATURE

1. A horse and a donkey. 2. He rolls himself into a ball. 3. The chameleon. 4. They are made of ivory. 5. It sheds its needles in the winter. 6. Australia. 7. The female lion has no mane. 8. The giraffe. 9. None. 10. Nectar. 11. The tail. 12. A foal. 13. An acorn. 14. A rodent. 15. Eight. 16. Gills. 17. The blue whale. 18. A caterpillar. 19. None, they are deaf. 20. Leopard fur has black spots, while that of a tiger is stripy. 21. Their newborn babies. 22. The hyena. 23. Yellow. 24. No, it is a type of rodent. 25. Mongrels. 26. A turtle. 27. His ability to fly. 28. A drone. 29. A vixen. 30. Dead animals. 31. To find insects. 32. Ink. 33. In underground burrows. 34. A reptile. 35. A mushroom. 36. It can inflate it by expanding its skin. 37. Blood. 38. A rooster. 39. The ostrich. 40. Bamboo. 41. Packs. 42. Slugs have no shell; snails do. 43. The arachnids. 44. Near water, mainly rivers and lakes. 45. They are not caught as kippers, they are smoked herrings. 46. A bitch. 47. Dozing in warm muddy water; they feed by night. 48. It hibernates. 49. A freshwater fish with razor-sharp teeth, capable of killing human beings. 50. An amphibian.

Quiz 19 — Pot Luck

EASY - LEVEL ONE

1 What do you call the fortified section of an Ancient Greek city?
2 What type of plant is known as a sapling?
3 What distinguishes a nectarine from a peach?
4 Which is the largest planet?
5 What do caterpillars feed on?
6 What do you call the control panel of a car?
7 What do you call the process by which birds fly to warmer regions in winter?
8 What was the name of Kurt Cobain's group?
9 What do you call that part of the skin that contains the root of the hair?
10 Which sign of the Zodiac represents twins?
11 Who was the drummer with the Beatles?
12 What type of crystal is used in electronic watches?
13 In which part of the Americas did the Aztecs live?
14 What do you call the material Egyptians used to write on?
15 What do you call a young lion?
16 In which country would you find Florence?
17 What do the letters of the film "E.T". stand for?
18 What do you call the meat produced from deer?
19 In which US city would you find Wall Street?
20 Which pop album has sold the most copies?
21 Who played the leading role in the film "Mrs Doubtfire"?
22 From which country does the flamenco dance originate?
23 In which part of the world is Laos?
24 What do you call trees that shed their leaves in the autumn, or fall?
25 What is the name of the molten rock which comes out of an erupting volcano?
26 Who uses Braille?
27 What type of vegetable is used for making sauerkraut?
28 Which animal's diet consists solely of eucalyptus leaves?
29 A horn belongs to which class of musical instruments?
30 What do the letters VIP stand for?
31 Which female singer released the album "Foreign Affair"?
32 What sort of animals are dolphins?
33 What type of medicine would you take to fight off bacteria?
34 What do you call a dog that descends from several species?
35 What are the colors of the Japanese flag?
36 What implement did farmers use to cut their crops by hand?
37 Which is the hottest planet?
38 What type of animal is a jackal?
39 Mick Jagger is the lead singer of which group?

42

40 The weight of which precious metal is measured in carats?

41 What type of writing was used in Ancient Egypt?

42 In Greek mythology, who was Icarus's father?

43 What do you call paintings on plaster which are found in old palaces and churches?

44 Which period of history means 'rebirth'?

45 What do you call a five-sided figure?

46 What do you call a thousand years?

47 Which awards are given out anually in Hollywood for achievements in movies?

48 What do you call the arms of an octopus?

49 What people used a tepee as a dwelling?

50 How did the Ancient Egyptians preserve the bodies of their kings?

A nswers to Quiz 18, GEOGRAPHY

1. Spain. 2. India andPakistan.3.Northumberland. 4. Peking. 5. Buckingham Palace. 6. Austria. 7. Devon. 8. Red. 9. Derbyshire. 10. Italy. 11. Africa. 12. West. 13. Argentina. 14. Paris. 15. Portugal. 16. Algeria. 17. Thailand. 18. Scotland. 19. Oslo. 20. Africa. 21. Netherlands. 22. Florida. 23. France. 24. Birmingham. 25. Washington. 26. Pacific. 27. Brazil. 28. Europe. 29. Sweden. 30. Belgium. 31. Perth. 32. Beijing. 33. Emus don't fly. 34. Mediterranean. 35. South Africa. 36. Bay of Biscay. 37. Bulgarian. 38. Italy. 39. East Germany. 40. Jerusalem. 41. South. 42. Seven. 43. Italy. 44. Casablanca. 45. Germany. 46. Cocaine. 47. Nile. 48. Barcelona. 49. Colchester. 50. Jodhpurs.

QUIZ 20 | Books

EASY - LEVEL ONE

1 Who wrote "Little Women"?

2 Name the little creatures in the Moomin books who were attracted by thunder storms?

3 In which book would you find Mayella Ewell?

4 Who wrote "Jane Eyre"?

5 In which series of books would you find the fortress of Salamandastron?

6 In which William Golding book did a party of schoolboys turn cannibal?

7 Which Astrid Lindgren character has a propeller protruding from his back?

8 In which book would you meet Vermicious Knids?

9 Where did Mr Badger live in "The Wind in the Willows"?

10 Who was the author of "Farmer Giles of Ham"?

11 Which creatures lived in Arnold Bros (est. 1905)?

12 Which comic book heroes lived in a sewer and enjoyed martial arts?

13 In which novel was a toad taken in hand by a mole, a rat, and a badger?

14 In which Conan Doyle novel did explorers find live dinosaurs?

15 In which novel do we meet Gagool the witch-finder?

16 What finally killed the invading aliens in "War of the Worlds"?

17 What is the connection between birds, mythical female warriors, and an Arthur Ransom novel?

18 Which novel opens with the words, 'Marley was dead, to begin with'?

19 In the book "Five Children and It" what was It's proper name?

20 C.S. Lewis's Narnia novels had a religious significance. Who did the lion represent?

21 In which novel was it 'always winter but never Christmas'?

22 Why don't hobbits wear shoes?

23 In the New Testament, which John was beheaded for the sake of a dance?

24 In "Great Expectations", what trade did Pip's guardian follow?

25 In which country does Tolstoy's "War and Peace" take place?

26 Who was the villain of "The Adventures of Tom Sawyer"?

27 Who maintained law and order in Noddy's Toyland?

28 Who wrote "The Indian in the Cupboard"?

29 Which girl had a cannibal king for a father and lived with a horse and a monkey?

30 In the book "The Once and Future King", who was the king?

31 In what situation might you need the help of Nancy Drew?

32 After "The Adventures of Tom Sawyer", Tom and Huck meet up

44

again and make a long journey. What transport do they use?

33 What were the names of the Hardy Boys?

34 Which Dickens novel takes place during the French Revolution?

35 Which fictional hero, named after a flower, helped people to escape the guillotine?

36 Which Rosemary Sutcliffe novel concerned a Roman legion?

37 What was Scrooge's first name?

38 Who found himself in Lilliput?

39 Who wrote Dido and Pa?

40 Who is the main character in The Sign of Four and The Speckled Band?

41 Who wrote "The Call of the Wild"?

42 The hero of a Rudyard Kipling novel played a game to improve his memory. What is it called?

43 Which small children's hero was, at the end of the original story, eaten by a spider?

44 Which pirate was handed the black spot in "Treasure Island"?

45 What sort of creature was Tarka?

46 Where does the action of "Lorna Doone" take place?

47 In which novel would you find Heathcliff and Catherine?

48 What is the connection between E. Nesbitt and railways?

49 In which country is the action of "War and Peace" set?

50 Two German brothers wrote a collection of fairy tales. Who were they?

1. An acropolis. 2. A young tree. 3. A nectarine has a smooth, waxy skin, whereas peach skin is fuzzy. 4. Jupiter. 5. Leaves. 6. The dashboard. 7. Migration. 8. Nirvana. 9. A follicle 10. Gemini. 11. Ringo Starr. 12. Quartz. 13. Mexico. 14. Papyrus. 15. A cub. 16. Italy. 17. Extra Terrestrial. 18. Venison. 19. New York. 20. Thriller by Michael Jackson. 21. Robin Williams. 22. Spain. 23. SE Asia 24. Deciduous. 25. Lava. 26. Blind people. 27. White cabbage. 28. The koala's. 29. Brass instruments. 30. Very Important Person. 31. Tina Turner. 32. Mammals. 33. An antibiotic. 34. A mongrel. 35. Red and white. 36. A sickle. 37. Venus. 38. A wild dog. 39. The Rolling Stones. 40. Gold. 41. Hieroglyphics. 42. Daedalus. 43. Frescoes. 44. The Renaissance. 45. A pentagon. 46. A millennium. 47. Oscars. 48. Tentacles. 49. Native Americans. 50. They mummified them.

QUIZ 21 | Places

FOR ANSWERS SEE QUIZ NO 22

EASY - LEVEL ONE

1 Which waterway separates Africa from Asia?

2 What is the capital city of Australia?

3 What is the city of Constantinople now called?

4 Which country does Greenland belong to?

5 Which city is further north – Paris or New York?

6 Which two countries does Norway have borders with?

7 Which is the second largest country in the world?

8 What do you call the narrow coastal inlets in Scandinavia?

9 Which are the two official languages of South Africa?

10 In which city would you find the Parthenon?

11 Which is the highest peak in the Alps?

12 Which country has the largest supplies of gold?

13 What is the capital of Massachusetts?

14 Which is the most southerly point of South America?

15 Which is the longest river in North America?

16 In which US city would you find the Sears Tower?

17 Which two languages are spoken in Belgium?

18 If you are at Orly Airport which city would you be in?

19 Which country has about 40% of its land situated below sea level?

20 In which Italian city would you find the Bridge of Sighs?

21 Which two countries make up the Iberian Peninsula?

22 In which country would you pay in drachmas?

23 Which volcano is situated on the island of Sicily?

24 Which country does Corsica belong to?

25 Which of these countries does the Equator not go through: Zaire, Indonesia, Argentina, Kenya, or Brazil?

26 In which continent is Lake Victoria?

27 Which city does the Sugar Loaf Mountain overlook?

28 Which country does Iceland belong to?

29 In which city is the church Sacre Coeur situated?

30 What language is spoken in Syria?

31 Which is the largest state of the USA?

32 Which country is Helsinki the capital of?

33 Which religious community has its headquarters in Salt Lake City?

34 Which is the largest country in South America?

35 In which city would you find the Brandenburg Gate?

36 Which is the highest mountain peak in Africa?

37 What is the name of the island state situated south of the Malay Peninsula?

38 On which river is Paris situated?

39 To which group of islands does Lanzarote belong?

40 On which lake is Chicago situated?

41 Under what name was Thailand formerly known?

42 What is the name of the Italian island to the South of Corsica?

43 Where are the Atlas Mountains?

44 Where is the seat of the International Red Cross?

45 What is the capital of Argentina?

46 Which is the largest of the Greek islands?

47 What language is spoken in Brazil?

48 What is Leningrad now called?

49 In which country would you pay with guilders?

50 Before Kenya gained independence, which country had been its governor?

A nswers to Quiz 20, BOOKS

1. Louisa May Alcott. 2. The Hattifatteners. 3. To Kill a Mockingbird. 4. Charlotte Brontë. 5. Redwall. 6. Lord of the Flies. 7. Karlson on the Roof. 8. Charlie and the Great Glass Elevator. 9. The Wild Wood 10. J.R.R. Tolkien. 11. The Nomes. 12. Diggers. 13. The Teenage Mutant Ninja Turtles. 14. The Lost World. 15. King Solomon's Mines. 16. Bacteria. 17. Ransom wrote Swallows and Amazons. 18. A Christmas Carol. 19. The Psammead. 20. Jesus. 21. The Lion, The Witch and the Wardrobe. 22. They have furry feet with leathery soles. 23. John the Baptist. 24. He was a blacksmith. 25. Toto. 26. Injun Joe. 27. Russia. 28. Lynn Reid Banks. 29. Pippi Longstocking. 30. King Arthur. 31. To solve a crime. 32. A hot air balloon. 33. Frank and Joe. 34. A Tale of Two Cities. 35. The Scarlet Pimpernel. 36. The Eagle of the Ninth. 37. Ebeneezer. 38. Gulliver. 39. Joan Aiken. 40. Sherlock Holmes. 41. Jack London. 42. Kim's game. 43. Tom Thumb. 44. Long John Silver. 45. An otter. 46. Exmoor. 47. Wuthering Heights. 48. She wrote The Railway Children. 49. Russia. 50. The Brothers Grimm.

QUIZ 22 Pot Luck

1 What was the prehistoric predecessor of the elephant?

2 Which sign of the Zodiac represents a pair of scales?

3 What is the main difference between a guitar and a violin?

4 Who was the lead singer of the group Queen?

5 What type of entertainment was Fred Astaire famous for?

6 How many minutes does a soccer match last?

7 What type of instrument would you use to view a distant star?

8 Which people built longships?

9 During a period of high pressure, would you expect sunny or changeable weather?

10 Which was Walt Disney's first full-length animated cartoon?

11 Which title was given to the kings of Ancient Egypt?

12 In which historical period does Gone with the Wind take place?

13 What is the name of the layer that protects the Earth from the ultra violet rays of the Sun?

14 In which country was paper invented?

15 From which European country does the paella originate?

16 What does a flag at half mast indicate?

17 In which Steven Spielberg film would you find dinosaurs living in modern times?

18 Which group of animals form a shoal?

19 What type of stories did Hans Christian Andersen write?

20 What is special about the Dog Star (Canis Major)?

21 What does a skunk do to ward off predators?

22 In which country is Krakow situated?

23 In which country would you find the river Seine?

24 What is the name of the professional fighters in Ancient Rome who engaged in public performances?

25 What distinguishes a British stamp from all other stamps in the world?

26 Which country is also referred to as Eire?

27 What do you call a person that studies the stars?

28 A silkworm feeds on the leaves of which tree?

29 In which country did people first have a Christmas tree?

30 In which European city would you find Eurodisney?

31 What are the colors of the German flag?

32 The Marseillaise is the national anthem of which country?

33 In Greek mythology, what was the most prominent feature of a Cyclops?

34 Where is Robin Hood supposed to have lived?

35 What does supersonic mean?

36 Which of the following is not a measurement of length: meter, cubic feet, inch, yard, or mile?

37 In a soccer team, who is the only player who can pick up a ball with his hands?

38 What is a gaucho?

39 Which of the following countries are not monarchies: The Netherlands, Sweden or Italy?

40 What do you call a flesh-eating animal?

41 What do you call a person who prepares weather forecasts?

42 What do you call the figure written below the line in a fraction?

43 What do you call the process by which gas or vapor turns liquid?

44 What do you call the place a rabbit lives in?

45 Which Greek goddess is believed to have emerged from the sea?

46 Which country would a cosmonaut come from?

47 What do you call it when the Moon moves in front of the Sun and blocks out all the light?

48 What sort of animal is a gibbon?

49 In a soccer match, what does a player have to do if he is shown a red card?

50 What do you call a group of lions?

Answers to Quiz 21, PLACES

1. The Suez Canal. 2. Canberra. 3. Istanbul. 4. Denmark. 5. Paris. 6. Sweden and Finland. 7. Canada. 8. Fjords. 9. English and Afrikaans. 10. Athens. 11. Mont Blanc. 12. South Africa. 13. Boston. 14. Cape Horn. 15. Mississippi-Missouri. 16. Chicago. 17. French and Flemish. 18. Paris. 19. The Netherlands. 20. Venice. 21. Spain and Portugal. 22. Greece. 23. Mount Etna. 24. France. 25. Argentina. 26. Africa. 27. Rio de Janeiro. 28. None – it is an independent republic. 29. Paris. 30. Arabic. 31. Alaska. 32. Finland. 33. The Mormons. 34. Brazil. 35. Berlin. 36. Kilimanjaro. 37. Singapore. 38. Seine. 39. Canaries. 40. Lake Michigan. 41. Siam. 42. Sardinia. 43. In North Africa, between the Mediterranean and the Sahara desert. 44. Geneva. 45. Buenos Aires. 46. Crete. 47. Portuguese. 48. Saint Petersburg. 49. The Netherlands. 50. Great Britain.

Q UIZ 23 | Books

EASY - LEVEL ONE

1 What is the best selling book of all time?

2 Who created the character of Miss Marple?

3 Which Emily wrote "Wuthering Heights"?

4 Which creator of Jeeves and Wooster is known by his initials P.G.?

5 Whose first Secret Diary was written when he was 13 3/4?

6 What was the profession of James Herriot?

7 What is the surname of romantic novelist Dame Barbara?

8 Which London barrister was created by John Mortimer?

9 Whose Lover was the subject of a book by D.H. Lawrence?

10 Which sport are Dick Francis' novels about?

11 Which politician Jeffrey wrote "Kane and Abel"?

12 Which novelist Jackie has an actress sister called Joan?

13 Which Ruth created Inspector Wexford?

14 What did Tolstoy write about together with War?

15 What was on the Island Robert Louis Stevenson wrote about?

16 What was the surname of the Dickens character Oliver?

17 Which Peter took the Darling children to Never Never Land?

18 Which bird of prey Has Landed, in the book by Jack Higgins?

19 What is the first name of novelist Miss Cookson?

20 Which detective novelist is known by her initials P.D.?

21 Which little girl had Adventures Through the Looking Glass?

22 How many Musketeers were there in the title of the book by Dumas?

23 Which Robinson was shipwrecked on a desert island?

24 Where is the Wind in the story about Toad and Badger?

25 What was the surname of Ebenezer in "A Christmas Carol"?

26 Which Jilly wrote about Polo and Riders?

27 Which popular yellow spring flower did Wordsworth write about?

28 What type of writing is John Betjeman famous for?

29 What is the nationality of Agatha Christie's detective Poirot?

30 What is the religious occupation of medieval detective Cadfael?

31 Charles Dodgson wrote his classic children's story under what name?

32 Which Frederick wrote "The Day of The Jackal"?

33 Fitzwilliam Darcy appears in which novel?

34 Whom did Bertie Wooster have

as his manservant?

35 Which Irving Welsh novel was about Scottish heroin addicts?

36 Which county in England did Laurie Lee come from?

37 Which Arthur wrote the children's classic "Swallows and Amazons"?

38 Which James became Britain's most read vet?

39 Who created Thomas the Tank Engine?

40 Which French detective was created by Georges Simenon?

41 What was the first name of the girl who went to live at Green Gables?

42 Who created the Discworld books?

43 Which Ian created James Bond?

44 Which creatures are the central characters in "Watership Down"?

45 Who wrote "Rebecca"?

46 What was the name of the boy in "The Jungle Book"?

47 What term is used for writing a novel that will go out under someone else's name?

48 Which novelist born in 1886 had the initials H.G.?

49 What is Joseph Heller's novel with a number in its catchy title?

50 Which children's publisher has a black-and-red insect as its logo?

Answers to
Quiz 22, POT LUCK

1. The mammoth. 2. Libra. 3. A violin is played with a bow, while the guitar is plucked. 4. Freddie Mercury. 5. Dancing. 6. Ninety minutes. 7. A telescope. 8. The Vikings. 9. Sunny weather. 10. Snow White and the Seven Dwarfs. 11. Pharaoh. 12. The American Civil War. 13. The ozone layer. 14. China. 15. Spain. 16. That somebody has died. 17. Jurassic Park. 18. Fish. 19. Fairy tales. 20. It is the brightest star in the sky. 21. It sprays them with a bad-smelling liquid. 22. Poland. 23. France. 24. Gladiators. 25. It does not have the name of the country printed on it. 26. The Republic of Ireland. 27. An astronomer. 28. The mulberry tree. 29. Germany. 30. Paris. 31. Black, red, and gold. 32. France. 33. He has only one eye. 34. Sherwood Forest, England. 35. Faster than the speed of sound. 36. Cubic feet. 37. The goalkeeper. 38. A South American cowboy. 39. Italy. 40. A carnivore. 41. A meteorologist. 42. The denominator. 43. Condensation. 44. A warren. 45. Aphrodite. 46. Russia. 47. A total eclipse of the Sun. 48. An ape. 49. Leave the pitch. 50. A pride.

Q_{24}^{UIZ} Pot Luck

EASY - LEVEL ONE

1 Who designed Coventry cathedral?

2 In which TV programme do Ian Botham and Bill Beaumont appear as team captains?

3 In 1979, Brighton Council decided to allow what type of beach?

4 Which David told his life story in "The Moon's a Balloon"?

5 Rocks are broken down by the elements by what gradual process?

6 Which tenor took the title role in "The Great Caruso"?

7 The word lupine relates to which animals?

8 In which country is the volcano Popocatépetl?

9 What number does the Roman numeral D stand for?

10 What was Jed Clampett's daughter called in "The Beverley Hillbillies"?

11 In which month is the first day of spring?

12 Who co-wrote a "Liverpool Oratorio" with Carl Davis?

13 Which stage direction means to go off stage?

14 What are the two initials of Narnia creator Lewis?

15 What was the name of the Spanish waiter in "Fawlty Towers"?

16 What dramatic event happened to Terry Kath of rock group Chicago at a party in 1978?

17 Which element is found in bones, shells and teeth?

18 In the early 1700s who invented a seed drill?

19 What are Gary Barlow, Howard Donald, Jason Orange and Mark Owen better known as?

20 What part of a garment is a raglan?

21 What scale is used to measure wind velocity?

22 In which country is the Table Mountain?

23 Which soap character had a secretary called Sly?

24 What is a young stallion called?

25 What is the Republic of Ireland's airline called?

26 What does the French word *vacances* mean?

27 What is the first name of TV cook Mosimann?

28 In tennis, what is a score of 40 all called?

29 Threshers and hammerheads are types of what?

30 The NUM is the National Union of what?

31 Which extra title was given to Catherine II of Russia?

32 Which constituency returned the MP with the highest majority in the 1992 General Election?

33 Which country is a car from if it

has the international registration
letter H?

34 Which came first the House of
Tudor or the House of Stuart?

35 Which Norman said, "He got on
his bike and looked for work."

36 What was the name of the witch
played by Agnes Moorhead in
"Bewitched"?

37 Zn is the symbol of which
chemical element?

38 In "Coronation Street" what is
Ken Barlow's job?

39 According to proverb, one man's
meat is another man's what?

40 Which radio DJ urged listeners
to 'fight the flab'?

41 Williams and Conference are
types of what?

42 Who recorded the album
"Medusa"?

43 How many times did Will Carling
skipper England before giving up
the captaincy in '96?

44 What is capital of Afghanistan?

45 Who was the female lead in the
TV sitcom "Terry and June?"

46 In which country was "The Flame
Trees of Thika" set?

47 What's the link between Shag,
The Weatherman and Sakkarin?

48 Which Irish entertainer Val used
to sing in a rocking chair?

49 How many yards in a mile?

50 Who was the only British female
singer to have three UK No 1s
in the 60s?

A nswers to
Quiz 23, Books

1. The Bible. 2. Agatha Christie. 3. Brontë. 4.
Wodehouse. 5. Adrian Mole. 6. Vet. 7. Cartland.
8. Rumpole. 9. Lady Chatterley. 10. Horse racing.
11. Archer. 12. Collins. 13. Rendell. 14. Peace.
15. Treasure. 16. Twist. 17. Pan. 18. Eagle. 19.
Catherine. 20. James. 21. Alice. 22 .Three. 23.
Crusoe. 24. The Willows. 25. Scrooge. 26.
Cooper. 27. Daffodils. 28. Poetry. 29. Belgian. 30.
Monk. 31. Lewis Carroll. 32. Forsyth. 33. Pride
and Prejudice. 34. Jeeves. 35. Trainspotting. 36.
Gloucestershire. 37. Rackham. 38. Herriot. 39.
Rev Awdry. 40. Maigret. 41. Anne. 42. Terry
Pratchett. 43. Fleming. 44. Rabbits.
45. Daphne Du Maurier. 46. Mowgli. 47.
Ghosting. 48. Wells. 49. Catch-22. 50. Ladybird.

QUIZ 25 | Places

EASY - LEVEL ONE

1 Which country is associated with bullfighting?

2 In which European city would you find Westminster Abbey?

3 Which is the largest country in South America?

4 In which European country, apart from Germany, is German the only official language?

5 Which is the smallest continent?

6 In which country would you find the pyramids?

7 What region are Denmark, Sweden, Norway, and Finland known as?

8 On which continent is Israel situated?

9 What is the capital of Japan?

10 Which canal links the Atlantic and Pacific Oceans in Central America?

11 In which country would you find Cape Town?

12 In which European city would you find the Colosseum?

13 In which city would you find the Kremlin?

14 On which ocean is San Francisco situated?

15 Which is the highest mountain range in the world?

16 Which language is spoken in Mexico?

17 What do the stars on the American flag stand for?

18 Which is the most famous building in Pisa?

19 What is the capital of Germany?

20 Which island state lies to the south-east of Australia?

21 What is the Serengeti known for?

22 What is the Sahara?

23 Which is the most northerly state in the USA?

24 In which continent would you find the country of Zaire?

25 What religion are the majority of people of India?

26 Which city is further north – New York or Moscow?

27 Which country would you go through in order to travel by land from France to Portugal?

28 Which island state lies to the west of Great Britain?

29 Which continents do the Ural Mountains separate?

30 In which US city would you find the Golden Gate Bridge?

31 With which countries does Iceland border?

32 What is the capital of Egypt?

33 Which is the largest mountain range in Europe?

34 In which European city would you find the Parthenon?

35 Rio de Janeiro is situated in which country?

36 What type of fish can you find in the Dead Sea?

37 Which inhabited continent is entirely in the Southern Hemisphere?

38 Which ocean would you have to cross to travel from London to New York?

39 In which city would you find the Hermitage Museum?

40 In which island group would you find Honolulu?

41 Ottawa is the capital of which country?

42 In which city would you find the Empire State Building?

43 Which of these cities is the odd one out: Calcutta, Bombay, New Delhi, Bangkok, Madras?

44 The Bloody Tower is part of which English castle?

45 The island of Sicily belongs to which country?

46 What is the capital of China?

47 Which island state lies to the South of Florida?

48 In which European city would you find the Eiffel Tower?

49 Which is the main language spoken in Israel?

50 On which continent is Sydney situated?

Answers to Quiz 24, Pot Luck

1. Basil Spence 2. A Question of Sport. 3. Nudist. 4. Niven. 5. Weathering. 6. Mario Lanza. 7. Wolves. 8. Mexico. 9. 500. 10. Elly May. 11. March. 12. Paul McCartney. 13. Exit. 14. C.S. 15. Manuel. 16. Accidentally shot himself dead. 17. Calcium. 18. Jethro Tull. 19. Take That. 20. Sleeve. 21. Beaufort. 22. South Africa. 23. J.R. Ewing. 24. Colt. 25. Aer Lingus. 26. Holidays. 27. Anton. 28. Deuce. 29. Shark. 30. Mineworkers. 31. The Great. 32. Huntingdon (J. Major 36,320). 33. Hungary. 34. The House of Tudor. 35. Tebbit. 36. Endora. 37. Zinc. 38. Teacher. 39. Poison. 40. Terry Wogan. 41. Pear. 42. Annie Lennox. 43. 57. 44. Kabul. 45. June Whitfield. 46. Kenya. 47. All guises of Jonathan King. 48. Doonican. 49. 1,760. 50. Sandie Shaw.

Q^{UIZ} 26 **Science**

EASY - LEVEL ONE

1 What happens to objects in zero gravity?

2 What do you call the thin coil of wire inside a light bulb?

3 Why do water pipes often burst in freezing weather?

4 What happens if you push a north pole of one magnet towards a north pole of another magnet?

5 Which are the primary colors?

6 Which instrument would you use to measure air pressure?

7 Why would a balloon filled with hot air fly better on a cold day than on a warm day?

8 What do vibrations in the air produce?

9 What do you call a material that can carry electricity?

10 What would you test with litmus paper?

11 What is electric current measured in?

12 What is the so-called 'greenhouse effect'?

13 Which two metals does bronze mainly consist of?

14 Which theory is express by the equation $E = mc^2$?

15 Which of the following was not a scientist: Copernicus, Gogol, or Pasteur?

16 What is the process by which seeds produce roots and shoots?

17 What is the process by which iron rusts?

18 Can water fall below freezing point without turning to ice?

19 Some parts of the Sun are cooler and darker than others. What are these called?

20 If a creature is described as 'saurian' what is it like?

21 What do botanists study?

22 Do heavy objects fall faster than light ones?

23 In the northern hemisphere, in which direction would the winds of a low pressure system circulate?

24 What process describes the moving of continents?

25 What is the hottest part of a candle flame?

26 What force makes objects fall to earth?

27 What is meant by the 'escape velocity' of a rocket leaving the earth?

28 Which type of carbon is used both as a lubricant and as the 'lead' in pencils?

29 Iron pyrites has a golden colour. What is its nickname?

30 Which very precious stone is made from heavily compressed carbon?

31 Which strong metal is composed mainly of iron and carbon?

32 If at least 10% chromium is added to steel to prevent corrosion, what is the resulting metal called?

33 Where in the garden would you

expect to find humus?

34 What useful function does the Earth's ozone layer perform?

35 What is a common name for the Aurora Borealis?

36 What is the storage capacity of a floppy disk measured in?

37 What is the full name for the 'tube' of a television?

38 Does water ice exist on Mars?

39 The planet Uranus is orbited by at least 15 moons. What other objects surround the planet?

40 If something is called 'vitreous', what does this mean?

41 What is the difference between flammable and inflammable?

42 What gas is found in marshes and down coal mines?

43 Where would you expect to find gluten?

44 Neon signs contain the gas neon, of course, but what other gas is also commonly used?

45 With the development of what weapon is J. Robert Oppenheimer associated?

46 In computers what does BIOS stand for?

47 What does CD-ROM stand for?

48 What is solid carbon dioxide called?

49 Apart from freezing water vapour, what else is necessary for a snow flake to form?

50 The air mixture breathed by divers contains oxygen mixed with what other gas?

Answers to Quiz 25, PLACES

1. Spain. 2. London. 3. Brazil. 4. Austria. 5. Australia. 6. Egypt. 7. Scandinavia. 8. Asia. 9. Tokyo. 10. The Panama Canal. 11. South Africa. 12. Rome. 13. Moscow. 14. The Pacific. 15. The Himalayas. 16. Spanish. 17. There is one star for every state. 18. The Leaning Tower. 19. Berlin. 20. New Zealand. 21. It is a national park created to preserve species of wild animal. 22. The world's largest desert. 23. Alaska. 24. Africa. 25. Hindu. 26. Moscow. 27. Spain. 28. Ireland. 29. Europe and Asia. 30. San Francisco. 31. None, it is an island. 32. Cairo. 33. The Alps. 34. Athens. 35. Brazil. 36. Because of its high level of salt there are no living creatures. 37. Australia. 38. The Atlantic Ocean. 39. St Petersburg. 40. Hawaii. 41. Canada. 42. New York City. 43. Bangkok. It is the capital of Thailand, and all the others are Indian cities. 44. The Tower of London. 45. Italy. 46. Beijing. 47. Cuba. 48. Paris. 49. Hebrew. 50. Australia.

Pot Luck

EASY - LEVEL ONE

1 In Greek mythology, who slew the Minotaur?

2 Lufthansa is the national airline of which country?

3 A muslim is a follower of which religion?

4 What do you call a plant-eating animal?

5 What do you call a group of stars?

6 Which painter created the Mona Lisa?

7 What does a philatelist collect?

8 Which instrument would a doctor use to listen to your chest?

9 From which material is a xylophone made?

10 Which prize is awarded annually in Norway for outstanding achievements in promoting world peace?

11 Christopher Reeve became famous for his portrayal of which comic book character?

12 Which country's flag is referred to as "Tricolor"?

13 What do you call a person who studies the history, structure and, origin of the Earth?

14 Which sign of the zodiac represents a goat?

15 Which title does a Jewish religious leader carry?

16 What are teeth used for cutting called?

17 In which country would you hear Flemish being spoken?

18 On which islands do people dance the Hula Hula?

19 In which state does the Pope live?

20 Who played James Bond in the film "The Spy Who Loved Me"?

21 What treasure is kept in Fort Knox?

22 In which building does the president of the USA live?

23 What is a person with arachnophobia frightened of?

24 What kind of animals were Lady and the Tramp?

25 Which actor played Kojak on television?

26 Which direction does the needle on a compass always point to?

27 Which European city does the Greenwich Meridian go through?

28 What do you call the wind that accompanies the wet season in India and South-east Asia?

29 What was the sequel to "Star Wars"?

30 How many degrees does a right angle have?

31 What would you find in the Louvre?

32 What is the capital of Belgium?

33 What sort of animal is a gerbil?

34 What would somebody perform an autopsy on?

35 Who directed the film Jaws?

36 Which character's nose grew longer when he told a lie?

37 What system do the brain and spinal cord form?

38 In which country would you find Adelaide and Brisbane?

39 What is the name for a river that flows into a larger river?

40 What suits are there in a pack of cards?

41 Which film features the song 'Take My Breath Away'?

42 If it is lunchtime in London, what time of day would it be in New York?

43 What are 100 acres called?

44 Which country does Edam cheese come from?

45 Which country has the largest population?

46 A person with the most common form of color blindness cannot distinguish between which two colors?

47 What do you call animals with a pouch?

48 In which country is the Black Forest situated?

49 In which part of the body are the vertebrae?

50 Which country would you have to cross to travel from Alaska to the rest of the USA?

A nswers to Quiz 26, SCIENCE

1. They float. 2. A filament. 3. Because water expands when it turns into ice. 4. They repel each other. 5. Red, yellow, and blue. 6. A barometer. 7. Hot air always rises, and the difference in temperature is greater on a cold day. 8. A sound. 9. A conductor. 10. Whether a substance is acid or alkaline. 11. Ampere. 12. Heat enters the atmosphere from the sun and is trapped by gases. Therefore the heat of the atmosphere increases. 13. Copper and tin. 14. The Theory of Relativity. 15. Gogol. 16. Germination. 17. Oxidation. 18. Yes. 19. Sun spots. 20. Like a lizard. 21. Plants. 22. No, though some objects, for example feathers, experience air resistance which makes them fall more slowly than a compact object of the same weight. 23. Anticlockwise. 24. Continental drift. 25. The tip. 26. Gravity. 27. The speed at which it must travel to escape Earth's gravity. 28. Graphite. 29. Fool's gold. 30. Diamond. 31. Steel. 32. Stainless steel. 33. In soil. 34. It prevents ultraviolet and other harmful radiation from penetrating the atmosphere. 35. The Northern Lights. 36. Megabytes. 37. Cathode ray tube. 38. Yes. 39. Rings. 40. It resembles glass. 41. There is no difference: they both mean 'easily set on fire'. 42. Methane. 43. In cereal grains (especially corn and wheat). 44. Argon. 45. The atomic bomb. 46. Basic Input Output System. 47. Compact Disk – Read Only Memory. 48. Dry ice. 49. A dust particle. 50. Helium.

Q^{UIZ} 28 | Places

EASY - LEVEL ONE

1 What is the capital of Italy?

2 Which ocean lies between North America and Japan?

3 In which European city do people travel around by gondolas?

4 Which is the main language spoken in Egypt?

5 On which sea are Italy, Greece, and the south of France situated?

6 In which country would you pay in Deutschmarks?

7 On which continent is Mexico situated?

8 What is the capital of the USA?

9 Which city is further north – London or Los Angeles?

10 Which is the highest mountain in the world?

11 With which of these countries does France not border: Germany, Spain or Russia?

12 In which country would you find the Rocky Mountains?

13 If you are travelling to Heathrow Airport, which country would be your destination?

14 Which city is the odd one out: New York, Paris or New Orleans?

15 Which waterway must you cross to travel from England to France?

16 Los Angeles, San Francisco and San Diego are all in which US state?

17 On which continent is Spain situated?

18 Which are the only two continents that are joined together?

19 Which is the odd country out: Great Britain, Greenland or Germany?

20 What is the capital of Russia?

21 Does Canada lie north or south of the Equator?

22 Which country lies to the north of England?

23 In which city is Red Square situated: New York, Moscow, or Athens?

24 If you travelled to Australia in July, what season would it be?

25 In which European city would you find Big Ben?

26 Which is the largest city in the Netherlands?

27 On which ocean is New York situated?

28 In which country would you find Barcelona, Madrid and Malaga?

29 Which two languages are spoken in Wales?

30 Which is the odd country out: USA, France, Australia, Ireland, or Great Britain?

31 In which city would you find Manhattan and Central Park?

32 Which country would you need to cross to travel from Canada to Mexico?

33 What is the capital of Israel?

34 Which pole is New Zealand nearest to?

35 With which country does China

not form a border: Russia,
Mongolia or Israel?

36 Which US state is further west,
Texas or Florida?

37 What type of mountain is
Fujiyama?

38 Athens is the capital of which
country?

39 Apart from France, which other
country uses Francs?

40 Which of the following cities is
not situated at the coast: Boston,
Copenhagen or Moscow?

41 In which US state is Disneyland
situated?

42 In which European city would you
find the Champs Elysées and the
Arc de Triomphe?

43 In which of the following countries
would you not find any Inuit:
Canada, Mexico or Greenland?

44 In which country would you most
likely find a mosque as a country's
main place of worship?

45 In which African state is
Johannesburg situated?

46 Which European country has the
shape of a boot?

47 Which continent is situated south
of Europe?

48 Which of the following countries
does not border the Atlantic:
France, USA or China?

49 Where would the climate be
warmer – Norway or Portugal?

50 Which is the odd one out:
Paris, Oxford, Rome, Tokyo or
Moscow?

A nswers to
Quiz 27, Pot Luck

1. Theseus. 2. Germany. 3. Islam. 4. A herbivore.
5. A constellation. 6. Leonardo da Vinci. 7.
Stamps. 8. A stethoscope. 9. Wood. 10. The
Nobel Peace Prize. 11. Superman. 12. France's.
13. A geologist. 14. Capricorn. 15. Rabbi. 16.
Incisors. 17. Belgium. 18. Hawaii. 19. Vatican
City. 20. Roger Moore. 21. The bulk of the gold
bullion reserves of the USA. 22. The White
House. 23. Spiders. 24. Dogs. 25. Telly Savalas.
26. North. 27. London. 28. Monsoon. 29. The
Empire Strikes Back. 30. Ninety. 31. Works of
art: it's an art gallery. 32. Brussels. 33. A rodent.
34. A dead body. 35. Steven Spielberg. 36.
Pinocchio's. 37. The central nervous system. 38.
Australia. 39. A tributary. 40. Hearts, spades, diamonds, and clubs. 41. Top Gun. 42. Morning. 43.
A hectare. 44. Holland. 45. China. 46. Red and
green. 47. Marsupials. 48. Germany. 49. The
back; they form the spinal column. 50. Canada.

QUIZ 29 | Pot Luck

EASY - LEVEL ONE

1 Do stalactites grow up or down?
2 What is another name for the constellation Orion?
3 Lakota, Dakota, and Arapaho are all what sort of people?
4 What are clouds usually made of?
5 Who was imprisoned and executed at Fotheringay?
6 Do daffodils grow from seeds, bulbs, or corms?
7 'Bald', 'golden', and 'sea' are all varieties of what sort of bird?
8 What completely harmless creature is sometimes called a devilfish because of its horned head?
9 What sort of creature is a flying fox?
10 Vampire bats exist only in stories. True or false?
11 What weather phenomenon was the Norse god Thor thought to control?
12 What was strange about the appearance of a cyclops?
13 Which constellation can be seen in Australia but not in the Northern Hemisphere?
14 What does a snake do to aid its growing process?
15 Which soldiers were known as 'iron sides'?
16 Narcissus stared at his reflection in a pond for so long that some thing unfortunate happened to him. What was it?

17 What causes the phenomena known as shooting stars?
18 By what other name is the Yeti known?
19 Of which community is the Dalai Lama the spiritual head?
20 Of which country was Lenin the leader?
21 What number is meant by a 'gross'?
22 Which town lost its children to the Pied Piper?
23 What was the name of the uncouth savages in "Gulliver's Travels"?
24 What is the difference between pianoforte and forte-piano?
25 Antonio Stradivari was a famous maker of musical instruments. In what did he specialize?
26 On which side of a tree would you expect to see lichen growing?
27 In which country does most of Siberia lie?
28 Which so-called sea is actually the world's largest lake?
29 Where would you find the Sea of Tranquillity?
30 Which lake in north-central Scotland is reputed to contain a monster?
31 What is a kumquat?
32 What is meant by the expressions 'in the land of Nod' and 'in the arms of Morpheus'?
33 How many bits make one byte?

34 What mysterious event took place at Belshazzar's feast?

35 Which building is occupied by the US Defense Department?

36 What does 1760 yards make?

37 Is a tomato a vegetable?

38 What is a prickly pear?

39 What is another name for egg plant?

40 What wood was frequently used for making longbows?

41 What wood did the British Navy use to build its ships?

42 How was Hamlet's father murdered?

43 Who wore an ass's head in "A Midsummer Night's Dream"?

44 Who was the villain in "Tom Brown's Schooldays"?

45 How often does Halley's comet return to the vicinity of Earth?

46 How did the Invisible Man cover up his problem?

47 Which H. G. Wells story showed horrific visions of the future?

48 Which character in ancient mythology had a sword suspended over his head, held by a single hair?

49 Who turned his daughter to gold with a kiss?

50 What supposedly happens to trolls caught in the daylight?

Answers to Quiz 28, PLACES

1. Rome. 2. The Pacific. 3. Venice. 4. Arabic. 5. The Mediterranean. 6. Germany. 7. North America. 8. Washington DC. 9. London. 10. Mount Everest. 11. Russia. 12. The USA. 13. England. 14. Paris; all the others are American cities. 15. The English Channel. 16. California. 17. Europe. 18. Europe and Asia. 19. Germany; all the others are island states. 20. Moscow. 21. North. 22. Scotland. 23. Moscow. 24. Winter. 25. London. 26. Amsterdam. 27. The Atlantic. 28. Spain. 29. English and Welsh. 30. France; in all the others English is the main language. 31. New York. 32. The USA. 33. Jerusalem. 34. The South Pole. 35. Israel. 36. Texas. 37. A volcano. 38. (a) Greece. 39. (c) Switzerland. 40. Moscow. 41. California. 42. Paris. 43. Mexico. 44. Saudi Arabia. 45. South Africa. 46. Italy. 47. Africa. 48. China. 49. Portugal. 50. Oxford; all the others are capital cities.

QUIZ 30 | Human Body

EASY - LEVEL ONE

1 What name is more usually given to the epidermis?

2 What do we call the collection of bones that supports the body?

3 What part of your body has auricles and ventricles?

4 What is a more common name for the patella?

5 Do your hair and nails continue to grow after you are dead?

6 What part of the mouth is affected by periodontitis?

7 How many milk (first) teeth do we have?

8 What are the bones of the spine called?

9 In which body organ would you find a retina?

10 The body has two intestines; what are they called?

11 Men have a lump clearly visible at the front of the throat. What is the common name for it?

12 Is it true that men and women have different numbers of ribs?

13 What is the common name for the esophagus?

14 What is the hard substance just under the white enamel of your teeth?

15 What is the average pulse rate for an adult at rest?

16 We have much more liver than we actually need. True or false?

17 Which human organ, shaped rather like a small sack, can become full of stones?

18 What is the technical name for the vertical bone that runs down the middle of the chest?

19 Where would you find the ulna and radius?

20 What is the technical name for the liquid waste which is collected in the bladder?

21 What are the millions of holes covering skin called?

22 What effect does the diasease hemophilia have on the blood?

23 What is the name given to the large chewing teeth at the back of the mouth?

24 What is the pigment that gives some people brown skin?

25 Where in the body is saliva found?

26 What is dandruff?

27 What is the disease in which the body's joints wear out?

28 Which are the smallest blood vessels: arteries, capillaries or veins?

29 What is myopia?

30 Where would you find the tibia and fibula?

31 What is the name for the two spongy organs with which we breathe?

32 Which of these is not a body organ: eulogy, spleen, or pancreas?

33 What organs transmit messages from parts of the body to the brain?

34 By what other name are the front cutting teeth known?

35 In what part of the body would you find a drum?

36 What is the mat of muscle that makes the lungs move?

37 What is inside the eyeball?

38 In which organ of the body would you find the pituitary gland?

39 What is the bone to which the legs are attached?

40 Why do we sweat?

41 In which part of the body would you find biceps and triceps?

42 Which part of the body is attacked by the disease meningitis?

43 Which childhood disease causes the salivary glands in the jaw to swell dramatically?

44 Which of these is not part of the body: coccyx, occiput, or pachyderm?

45 What is the process called by which food is broken down and nutrition extracted?

46 What is the technical name for breathing?

47 Where would you find the gluteus maximus muscles?

48 Which part of the inner ear controls our sense of balance?

49 What is the condition in which part of the stomach lining inflamed by gastric juices?

50 Which substance, associated with animal fat, is responsible for the narrowing of arteries?

Answers to Quiz 29, Pot Luck

1. Down. 2. The Hunter. 3. Native American Indians. 4. Water vapor (sometimes ice crystals). 5. Mary Queen of Scots. 6. Bulbs. 7. Eagle. 8. The manta ray. 9. A type of bat. 10. False. 11. Thunder. 12. They had only one eye. 13. The Southern Cross. 14. It sheds its skin. 15. Oliver Cromwell's roundheads. 16. He turned into a flower. 17. Meteors burning up in Earth's atmosphere. 18. The Abominable Snowman. 19. Tibetan Buddhists. 20. The Soviet Union. 21. 144. 22. Hamlin. 23. Yahoos. 24. Pianoforte is an instrument, forte-piano means playing loudly and then suddenly softly. 25. Violins. 26. The south side. 27. Russia. 28. The Caspian Sea. 29. On the Moon. 30. Loch Ness. 31. A fruit resembling a small orange. 32. Sleeping. 33. Eight. 34. Writing magically appeared on the wall. 35. The Pentagon. 36. One mile. 37. No; botanically it is a fruit. 38. A type of cactus with a prickly but edible fruit. 39. Aubergine. 40. Yew. 41. Oak. 42. Poison was poured into his ear. 43. Bottom. 44. Flashman. 45. About every 76 years. 46. He wore bandages. 47. The Time Machine. 48. Damocles. 49. King Midas. 50. They turn to stone.

Q^{UIZ}₃₁ Pot Luck

EASY - LEVEL ONE

1 What was the original name of Drake's ship "The Golden Hind"?

2 What is the term for a positive electrode?

3 In "Last Of The Summer Wine" what was Nora's husband called?

4 Which swimming stroke is named after an insect?

5 Which English queen has the same name as a type of plum?

6 Which Rovers does veteran cartoon character Roy play for?

7 How many dots are used in each letter in the Braille system?

8 Who won the Oscar for best actor in both 1993 and 1994?

9 What is a female deer called?

10 Who was the first player to score a maximum 147 break in World Championship snooker?

11 What can be an island, a sweater or a potato?

12 What unit is used to measure horses?

13 Who is Reg Dwight better known as?

14 Who is the lead singer with folk-rock group Steeleye Span?

15 In "Red Dwarf" what was the ranking of Technician Dave Lister?

16 How many tenpin bowling skittles need knocking down for a strike?

17 How is 77 represented in Roman numerals?

18 Who is the patron saint of music?

19 What are birds of a feather said to do?

20 "Kiss Me Kate" is a musical version of which play by Shakespeare?

21 The single "Papa Don't Preach" came from which Madonna album?

22 Betz cells are found in which part of the body?

23 What is the only bird that can hover in the air and also fly backwards?

24 Who earned the nickname "Slow-hand"?

25 In the Bible who goes after Mark and before John?

26 Which country does opera singer Pavarotti come from?

27 Which is the third largest of the Channel Islands?

28 Who was Liverpool manager for the '84 European Cup triumph?

29 In which Puccini opera does Mimi appear?

30 How many sides has an octagon?

31 Which type of calendar is used today in the western world?

32 What instrument can be bass, electric or Spanish?

33 What was most remarkable about Edward VIII's reign?

34 In which month of the year would you go to Munich for the beer festival?

35   What do the numbers add up to on the opposite sides of a dice?

36   Which city is said to have been founded by Romulus and Remus?

37   In the zodiac, which animal is linked with Capricorn?

38   How many years are involved in a silver anniversary?

39   Who scripted "Only Fools And Horses"?

40   In music, how many quavers equal a minim?

41   Which country originated the term 'plonk' for wine?

42   How did Cherilyn Sarkasian LaPierre become better known?

43   What was the final battle that Napoleon fought in?

44   Which men used to perform with Ken Dodd?

45   On which day are British elections held?

46   Which poet wrote about the charms of Miss Joan Hunter Dunn?

47   What was the name of the land where Gulliver met the Little People?

48   In the nursery rhyme, who ran away with the spoon?

49   Which animal's name comes first in the dictionary?

50   How many sides has a 20-pence piece?

Answers to Quiz 30, THE HUMAN BODY

1. Skin. 2. The skeleton. 3. The heart. 4. The kneecap. 5. Yes. 6. The gums. 7. Twenty. 8. Vertebrae. 9. The eye. 10. The large and small intestines. 11. The Adam's apple. 12. No. 13. The throat. 14. Dentine. 15. About 70 beats per minute. 16. True. 17. The gall bladder. 18. The sternum. 19. In the forearm. 20. Urine. 21. Pores. 22. It prevents it from clotting. 23. Molars. 24. Melanin. 25. In the mouth. 26. Flakes of skin from the scalp. 27. Arthritis. 28. Capillaries. 29. Short-sightedness. 30. In the lower leg. 31. Lungs. 32. Eulogy. 33. Nerves. 34. Incisors. 35. The ear. 36. The diaphragm. 37. A jelly-like liquid called aqueous humor. 38. The brain. 39. The pelvis. 40. To reduce body temperature. 41. In the arm. 42. The membrane covering the brain. 43. Mumps. 44. Pachyderm. 45. Digestion. 46. Respiration. 47. In the buttocks. 48. The semi-circular canals. 49. An ulcer. 50. Cholesterol.

QUIZ 32 | 60s Music

EASY - LEVEL ONE

1 Who went "Surfin' USA"?

2 Micky Dolenz found fame in which simian-sounding group?

3 Who was Crying In the Chapel?

4 Which Beatles hit starts "Dear Sir or Madam, will you read my book"?

5 Brothers Barry, Maurice and Robin formed which group?

6 Who mocked the clothes conscious with "Dedicated Follower of Fashion"?

7 Diana Ross fronted which Tamla group?

8 Which group loved Jennifer Eccles?

9 Which part of her body did Sandie Shaw bare on stage?

10 Who sang "Don't Treat Me Like A Child" while still at school?

11 Were the Everley brothers actually brothers?

12 Which Dusty was Going Back?

13 Status Quo first charted with Pictures of what type of Men?

14 Which country-style singer was known as Gentleman Jim?

15 Who backed Brian Poole?

16 Which city did the Searchers come from?

17 Which Australian yodelled "I Remember You"?

18 Who completed the line-up with Dave Dee, Beaky, Mick and Tich?

19 Which trouser splitting singer had the initials PJ ?

20 Which city did the Flowerpot Men want to go to?

21 Whose Five were in Bits And Pieces?

22 Critics said Donovan was a British copy of which US performer?

23 Which Marianne was linked with Mick Jagger?

24 Which country did Roy Orbison come from?

25 Which George produced the Beatles' records?

26 Which group recorded "Flowers In The Rain"?

27 Who was backed by Hermits?

28 Who managed to get to No. I with a song about a dustman?

29 Which John wanted to Give Peace A Chance at the end of the 60s?

30 Which dance was Chubby Checker doing at the start of the 60s?

31 What was Helen Shapiro Walking Back to in 1961?

32 What was Venus wearing in 1962 according to Mark Wynter?

33 What was the occupation of Lonnie Donegan's old man?

34 In which part of town was Petula Clark in the 1960s?

35 What was the title of Cliff Richard's 1968 Eurovision song?

36 Who was Cher's first singing partner with a hit song?

37 Who was lead singer with The Supremes?

38 What did The Searchers sing about along with Needles?

39 What shade of Pale did Procol Harum sing about?

40 Who was Gerry's backing group?

41 How many Hours was Gene Pitney from Tulsa?

42 Who sang with The Dreamers?

43 Who had Hermits?

44 Who was known as 'The Big O'?

45 What followed Ready, Steady in the title of the pop show?

46 My Boy, according to Millie, is called what?

47 What were The Kinks Dedicated Followers of in 1966?

48 Who sang with The Dakotas?

49 According to The Animals, what was the name of The House in New Orleans?

50 Who was heard to "Shout" in 1964?

1. The Pelican. 2. Anode. 3. Wally. 4. Butterfly. 5. Victoria. 6. Melchester. 7. Six. 8. Tom Hanks. 9. Doe. 10. Cliff Thorburn. 11. Jersey. 12. Hands. 13. Elton John. 14. Maddy Prior. 15. Third Class. 16. Ten. 17. LXXVII. 18. St Cecilia. 19. Flock together. 20. The Taming of the Shrew. 21. True Blue. 22. The brain. 23. Hummingbird. 24. Eric Clapton. 25. Luke. 26. Italy. 27. Alderney. 28. Joe Fagan. 29. La Bohème. 30. Eight. 31. Gregorian. 32. Guitar. 33. He abdicated. 34. October. 35 Seven. 36. Rome. 37. Goat. 38. 25. 39. John Sullivan. 40. Four. 41. Australia. 42. Cher. 43. Waterloo. 44. The Diddymen. 45. Thursday. 46. John Betjeman. 47. Lilliput. 48. Dish. 49. Aardvark. 50. Seven.

QUIZ 33 Pot Luck

EASY - LEVEL ONE

1 Which actor played Jim Hacker in TV's "Yes Prime Minister"?

2 How many children were there in Enid Blyton's Famous Five?

3 Who appeared with The Coconuts?

4 What kind of animal was Phillip Schofield's puppet pal Gordon?

5 What is the stage name of Harry Webb?

6 What was Conrad Phillips most famous TV role?

7 Which film gave Jack Nicholson his first Oscar?

8 Which season do Americans call the Fall?

9 The fabled bird the griffin had the head of which real bird?

10 On which Common would you find the Wombles?

11 Whose catchphrase is, "Nice to see you to see you nice"?

12 Who was the first Labour MP?

13 Who at the age of fourteen became Britain's youngest chess International Master?

14 Which country does Bryan Adams come from?

15 Who was known as the lady with the lamp?

16 What is the plural of the word sheep?

17 How is Rebecca Rolfe better known?

18 What is the symbol for the Gemini sign of the zodiac?

19 Where in a horse is the coffin joint?

20 What word can go before cheese, plant and roll?

21 Which Simon and Garfunkel song features the words "Jesus loves you more than you can say"?

22 Which 'famous first' is attributed to asparagus in Britain?

23 Which substance is most used for pencil lead?

24 To ten years either way, in which year did Charles Dickens die?

25 Which long-running radio programme was devised by Roy Plomley?

26 Which Lloyd Webber musical does the song "Memory" come from?

27 What drink does pear juice make?

28 What name can be a lettuce or a mass of floating frozen water?

29 Which vegetable did Sir Walter Raleigh bring to England?

30 In the strip cartoon, what is the name of Snoopy's brother?

31 "Half A Sixpence" is based on which story by H.G. Wells?

32 At which course are the Coventry Stakes run?

33 Soyuz was the name of a Russian spacecraft, but what does the name mean?

34 Who talked of an "early bath" and an "up and under"?

35	Who wrote the Savoy operas?
36	Who lost her pocket?
37	In the film "The Day of the Jackal", who played the Jackal?
38	What colour is a sapphire?
39	Does Elizabeth II face to the left or right on a British coin?
40	How were the musical duo Asher and Weller better known?
41	What did Bo and Luke Duke call their car?
42	In Shakespeare's "Othello", who is the female lead?
43	In the pirate song, how many men were on the dead man's chest?
44	Mike Hawthorne was the first Briton to win the World Champion in which sport?
45	Venetian blinds originated in which country?
46	A poult is the young of which creature?
47	Which group recorded the original of "Light My Fire"?
48	In an English trial, how many people sit on the jury?
49	Where - apart from the Moon - are the Mountains Of The Moon?
50	Which great soprano earned the name of 'La Divina'?

Answers to Quiz 32, 60s Music

1. The Beach Boys. 2. Monkees. 3. Elvis Presley. 4. Paperback Writer. 5. The Bee Gees. 6. The Kinks. 7. Supremes. 8. The Hollies. 9. Her feet. 10. Helen Shapiro. 11. Yes. 12. Springfield. 13. Matchstick. 14. Jim Reeves. 15. The Tremeloes. 16. Liverpool. 17. Frank Ifield. 18. Dozy. 19. Proby. 20. San Francisco. 21. Dave Clark. 22. Bob Dylan. 23. Faithfull. 24. US. 25. Martin. 26. Move. 27. Herman. 28. Lonnie Donegan. 29. John Lennon. 30. The Twist. 31. Happiness. 32. Blue Jeans. 33. Dustman. 34. Downtown. 35. Congratulations. 36. Sonny. 37. Diana Ross. 38. Pins. 39. Whiter. 40. The Pacemakers. 41. 24. 42. Freddie. 43. Herman. 44. Roy Orbison. 45. Go. 46. Lollipop. 47. Fashion. 48. Billy J. Kramer. 49. The Rising Sun. 50. Lulu.

Q UIZ 34 | 60s Films

FOR ANSWERS SEE QUIZ NO 35

EASY - LEVEL ONE

1 Who won a BAFTA for his role in Lawrence of Arabia but not an Oscar?

2 Who starred in "Funny Gir"l and "Lawrence of Arabia"?

3 Who starred in "Mary Poppins" and "The Sound of Music"?

4 What is Bert's, alias Dick Van Dyke, job in "Mary Poppins"?

5 In which Disney film does "The Bare Necessities" appear?

6 Which daughter of Charlie Chaplin appeared in "Doctor Zhivago"?

7 Who was Butch in "Butch Cassidy and the Sundance Kid"?

8 Which classic had the line "This is Benjamin. He's a little worried about his future"?

9 Who played Eliza Doolittle in "My Fair Lady"?

10 In which city does "One Hundred and One Dalmatians" take place?

11 Which 1963 BAFTA winner shared its name with a 60s Welsh singer?

12 How many "years BC" were in the title of the 1966 Raquel Welch film?

13 Which "The Upper Hand" actress starred in Goldfinger?

14 In which film does 007 seek a diamond smuggler?

15 How many were there in the Dirty band led by Charles Bronson?

16 Which Romeo and Juliet type of musical won most Oscars in the 60s?

17 In which 1968 musical did Bill Sikes murder Nancy?

18 What was Paul Scofield A Man For in 1966?

19 Who co-starred with Jon Voight as Ratso Rizzo in "Midnight Cowboy"?

20 Who is the Inspector in the Pink Panther films?

21 Which Carry On film tells of the all-female Glamcabs firm?

22 Who starred in "True Grit"?

23 In "Easy Rider" what are the riders riding?

24 In which 60s film did Norman Bates appear?

25 Which Mrs Richard Burton starred in "Who's Afraid of Virginia Woolf"?

26 Which Goon starred in "Dr Strangelove"?

27 Who co-starred with Walter Matthau in "The Odd Couple"?

28 Tommy Steele sang the title song in Half a what in 1967?

29 Who was a GI and was the star of a film with that in the title?

30 Which blonde's last film was 'The Misfits" in 1960?

31 On which Side of New York was the musical about rival gangs?

32 Who starred as Cleopatra and

married co-star Richard Burton?

33 With which country is Lawrence associated in the film with Peter O'Toole?

34 Which role did Warren Beatty play to Faye Dunaway's Bonnie?

35 What type of Cowboy was Jon Voight in the 1969 film?

36 Who was The Graduate in the film of the same name?

37 Who won an Oscar as Professor Higgins in "My Fair Lady"?

38 Which musical by Lionel Bart was based on a Dickens novel?

39 Which western actor won his only Oscar for "True Grit"?

40 Which actress Mia starred in the controversial "Rosemary's Baby"?

41 What were the hills alive with in the musical set in Austria?

42 What was the nationality of Zorba in the film with Anthony Quinn?

43 Who's Coming to which meal in the Katharine Hepburn film?

44 Which nanny did Julie Andrews win an Oscar for playing?

45 Who played Alfie?

46 Which blonde Julie was a Darling?

47 Who played Fanny Brice in "Funny Girl"?

48 Which Doctor did Omar Sharif play in the film set in the USSR?

49 Which Gregory won an Oscar for "To Kill A Mockingbird"?

50 Which Miss was Maggie Smith whose Prime won an Oscar in '69?

1. Paul Eddington. 2. Four – one was a dog. 3. Kid Creole. 4. Gopher. 5. Cliff Richard. 6. William Tell. 7. One Flew over the Cuckoo's Nest. 8. Autumn. 9. Eagle. 10. Wimbledon. 11. Bruce Forsyth. 12. Keir Hardie. 13. Nigel Short. 14. Canada. 15. Florence Nightingale. 16. Sheep. 17. Pocahontas 18. Twins. 19. Foot. 20. Swiss. 21. Mrs Robinson. 22. First frozen food. 23. Graphite. 24. 1870. 25. Desert Island Discs. 26. Cats. 27. Perry. 28. Iceberg. 29. Potato. 30. Spike. 31. Kipps. 32. Ascot. 33. Union. 34. Eddie Waring. 35. Gilbert and Sullivan. 36. Lucy Locket. 37. Edward Fox. 38. Blue. 39. Right. 40. Peter and Gordon. 41. The General Lee. 42. Desdemona. 43. 15. 44. Motor racing. 45. Japan. 46. Turkey. 47. The Doors. 48. 12. 49. Uganda. 50. Maria Callas.

Quiz 35 Pot Luck

1   What do the letters AIDS stand for?

2   How many stomachs has a cow?

3   With which swimming stroke do races begin in the water?

4   What have you been doing if you finish by casting off?

5   How is the Roman city of Verulamium known today?

6   Roy Jenkins was a founder of which political party?

7   What does Susan Hampshire suffer from?

8   Film star Roy Scherer died in 1985. What was his screen name?

9   Which city in the world has the largest population?

10 Whose ship was the first to sail round the world?

11 In music hall, who was the 'Prime Minister of Mirth'?

12 Who composed "The Flight Of The Bumble Bee"?

13 Which actor can be found in The Nag's Head and The Royal Oak?

14 What is the full name of BBC Radio 5?

15 What was invented by Lewis Waterman in the 1880s?

16 Which illustrator was famous for detailed drawings of weird and wonderful mechanical inventions?

17 Who appears with Lamb Chop?

18 Following the 1963 Peerage Act, who was the first peer to disclaim his title?

19 What was "Prisoner: Cell Block H" originally called?

20 Which instrument usually has 47 strings?

21 What is the name of Dennis the Menace's dog?

22 For over a quarter of a century, which tobacco company has produced a football yearbook?

23 Who wrote "Help Me Make It Through The Night"?

24 Moving anti-clockwise on a dartboard what is the number next to 4?

25 Who created the detective Paul Temple?

26 Who pricked her finger on a spinning wheel and slept for 100 years?

27 Who became Earl of Stockton on his 90th birthday?

28 Which traffic light follows green?

29 In "My Friend Flicka" who or what was Flicka?

30 Which is the first month of the year to have exactly 30 days?

31 In which TV show did the 'Mr Puniverse' contest take part?

32 How many more letters are there in the English than the Greek alphabet?

33 Which food item is used in an annual race at Olney?

34 Which part of the mint plant is used to make mint sauce?

35 In legend, who slew the gorgon

Medusa?

36 Who had sons called Ham, Shem and Japheth?

37 What was the name of Rolf Harris's puppet koala bear?

38 Which British olympic gold ice skating medallist died in 1995?

39 When did Halley's Comet last appear?

40 How many legs has a lobster?

41 Louise Brown will always hold which famous first?

42 What was the name of King Arthur's sword?

43 Who on TV often used the phrase "you are, are you not..."?

44 On the radio where are you sent with eight records of your choice?

45 Which part of its body does a snake use to detect noise?

46 Who was the first American president to resign from office?

47 In "The Naked Civil Servant" who did John Hurt portray?

48 "Thanks For The Memory" is the theme song of which comedian?

49 Who did Michael Caine play in "The Ipcress File"?

50 Which magazine has been edited by Richard Ingrams and Ian Hislop?

A nswers to Quiz 34, 60s Films

1. Peter O'Toole. 2. Omar Sharif. 3. Julie Andrews. 4. Chimney sweep. 5. The Jungle Book. 6. Geraldine. 7. Paul Newman. 8. The Graduate. 9. Audrey Hepburn. 10. London. 11. Tom Jones. 12. One Million. 13. Honor Blackman. 14. Diamonds Are Forever. 15. Dozen. 16. West Side Story. 17. Oliver!. 18. All Seasons. 19. Dustin Hoffman. 20. Clouseau. 21. Cabby. 22. John Wayne. 23. Motorbikes. 24. Psycho. 25. Elizabeth Taylor. 26. Peter Sellers. 27. Jack Lemmon. 28.Sixpence. 29. Elvis Presley. 30. Marilyn Monroe. 31. West. 32. Elizabeth Taylor. 33. Arabia. 34. Clyde. 35. Midnight. 36. Dustin Hoffman. 37. Rex Harrison. 38. Oliver! 39. John Wayne. 40. Farrow. 41. The Sound of Music. 42. Greek. 43. Dinner. 44. Mary Poppins. 45. Michael Caine. 46. Christie. 47. Streisand. 48. Zhivago. 49. Peck. 50. Jean Brodie.

Q^{UIZ}₃₆ | Sitcoms

EASY - LEVEL ONE

1 In "Dad's Army" who called Sgt Wilson Uncle Arthur?

2 What is the nationality of Margaret Meldrew?

3 Which family lived in Nelson Mandela House, Peckham?

4 Which space-age sitcom stars Craig Charles and Chris Barrie?

5 Which Scottish pop star played Adrian Mole's mum?

6 Which Felicity was the star of "Solo"?

7 Who plays Jean, husband of Lionel, in "As Time Goes By"?

8 Where did Hester and William Fields head for in the 80s/90s sitcom?

9 Which 70s character wore a knitted tanktop, long mac and a beret?

10 Which sitcom featured Mimi La Bonc and a painting by Van Clomp?

11 What was the occupation of Gladys Emmanuel in "Open All Hours"?

12 In which show does Tracey have a husband Darryl and son Garth?

13 Where were Miss Tibbs, Miss Gatsby and Major Gowen permanent guests?

14 In the 80s how were Candice, Amanda, Jennifer and Shelley known?

15 On which birthday did Tom Good begin "The Good Life"?

16 Whose dreams of his mother-in-law featured a hippopotamus?

17 Which 70s sitcom saw Wendy Richard as Miss Brahms?

18 Which Birmingham comic starred as Bob Louis in "The Detectives"?

19 What was the profession of Tom and Toby in "Don't Wait Up"?

20 How were the mature Dorothy, Blanche, Rose and Sophia known?

21 How was Bombadier Beaumont known in "It Ain't Half Hot Mum"?

22 In which show did Paul Nicholas play Vince Pinner?

23 What is the first name of Mr Bucket in "Keeping Up Appearances"?

24 Which sitcom was set in HMP Slade?

25 Which blonde does Leslie Ash play in "Men Behaving Badly"?

26 "Drop the Dead Donkey" takes place in what type of office?

27 In which show did Baldrick first appear?

28 Which sitcom chronicled the life of Zoë and Alec Callender?

29 Which show's theme song was "Holiday Rock"?

30 Which decade does Gary return to in "Goodnight Sweetheart"?

31 What is the first name of Mrs Bucket of "Keeping Up Appearances"?

32 Which actress Joanna played Patsy in "Absolutely Fabulous"?

33 Who was the café owner, played by Gorden Kaye, in "Allo Allo"?

34 In which sitcom does grumpy Victor Meldrew appear?

35 What is the surname of Del Boy and Rodney?

36 Which sport is the sitcom "Outside Edge" centred on?

37 What kind of Life did Jerry and Margo's neighbours lead?

38 What was the profession of Steptoe and Son?

39 In the sitcom title how many Children did Bill and Ben Porter have?

40 Which of Nora Batty's wrinkled garments turned on Compo?

41 Which two characters were "Just Good Friends"?

42 During which war was "Dad's Army" set?

43 Which senior political position did James Hacker MP reach?

44 In what type of establishment was "Are You Being Served?" set?

45 In which northeast city was "Auf Wiedersehen Pet" set?

46 Who is Tracey's sister in "Birds of a Feather"?

47 Whose servant was Baldrick?

48 Which sitcom was about the Boswell family from Liverpool?

49 At which hotel was Manuel the waiter?

50 In which series would you meet the Yellowcoats from Maplin's?

Answers to Quiz 35, Pot Luck

1. Acquired Immune Deficiency Syndrome. 2. Four. 3. Backstroke. 4. Knitting. 5. St Albans. 6. Social Democrat Party. 7. Dyslexia. 8. Rock Hudson. 9. Tokyo. 10. Ferdinand Magellan. 11. George Robey. 12. Rimsky-Korsakov. 13. Nicholas Lyndhurst. 14. Radio Five Live. 15. Fountain Pen. 16. Heath Robinson. 17. Shari Lewis. 18. Tony Benn. 19. Prisoner. 20. Harp. 21. Gnasher. 22. Rothmans. 23. Kris Kristofferson. 24. 18. 25. Francis Durbridge. 26. Sleeping Beauty. 27. Harold Macmillan. 28. Amber. 29. Horse. 30. April. 31. The Late, Late Breakfast Show. 32. Two. 24. Greek, 26. English.3 3. Pancakes. 34. Leaves. 35. Perseus. 36. Noah. 37. Kojee Bear. 38. John Curry. 39. 1986. 40. Eight. 41. First test tube baby. 42. Excalibur (also referred to as Caliburn). 43. Russell Harty. 44. Desert island. 45. Tongue. 46. Richard Nixon. 4. Quentin Crisp. 48. Bob Hope. 49. Harry Palmer. 50. Private Eye.

Quiz 37 | 40s & 50s Films

EASY - LEVEL ONE

1. Which Disney film released in 1942 was about a little fawn?

2. How many days did it take David Niven to go Around the World?

3. In the 1957 film about Japanese prisoners, where was the Bridge?

4. Which yuletide classic was first sung by Bing Crosby?

5. If Lady is a pedigree spaniel what is the name of the mongrel?

6. Which Ben won 11 Oscars in 1959?

7. In which 1940 film did Mickey Mouse conduct the orchestra?

8. In which film did Vivien Leigh play Scarlett O'Hara?

9. Who starred in the Road films with Dorothy Lamour and Bing Crosby?

10. Which film set in Rick's Café starred Humphrey Bogart and Ingrid Bergman?

11. Which actor, later a Lord, played the lead in "Henry V"?

12. Which film starred Celia Johnson, Trevor Howard and a train station?

13. Which Alfred directed the thrillers "Rebecca" and "Notorious"?

14. Which actor Orson starred in "Citizen Kane"?

15. Who played eight different characters in "Kind Hearts and Coronets"?

16. What was the series of comedies made in West London studios called?

17. Where was Gene Kelly Singin'?

18. How did Some Like It in the film with Marilyn Monroe?

19. What was the name of the car that involved Kenneth More and Dinah Sheridan in the London to Brighton road run?

20. Which star of "East of Eden" died in a car crash aged 24?

21. Which actress married Prince Rainier of Monaco?

22. Which French 'sex kitten' starred with Dirk Bogarde in "Doctor at Sea"?

23. In the Charlton Heston film how many commandments were there?

24. Where was there Room in the film starring Laurence Harvey?

25. Who was the young star of "National Velvet" in 1945?

26. Which dancer/actress Ginger won an Oscar in 1940?

27. Which actor Marlon starred in "On the Waterfront"?

28. What goes with Old Lace in the title of the Cary Grant film?

29. What is A Many Splendored Thing?

30. From Here to where?

31. Which film told of Moses leading the Israelites to the Promised Land?

32. Who starred as Moses?

33 What or who is Lady in Lady and the Tramp?

34 Which film of J.M. Barrie's book was described as "a painful travesty"?

35 Which 11-Oscar-winning film of 1959 cost four million dollars?

36 Who was the star of Around the World in Eighty Days?

37 Which film company released Sleeping Beauty?

38 The action of South Pacific takes place during which war?

39 Which Welsh actor Richard starred in The Robe?

40 Which 1957 film whistled "Colonel Bogey" as its theme?

41 Who played the pop star in Jailhouse Rock?

42 What completes the line from "All About Eve", "Fasten your ___, it's going to be a bumpy night"?

43 What was the surname of film the director Darryl F?

44 Which Maurice starred in Gigi?

45 Which US singer had an acting role in From Here to Eternity?

46 Which actress starred in From Here to Eternity and The King and I?

47 Who played the starring role of Terry in On the Waterfront?

48 Which film catapulted James Dean to stardom?

49 Which French star appeared in And God Created Woman set in St Tropez?

50 Which dancer/singer was the "American in Paris"?

Answers to Quiz 36, SITCOMS

1. Pike. 2. Scottish. 3. The Trotters. 4. "Red Dwarf". 5. Lulu. 6. Kendal. 7. Judi Dench. 8. France. 9. Frank Spencer. 10. "'Allo 'Allo". 11. Nurse. 12. "Birds of a Feather". 13. Fawlty Towers. 14. "Girls On Top". 15. 40th. 16. Reginald Perrin. 17. "Are You Being Served?". 18. Jasper Carrott. 19. Doctors. 20. The Golden Girls. 21. Gloria. 22. "Just Good Friends". 23. Richard. 24. "Porridge". 25. Deborah. 26. TV newsroom. 27. "Blackadder". 28. "May to December". 29. "Hi-De-Hi". 30. 1940s. 31. Hyacinth. 32. Lumley. 33. René. 34. One Foot in the Grave. 35. Trotter. 36. Cricket. 37. The Good Life. 38. Rag and bone men. 39. 2 Point 4. 40. Stockings. 41. Vince and Penny. 42. Second World War. 43. Prime Minister. 44. Department store. 45. Newcastle. 46. Sharon. 47. Blackadder. 48. Bread. 49. Fawlty Towers. 50. Hi de Hi!

Quiz 38 Pot Luck

EASY - LEVEL ONE

1 What does an arctophile collect?

2 Which of Verdi's operas is set in Ancient Egypt?

3 What gives red blood cells their colour?

4 Who has had hits with "Tutti Frutti" and "Rip It Up"?

5 On TV, what kind of creature was Flipper?

6 Which animals took Hannibal over the Alps?

7 How is the auracaria tree more commonly known?

8 In which team game do you try to move backwards all the time?

9 Which situation comedy had Wendy Craig and Geoffrey Palmer as a married couple?

10 Who was the first British monarch to visit New Zealand?

11 Who recorded the albums "John Wesley Harding" and "Nashville Skyline"?

12 Who does The Beast fall in love with?

13 What is the main ingredient in a brick?

14 What hangs down from the roof of cave – a stalagmite or a stalactite?

15 What is the body of a penguin covered with?

16 How does Saturday's child work for a living?

17 Who appeared with Keith Chegwin on "Multi Coloured Swap Shop" and later married him?

18 Which musical direction means at ease, at a slow comfortable pace?

19 Which bell said, "You owe me five farthings"?

20 Which king is said to have burnt the cakes?

21 Which British national daily newspaper ceased publication in 1995?

22 Which girl shares her name with a Christmas song?

23 How many edges in a cube?

24 Which dance comes from "Orpheus In The Underworld"?

25 At what age does a filly become classified as mare?

26 What type of creature is a Pacific sea wasp?

27 Who had a No 1 in 1995 with "You Are Not Alone"?

28 How many are there in a baker's dozen?

29 George Harrison's "My Sweet Lord" was claimed to sound like which other song?

30 Is the South Pole at the Arctic or the Antarctic?

31 Thomas Arnold was headmaster of which public school?

32 What kind of creature was Rikki-Tikki-Tavi?

33 In the story, how many men were in Jerome K. Jerome's boat?

34 In which town do the Flintstones live?

35 In 1930, which country did Amy Johnson fly to from England?

36 When "Coronation Street" moved from two to three programmes a week in 1989, what was the new day for transmission?

37 Who wrote "Watership Down"?

38 Which animal is regarded as the one with the longest life span?

39 Who in the Bible had a coat of many colours?

40 What is the outer layer of skin called?

41 What meat appears in a Punch and Judy show?

42 Who left "Take That" in July 1995?

43 What does an invertebrate not have?

44 Who was the tallest of Robin Hood's Men?

45 Who wrote "The Female Eunuch"?

46 In "Countdown" how many letters are selected for the letters game?

47 What was the actual first name of Hopalong Cassidy?

48 Della Street was secretary to which famous legal character?

49 What did Constantinople become known as in March 1930?

50 Who did Sri Lanka beat in the quarter finals of the '94 cricket World Cup?

Answers to Quiz 37, 40s & 50s FILMS

1. Bambi. 2. 80 days. 3. Over the River Kwai. 4. White Christmas. 5. Tramp. 6. Ben Hur. 7. Fantasia. 8. Gone With The Wind. 9. Bob Hope. 10. Casablanca. 11. Laurence Olivier. 12. Brief Encounter. 13. Hitchcock. 14. Welles. 15. Alec Guinness. 16. Ealing Comedies. 17. In The Rain. 18. Hot. 19. Genevieve. 20. James Dean. 21. Grace Kelly. 22. Brigitte Bardot. 23. Ten. 24. At The Top. 25. Elizabeth Taylor. 26. Rogers. 27. Brando. 28. Arsenic. 29. Love. 30. Eternity. 31. The Ten Commandments. 32. Charlton Heston. 33. Dog. 34. Peter Pan. 35. Ben Hur. 36. David Niven. 37. Walt Disney. 38. World War II. 39. Burton. 40. The Bridge on the River Kwai. 41. Elvis Presley. 42. Seatbelts. 43. Zanuck. 44. Chevalier. 45. Frank Sinatra. 46. Deborah Kerr. 47. Marlon Brando. 48. Rebel Without a Cause. 49. Brigitte Bardot. 50. Gene Kelly.

Quiz 39 Football

EASY - LEVEL ONE

1 Who plays home games at Ewood Park?

2 Which team are known as the Gunners?

3 What colour are Manchester United's home shirts?

4 Which footballer made a record with Lindisfarne?

5 Who was England's manager for the 1990 World Cup in Italy?

6 Which city has teams called Wednesday and United?

7 Which ground hosts the FA Cup Final?

8 Who plays against Rangers in an Auld Firm derby match?

9 How many minutes in the second half of a Premier League match?

10 What name is shared by Birmingham, Coventry and Leicester?

11 Which colour card is used to send a player off?

12 Who joined Liverpool from Nottingham Forest for £8 million plus in 1995?

13 Which country does Ryan Giggs play for?

14 Who was Ian St John's partner on TV?

15 Which East Anglian team is nicknamed The Canaries?

16 How many players should be on the pitch at the start of a game?

17 Who won the World Cup in 1958, 1962, 1970 and 1990?

18 Which team plays home games at Villa Park?

19 What is the name of BBC 1's long-running Saturday night soccer show?

20 Hearts and Hibs come from which Scottish city?

21 What number is traditionally worn on the goalie's shirt?

22 Which Geordie played for England and managed the Republic of Ireland?

23 Which country does Jurgen Klinsmann come from?

24 If you were at Goodison Park who would be playing at home?

25 Which London team earned the nickname "The Crazy Gang"?

26 Which Nottingham club was managed by Brian Clough?

27 What is the colour of the home strip of both Everton and Chelsea?

28 Which country do Hendry, Goram and McCoist play for?

29 Can a goalkeeper score a goal for his own team?

30 At which Lane do Spurs play when at home?

31 Which team is known as The Magpies?

32 Which David has played for Aston Villa, Milan, Sampdoria and Arsenal?

33 What two colours are in Blackburn's home strip?

34 How many linesmen are there in an international match?

35 In which country was the 1994 World Cup finals held?

36 Which city has teams called Rovers and City?

37 What position did Peter Shilton play?

38 Tommy Docherty and Jock Stein have both managed which country?

39 Who plays home games at Filbert Street?

40 Which club is linked with the playing career of Jimmy Armfield?

41 Which Joe managed Everton when they won the 1995 FA Cup?

42 Which country do Real Madrid come from?

43 In QPR what does the letter R stand for?

44 Which club did Steve Bruce play for in a Premiership winning season?

45 Which country did George Best play for?

46 What is the home colour of Nottingham Forest?

47 Which country does David Ginola come from?

48 At which club did Terry Venables and Alan Sugar clash?

49 Who did Alan Shearer play for before he joined Blackburn?

50 Why did France not play in qualifying games for the '98 World Cup?

A nswers to Quiz 38, POT LUCK

1. Teddy bears. 2. Aida. 3. Haemoglobin. 4. Little Richard. 5. Dolphin. 6. Elephants. 7. Monkey puzzle. 8. Tug of War. 9. Butterflies. 10. Elizabeth II. 11. Bob Dylan. 12. Beauty. 13. Clay. 14. Stalactite. 15. Feathers. 16. Hard. 17. Maggie Philbin. 18. Adagio. 19. St Martins. 20. Alfred. 21. "Today". 22. Carol. 23. 12. 24 .The can-can. 25. Five. 26. Jellyfish. 27. Michael Jackson. 28. 13. 29. He's So Fine recorded by the Chiffons. 30. Antarctic.31. Rugby. 32. Mongoose in a Rudyard Kipling story. 33. Three. 34. Bedrock. 35. Australia. 36. Friday. 37. Richard Adams. 38. The giant tortoise. 39. Joseph. 40. Epidermis. 41. Sausages. 42. Robbie. 43. A backbone. 44. Little John. 45. Germaine Greer. 46. Nine. 47. William. 48. Perry Mason. 49. Istanbul. 50. England.

Quiz 40 Pot Luck

1 What is the boiling point of water?

2 Alphabetically, which is the second sign of the zodiac?

3 What is Goldfinger's first name?

4 Who had a No 1 hit with the song "I Just Called To Say I Love You"?

5 Who wrote "The Owl and The Pussycat"?

6 What are beds of snooker tables traditionally made of?

7 By what name was travelling show tap dancer Luther Robinson known?

8 What was the name of the "Neighbours" character played by Kylie Minogue?

9 What word describes the permanent disappearance of a species?

10 The Star of Africa is what type of gem?

11 In education, what does BA stand for?

12 In the human body, what has four chambers?

13 Which creature can turn its stomach inside out?

14 There are 78 cards in which type of pack?

15 What is arachnophobia the fear of?

16 Which two writers created "Auf Wiedersehen, Pet"?

17 How many cards of the same suit are needed for a flush in poker?

18 What name is given to an athletics event such as running or hurdling?

19 Which war in Europe took place between 1936–9?

20 Under what name did Samuel Clemens write?

21 Who recorded the album "Tubular Bells"?

22 In which city is the Obelisk of Luxor?

23 Which day of the week is named after the moon?

24 In the USA what is a greenback?

25 Who composed the tune to "Twinkle Twinkle Little Star"?

26 Which Charles wrote "The Origin Of Species"?

27 Donnerstag is German for which day?

28 Jennyanydots was what kind of cat?

29 What is the federal republic of Switzerland divided into?

30 Who wrote "Rebecca"?

31 Which part did Michael Jackson play in "The Wiz"?

32 What is the currency of Austria?

33 Which childhood disease is also known as rubella?

34 Who recorded the album "Definitely, Maybe"?

35 In "Coronation Street", what is the name of Mike Baldwin's wife?

36 Cab is a shortening of which

word?

37 In rhyming slang what is meant by dickory dock?

38 How is Priscilla White better known?

39 Who wrote "Maple Leaf Rag"?

40 The Tsar Kolokol is the biggest what in the world?

41 Which David presented "Juke Box Jury"?

42 To five years either way, when was the Empire State Building finished?

43 Which comedy series featured the Boswell family?

44 Brassica oleracea is better known as what?

45 Who wrote home from Camp Grenada?

46 How many sides has an isosceles triangle?

47 What does a Geiger counter detect?

48 Whose catchphrase was, "Shut that door!"?

49 Which major river flows through Newcastle?

50 Who was the star of "Zorba The Greek"?

Answers to Quiz 39, FOOTBALL

1. Blackburn Rovers. 2. Arsenal. 3. Red. 4. Paul Gascoigne. 5. Bobby Robson. 6. Sheffield. 7. Wembley Stadium. 8. Celtic. 9. 45. 10. City. 11. Red. 12. Stan Collymore. 13. Wales. 14. Jimmy Greaves. 15. Norwich City. 16. 22. 17. Brazil. 18. Aston Villa. 19. Match of the Day. 20. Edinburgh. 21. 1. 22. Jack Charlton. 23. Germany. 24 . Everton. 25. Wimbledon. 26.. Forest. 27. Blue. 28. Scotland. 29. Yes. 30. White Hart. 31. Newcastle. 32. Platt. 33. Blue and white. 34. Two. 35. USA. 36. Bristol. 37. Goal. 38. Scotland. 39. Leicester. 40. Blackpool. 41. Royle. 42. Spain. 43. Rangers. 44. Manchester United. 45. Northern Ireland. 46. Red. 47. France. 48. Tottenham. 49. Southampton. 50. As hosts they automatically qualified.

Q UIZ 41 Soaps

EASY - LEVEL ONE

1 What is the name of the pub in Albert Square?

2 Whom did Raquel marry in secret in December 1995?

3 What was Trevor Jordache buried under in "Brookside"?

4 In which street is "Neighbours" set?

5 Which British actress played Alexis in "Dynasty"?

6 In which soap is there a pub called The Woolpack?

7 What is the name of the ranch in "Dallas"?

8 Which bird added to a Crest completes a soap series?

9 Which hospital soap is set in Holby City Hospital?

10 Which Australian soap is set in Summer Bay?

11 On which Cell Block might there be a Prisoner in an Australian soap?

12 Which Place was the the name of the first major US soap?

13 Which British soap was set in a motel?

14 In the 1960s series "Compact", what was Compact?

15 Which soap was a spin-off of "Dynasty"?

16 In which Landing did some members of Dallas's Ewing family settle?

17 Which soap has featured the Corkhills, the Grants and the Dixons?

18 Who left his role as Scott Robinson and became a West End Joseph?

19 Which couple took over The Rovers' Return after Bet Gilroy left?

20 Who was Sharon's mum in "EastEnders"?

21 By what initials was actor Larry Hagman known as in "Dallas"?

22 What was Blake and Krystle's surname in "Dynasty"?

23 In "Home and Away" was Bobby Simpson a boy or a girl?

24 Where was there a horrific air crash in December 1993?

25 In which Australian city is "Neighbours" set?

26 Which police series is based at Sun Hill police station?

27 In "Coronation Street" who owns The Kabin?

28 What was the first name of legendary Street character Mrs Sharples?

29 Which country did Michelle go to when she left Albert Square?

30 Which Carry On star became Phil and Grant's mum in "EastEnders"?

31 Who left "EastEnders" for France with two of her three children?

32 What is the name of Maureen's mum in "Coronation Street"?

33 Who is the Street's repetitive

butcher?

34 In which soap did Dave Glover perish in a fire?

35 Which "Coronation Street" MacDonald twin went to prison?

36 In which soap does Sinbad appear?

37 What is EastEnder Tiffany's daughter called?

38 What was Ivy Tilsley's surname when she died?

39 Former members of which soap starred in a BT ad in 1997?

40 In "Neighbours" what was the surname of Scott, Paul, Lucy and Julie?

41 Who was Frank Tate's murdered wife in "Emmerdale"?

42 What is the name of Jack and Vera Duckworth's wayward son?

43 Where was David Wicks heading for when he left "EastEnders"?

44 Who is Bianca's mum in "EastEnders"?

45 Who married Shane in "Home and Away"?

46 What is the name of the Barbara Windsor character in "EastEnders"?

47 In the Street what is Curly's real name?

48 Where was Curly's wife Raquel heading for on leaving Weatherfield?

49 Which Street character had a fling with gangster Fraser Henderson?

50 Which soap pub is famous for its Newton & Ridley beer?

A nswers to Quiz 40, POT LUCK

1. 100 degrees Celsius. 2. Aries. 3 . Auric. 4. Stevie Wonder. 5. Edward Lear. 6. Slate. 7. Bojangles. 8. Charlene. 9. Extinction. 10. Diamond. 11. Bachelor of Arts. 12. The Heart. 13. Starfish. 14. Tarot. 15. Spiders. 16 .Clement and La Frenais. 17. Five. 18. Track. 19. Spanish Civil War. 20. Mark Twain. 21. Mike Oldfield. 22. Paris. 23. Monday. 24. A dollar bill. 25. Mozart. 26. Darwin. 27. Thursday. 28. Gumbie Cat. 29. Cantons. 30. Daphne du Maurier.31. The Scarecrow. 32. Schilling. 33. Measles. 33. Oasis. 35. Alma. 36. Cabriolet. 37. Clock. 38. Cilla Black. 39. Scott Joplin. 40. Bell. 41. Jacobs. 42. 1931. 43. Bread. 44. Cabbage. 45. Allan Sherman. 46. Three. 47. Radioactivity. 48. Larry Grayson. 49. Tyne. 50. Anthony Quinn.

Quiz 42 — Pot Luck

EASY - LEVEL ONE

1. What colour is pure molten gold?
2. What is the zodiac sign of Pisces?
3. Whose face is on an American five-dollar bill?
4. Who had a No 1 hit with the song "Wuthering Heights"?
5. With which branch of medicine is Mesmer associated?
6. Who sang on a "Showboat" and ended up in "Dallas"?
7. In the nursery rhyme, what did Tom, Tom the piper's son steal?
8. Who wrote "Where Have All The Flowers Gone"?
9. In "HMS Pinafore" who did Sir Joseph Porter bring on boat along with his sisters?
10. According to the proverb, what begins at home?
11. Which birds are traditionally used by Japaneses fishermen to help them catch fish?
12. Who plays TV's Inspector Morse?
13. Called chequers in America, what's the name of this game in Britain?
14. Who was the last queen of England by succession before Elizabeth II?
15. What is the term for fear of enclosed spaces?
16. Name the consortium that runs the National Lottery?
17. What was the name of the Big River sung about by Jimmy Nail?
18. What is the name of the person who delivers the mail in Greendale?
19. Which city is the setting for "Saturday Night Fever"?
20. What was the No 1 recording made by Matthews Southern Comfort?
21. Which food item is most consumed by humans throughout the world?
22. Who says, "Know what I mean, 'Arry"?
23. Which day of the week is named after the god Thor?
24. Who first recorded "A Whiter Shade Of Pale"?
25. What is Sweden's national flower?
26. What do entomologists study?
27. What tree does a date grow on?
28. In the song, what did my true love send to me on the seventh day of Christmas?
29. Who was the famous son of Uther Pendragon?
30. Who has been world darts champion a record five times?
31. On the radio, what did ITMA stand for?
32. What was the most famous group managed by Andrew Loog Oldham?
33. Where is the steepest street in the world?
34. Who recorded the album

"Brothers In Arms"?

35 In which sport is the Davis Cup played for?

36 Which English king was said to be Unready?

37 In song, what colour toothbrush was Max Bygraves?

38 Which veteran entertainer brought his 'odd odes' to TV?

39 Which US president was assassinated in a Washington theatre?

40 Who had a rifle called "Old Betsy"?

41 David Lean's film was about a passage to which country?

42 Which city was "so good they named it twice"?

43 In song, where do the deer and the antelope play?

44 Which planet is fourth from the sun?

45 According to a Nick Berry song title every loser does what?

46 How many sides has a parallelogram?

47 Which film star dog had three names each containing three letters?

48 Where did Larry the Lamb live?

49 In which country did the Thuggee - from which we derive the word thug - operate?

50 What part did Joan Collins play in "Dynasty"?

A nswers to Quiz 41, Soaps

1. Queen Victoria. 2. Curly Watts. 3. The patio. 4. Ramsay. 5. Joan Collins. 6. Emmerdale. 7. Southfork. 8. Falcon. 9. Casualty. 10. Home and Away. 11. H. 12. Peyton. 13. Crossroads. 14. A magazine. 15. The Colbys. 16. Knot's. 17. Brookside. 18. Jason Donovan. 19. Jack and Vera Duckworth. 20. Angie Watts. 21. J.R. 22. Carrington. 23. Girl. 24. Emmerdale. 25. Melbourne. 26. The Bill. 27. Rita Sullivan. 28. Ena. 29. America. 30. Barbara Windsor. 31. Cindy Beale. 32. Maud Grimes. 33. Fred Elliott. 34. "Emmerdale". 35. Steve. 36. "Brookside". 37. Courtney. 38. Brennan. 39. "EastEnders". 40. Robinson. 41. Kim. 42. Terry. 43. Italy. 44. Carol. 45. Angel. 46. Peggy Mitchell. 47. Norman. 48. Malaysia. 49. Liz McDonald. 50 . The Rover's Return.

Q UIZ 43 70s Films

EASY - LEVEL ONE

1 Which Pink character appeared in three top films of the 70s?

2 Which 1977 film was rereleased 20 years later?

3 Which film was described as 'shark stew for the stupefied'?

4 In which decade does the action of "Grease" take place?

5 Which 1972 movie detailed the career of the Corleone family?

6 In which film did Clark Kent combat the Spider Lady?

7 Which Steven directed "Close Encounters of the Third Kind"?

8 In which gangster city does the action of "The Sting" take place?

9 Which brothers wrote most of the songs for "Saturday Night Fever"?

10 Which 1977 Movie had a frog as one of its main stars?

11 Which was the first Rice/Lloyd Webber musical made into a film?

12 Which Barbra starred in "A Star Is Born"?

13 Which film was based on "The Tower and The Glass Inferno"?

14 Which disaster movie was described as "Grand Hotel in the sky …"?

15 In which Californian city did "Earthquake" take place?

16 Which gorilla was the star of a 1976 remake of a 30s classic?

17 Who played James Bond in "Moonraker"?

18 Which 1970 war film led to a long-running TV spin off with Alan Alda?

19 Which Steve starred in "Papillon"?

20 Which 1975 Jack Nicholson film takes place in a mental hospital?

21 Which boxer was Sylvester Stallone on the big screen?

22 Which disaster movie tells of a capsized luxury liner?

23 Which Annie was an Oscar winner for Woody Allen?

24 Which future British MP won an Oscar for "Women in Love" in 1970?

25 Who Doesn't Live Here Any More in the 1974 movie?

26 Which Liza Minnelli Oscar-winning film was set in pre-war Germany?

27 Which Mr Moore starred opposite Bo Derek in "10"?

28 Which Asian war was "The Deer Hunter" about?

29 Where was the Fiddler in the 1971 film?

30 What was the profession of "hero" Doyle in "The French Connection"?

31 Which Wars were there in 1977?

32 Which 1972 film, with Marlon Brando, was about the Mafia?

33 What was Herbie?

34 Which creature took a starring

role in "Jaws"?

35 What Night was there Fever in the movie with John Travolta?

36 Who was versus Kramer in the Dustin Hoffman film?

37 Who is Clark Kent better known as?

38 Which bird's Nest did One fly over in 1975?

39 In which film did John Travolta and Olivia Newton-John sing "You're the One That I Want"?

40 What Kind of Close Encounters were there in 1977?

41 On which Egyptian river was there Death in the Agatha Christie film?

42 Which boxer did Sylvester Stallone play?

43 Name the frog in "The Muppet Movie"?

44 Which bird of prey Landed in the war movie based on Jack Higgins' novel?

45 Which 1970s film about a giant ape was a remake of a 1933 movie?

46 Which disaster movie was about a fire in the world's tallest building?

47 Which film told of a mobile hospital in the Korean War?

48 Which fruit was Clockwork in the Stanley Kubrick film?

49 Which animal's Day was it in the film about an assassin based on the Frederick Forsyth novel?

50 What was the first name of gangster Malone?

Answers to Quiz 42, Pot Luck

1. Green. 2. Fish. 3. Abraham Lincoln. 4. Kate Bush. 5. Hypnotism. 6. Howard Keel. 7. A pig. 8. Pete Seeger. 9. His cousins and his aunt. 10. Charity. 11. Cormorants. 12. John Thaw. 13. Draughts. 14. Queen Victoria. 15. Claustrophobia. 16. Camelot. 17. Tyne. 18. Postman Pat. 19. New York. 20. Woodstock. 21. Rice. 22. Frank Bruno. 23. Thursday. 24. Procol Harum. 25. Lily of the valley. 26. Insects. 27. Palm. 28. Seven swans a-swimming. 29. King Arthur. 30. Eric Bristow. 31. It's That Man Again. 32. The Rolling Stones. 33. Dunedin, N.Z. 34. Dire Straits. 35. Tennis. 36. Ethelred. 37. Blue. (You're A Pink Toothbrush, I'm A Blue Toothbrush) 38. Cyril Fletcher. 39. Abraham Lincoln. 40. Davy Crockett. 41. India. 42. New York. 43. Home On The Range. 44. Mars. 45. Wins. 46. Four. 47. Rin Tin Tin. 48. Toytown. 49. India. 50. Alexis Carrington.

QUIZ 44 Pot Luck

EASY - LEVEL ONE

1 Which creatures did St Patrick drive out of Ireland?

2 In which TV programme do Patsy and Edina appear?

3 A 1990 ad for jeans helped put which early 70s Steve Miller Band song to the top of the charts?

4 In which month does the grouse shooting season start in Britain?

5 What type of racing has only two cars competing on the track at the same time?

6 How many years are celebrated by a platinum anniversary?

7 What is an oblong bar of gold called?

8 Who has played Lord Peter Wimsey and Bertie Wooster on TV?

9 Which European soccer trophy did Spurs become the first British team to win?

10 In the Paul McCartney/Stevie Wonder hit what went with ebony?

11 In which month is Twelfth Night?

12 In which city is the Whitney art gallery?

13 In which soap do the Sugdens appear?

14 What are the initials of thriller writer James?

15 Who recorded the album "The Immaculate Collection"?

16 In the book title, who did writer Laurie Lee have cider with?

17 Which musical does "I Know Him So Well" come from?

18 Which fictional Scottish doctor kept a casebook?

19 Who made up Abba with Benny, Bjorn and Annifrid?

20 Which traveller had the unusual first name of Lemuel?

21 Who wrote the words to "The Boxer"?

22 In which country is Hampden Park Stadium?

23 What can be upside down, ginger or Dundee?

24 Who was presenter of the 60s pop show "Saturday Club"?

25 Who was the lead singer with Culture Club?

26 What do the French words au revoir mean ?

27 Who said, "Am I dying beyond my means?"?

28 Who played the character of Mrs Fawlty?

29 Which Marie is supposed to have said, "Let them eat cake"?

30 What do the initials TB stand for?

31 What do the letters in M*A*S*H actually stand for?

32 How many minutes in five hours?

33 A car with the international registration letter E comes from where?

34 Who came first King Edward VIII or George VI?

35	Ruth and Bobbo Patchett appear in which Fay Weldon novel?
36	Where were Norse gods said to live?
37	Fe is the symbol of which chemical element?
38	Which army commander was known as "The Desert Fox"?
39	In which early radio soap was Mary worried about Jim?
40	What is the first month of the year to have exactly 31 days?
41	On TV, who worked in "The Rag Trade" and "On The Buses"?
42	Which musical instrument has dampers, hammers and strings?
43	"You Don't Have To Say You Love Me" was which singer's first No 1?
44	Which fish is smoked and cured and called 'finnan'?
45	Which pear-shaped tropical fruit has given its name to a bathroom suite colouring?
46	The Spanish Riding School is in which country?
47	What was the original name of the line on a ship showing the level to which it could be loaded?
48	Bouillabaisse is what kind of fish dish?
49	John Ridd is the male lead in which book with a girl's name as its title?
50	Who wrote the music "The Four Seasons"?

A nswers to Quiz 43, 70s Films

1. Pink Panther. 2. Star Wars. 3. Jaws. 4. Fifties. 5. The Godfather. 6. Superman. 7. Spielberg. 8. Chicago. 9. Gibb. 10. The Muppet Movie. 11. Jesus Christ Superstar. 12. Streisand. 13. Towering Inferno. 14. Airport. 15. Los Angeles. 16. King Kong. 17. Roger Moore. 18. M*A*S*H. 19. McQueen. 20. One Flew Over the Cuckoo's Nest. 21. Rocky. 22. Poseidon Adventure. 23. Hall. 24. Glenda Jackson. 25. Alice. 26. Cabaret. 27. Dudley. 28. Vietnam. 29. On the Roof. 30. Cop. 31. Star Wars. 32. The Godfather. 33. A car. 34. A shark. 35. Saturday. 36. Kramer. 37. Superman. 38. Cuckoo's. 39. Grease. 40. Third. 41. Nile. 42. Rocky. 43. Kermit. 44. Eagle. 45. King Kong. 46. Towering Inferno. 47. M*A*S*H. 48. Orange. 49. Jackal. 50. Bugsy.

FOR ANSWERS SEE QUIZ NO 46

Geography

EASY – LEVEL ONE

1 Is Australia in the northern or the southern hemisphere?

2 What does each star on the flag of the United States stand for?

3 Which country does the holiday island of Ibiza belong to?

4 Which island would you visit to kiss the Blarney Stone?

5 In which country would you be if you were visiting the Taj Mahal?

6 The south of which continent is closest to the Falkland Islands?

7 In which mountain range would you find Mount Everest?

8 Which country is Luxembourg the capital of?

9 What colour is the spot in the middle of the Japanese flag?

10 The island of Sicily is at the toe of which country?

11 Which country is also known as The Netherlands?

12 In which country are Maoris the indigenous population?

13 In which Scandinavian country would you find fjords?

14 Which country's languages include English, Zulu and Afrikaans?

15 Which country's name could be part of a Christmas dinner?

16 In which city is the Vatican City?

17 What is K2?

18 In which country is the Yellow River, also known as Huang He?

19 Which country has four letters, the last one q?

20 Which country, capital Bangkok, used to be called Siam?

21 Which ocean lies between Europe and America?

22 Which European country has an area called Flanders?

23 Is the South Pole in the Arctic or the Antarctic?

24 Which Rock is on the south coast of Spain?

25 Which isle lies between England and Northern Ireland?

26 Which island to the south of India used to be called Ceylon?

27 Which sea separates Europe and Africa?

28 In which ocean is Fiji?

29 Which island, in the Arctic Ocean, is the largest in the world?

30 In which continent is the world's longest river, the Nile?

31 In which Swiss mountain range is the Jungfrau?

32 Which is the next largest island in the world after Australia?

33 Which seaside resort is Super-Mare?

34 On which continent is the Kariba Dam?

35 What are Lakes Michigan, Superior, Huron, Erie and Ontario known as collectively?

36 If the southern limit of the tropics is Capricorn what is the

northern limit called?

37 Which island is to the south of Australia?

38 In the south of which country was Saigon?

39 If you were in Benidorm in which country would you be?

40 Which London palace has a maze?

41 Which isle off the west coast of England has three legs as its symbol?

42 Which country is connected to Wales by the Severn Bridge?

43 Which US state is a collection of islands in the Pacific?

44 Which language do natives of Hamburg speak?

45 Which county has a red rose as its symbol?

46 Which Queen gave her name to the capital of Hong Kong?

47 Which Bank is made of sand in the North Sea?

48 In which county is Penzance?

49 Which islands are Sark and Alderney part of?

50 Greece is in which continent?

Answers to Quiz 44, POT LUCK

1. Snakes. 2. Absolutely Fabulous. 3. The Joker. 4. August. 5. Drag Racing. 6. 70. 7. Ingot. 8. Ian Carmichael. 9. European Cup Winners' Cup. 10. Ivory. 11. January. 12. New York. 13. Emmerdale. 14. P.D. 15. Madonna. 16. Rosie. 17. Chess. 18. Doctor Finlay. 19. Agnetha. 20. Gulliver. 21. Paul Simon. 22. Scotland. 23. Cake. 24. Brian Matthew. 25. Boy George. 26. Until we meet again. 27. Oscar Wilde. 28. Prunella Scales. 29. Antoinette. 30. Tuberculosis. 31. Mobile Army Surgical Hospital. 32. 300. 33. Spain. 34 . Edward VIII. 35. The Life And Loves Of A She Devil. 36. Valhalla. 37. Iron. 3 8. Rommel. 39. Mrs Dale's Diary. 40. January. 41. Reg Varney. 42. Piano. 43. Dusty Springfield. 44. Haddock. 45. Avocado. 46. Austria. 47. Plimsoll Line. 418. Soup. 49. Lorna Doone. 50. Vivaldi.

Quiz 46 Pot Luck

EASY – LEVEL ONE

1 Red, yellow and blue are what type of colour?

2 In which TV programme does Hyacinth Bucket appear?

3 Which John was Labour leader before Tony Blair?

4 Which soccer side has Alexandra in its name?

5 The Acol system is used in which game?

6 How many years are celebrated by a ruby anniversary?

7 What three colours are in the flag of Belgium?

8 Which Leo plays Rumpole?

9 What number does the Roman numeral C stand for?

10 What was the name of Miss Rigby in the song by the Beatles?

11 In which month is Valentine's Day?

12 Which Ron played Fagin on film?

13 Roberta Flack had a No 1 with a song about the First Time I Saw Your what?

14 What are the initials of the poet Eliot?

15 What did Polly Flinders do?

16 Which Frederick wrote "The Day Of the Jackal"?

17 Which term means related to the moon?

18 Which Roger has played James Bond?

19 What are John, Paul, George and Ringo better known as?

20 On what part of your body would you wear a muff?

21 Which Wendy starred in "Butterflies"?

22 In which city is The Oval cricket ground?

23 Which Florence was known as the lady with the lamp?

24 What is a young fox called?

25 On which course is the Derby run?

26 Which special name is given to a group of ravens?

27 Who recorded the album "Thriller"?

28 On TV, is "Brookside" a close, an avenue or a drive?

29 Grandfather, cuckoo and carriage are types of what?

30 RoSPA is the Royal Society for the Prevention of what?

31 What is Norman Watts' nickname in "Coronation Street" ?

32 In 1907, who was the first woman to receive the Order of Merit?

33 Which country does a car come from if it has the international registration letter D?

34 Which doctor had a pet chimp called Chee Chee?

35 Who played Miss Brahms?

36 Which company had Nipper the dog as its trade mark?

37 C is the symbol of which

chemical element ?

38 Which cartoon character has Bluto as his arch rival?

39 Which two colours appear on the flag of Denmark?

40 What is the last month of the year to have exactly 30 days?

41 In which city was the 1994 Eurovision Song Contest held?

42 In a Pink Floyd song who had the strange hobby of collecting clothes?

43 If you are playing Southern Cross you are playing a form of which game?

44 Euclid is associated with which branch of mathematics?

45 Which group had a No 1 with "Belfast Child"?

46 How many players are in a Rugby League team?

47 In the UK what is the maximum number of years between General Elections?

48 What type of dance involves moving under a low horizontal pole?

49 How many pints in a gallon?

50 Which brothers, Jacob and Wilhelm, wrote fairy tales?

A nswers to Quiz 45, GEOGRAPHY

1. Southern. 2. A state. 3. Spain. 4. Ireland. 5. India. 6. South America. 7. Himalayas. 8. Luxembourg. 9. Red. 10. Italy. 11. Holland. 12. New Zealand. 13. Norway. 14. South Africa. 15. Turkey. 16. Rome. 17. Mountain. 18. China. 19. Iraq. 20. Thailand. 21. Atlantic. 22. Belgium. 23. Antarctic. 24. Gibraltar. 25. Isle of Man. 26. Sri Lanka. 27. Mediterranean. 28. Pacific. 29. Greenland. 30. Africa. 31. Alps. 32. Greenland. 33. Weston. 34. Africa. 35. Great Lakes. 36. Tropic of Cancer. 37. Tasmania. 38. Vietnam. 39. Spain. 40. Hampton Court. 41. Isle of Man. 42. England. 43. Hawaii. 44. German. 45. Lancashire. 46. Victoria. 47. Dogger Bank. 48. Cornwall. 49. Channel Islands. 50. Europe.

Q^{UIZ}₄₇ Hollywood

EASY - LEVEL ONE

1 Which tough guy star of "Casablanca" married Lauren Bacall?

2 Who co-starred with Bob Hope in the Road films?

3 Which actress left her husband and children for director Roberto Rossellini?

4 What is the first name of actor Curtis, father of Jamie Lee?

5 Which Officer and a Gentleman married supermodel Cindy Crawford?

6 How was Ruth Elizabeth Davis better known?

7 Which director Cecil B. was famous for epic movies?

8 Which Kops were the creation of director Mack Sennett?

9 Which daughter of Judy Garland won an Oscar for "Cabaret"?

10 Who is Kirk Douglas's son?

11 Which actress Ava was Frank Sinatra's second wife?

12 What relation is Shirley Maclaine to fellow star Warren Beatty?

13 Which Katharine had a long relationship with Spencer Tracy?

14 Which actress Grace became Princess of Monaco?

15 Which British suspense film director worked in Hollywood from 1939?

16 Which actress daughter of Henry was known as Hanoi Jane because of her anti-Vietnam war activities in the 1970s?

17 Who co-starred with Vivien Leigh in "Gone With the Wind"?

18 How is Jack Lemmon's co-star in "The Odd Couple", Walter Matasschanskavasky better known?

19 Who was Fred Astaire's most frequent dancing partner?

20 Which child star Shirley went on to be a US Ambassador?

21 Which silent movie star Rudolph died at an early age?

22 Hollywood legends Lionel, Ethel and John share what surname?

23 Which actor Paul is the husband of actress Joanne Woodward?

24 Who was married to Sean Penn and played the role of Evita?

25 Who was born Doris Kappelhoff?

26 Which star of "Top Gun" married Nicole Kidman?

27 Which actor James, famous for gangster roles, is credited with the catchphrase "You dirty rat!"?

28 Why was Jimmy Durante nicknamed Schnozzle?

29 Who married Richard Burton twice?

30 Which actress Demi married Bruce Willis?

31 Who played the head of the Corleone family?

32 Which Welsh actor starred opposite Debra Winger in

Shadowlands?

33 Who played Han Solo?

34 Which Jack starred with Shirley Maclaine in Terms of Endearment?

35 Which Eddie's most famous role is in Beverley Hills Cop?

36 Which British Michael won an Oscar for Hannah and her Sisters?

37 Which Jack's films include Some Like It Hot?

38 Which Mrs Bruce Willis starred in Ghost?

39 Which Katherine has received a record 12 Oscar nominations?

40 Who starred in and wrote the song "Evergreen" for A Star is Born?

41 Which Warren starred in Dick Tracy and Bugsy Malone?

42 Which Paul was in The Sting and The Color of Money?

43 Although born in the US, where was Mel Gibson brought up?

44 Who won Oscars for Forrest Gump in '94?

45 Who was the female Kramer?

46 In which decade did Sylvester Stallone first play Rambo?

47 Which country was Sean Connery born in?

48 Which Al won an Oscar for his role in Scent of a Woman?

49 Who was in Rain Man and was one of Four Good Men?

50 What "Color" is in the title of Whoopi Goldberg's first major film?

Answers to Quiz 46, Pot Luck

1. Primary. 2. Keeping Up Appearances. 3. Smith. 4. Crewe. 5. Bridge. 6. 40. 7. Black, red and yellow. 8. McKern. 9. 100. 10. Eleanor. 11. February. 12. Moody. 13. Face. 14. T.S. 15. Sat among the cinders. 16. Forsyth. 17. Lunar. 18. Moore. 19. The Beatles. 20. Hands. 21. Craig. 22. London. 23. Nightingale. 24. Cub. 25. Epsom. 26. Unkindness. 27. Michael Jackson. 28. Close. 29. Clock. 30. Accidents. 31. Curly 32. Florence Nightingale. 33. Germany. 34. Dr Doolittle. 35. Wendy Richard. 36. HMV - His Master's Voice. 37. Carbon. 38. Popeye. 39. Red and white. 40. November. 41. Dublin. 42. Arnold Layne. 43. Poker. 44. Geometry. 45. Simple Minds. 46. 13. 47. Five. 48. Limbo. 49. Eight. 50. Grimm.

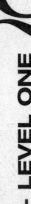

QUIZ 48 Pot Luck

EASY - LEVEL ONE

1 Which motorway was the first to be built in Britain?

2 What is the zodiac sign of the Bull?

3 On a dart board, which number is bottom centre?

4 Who had a No 1 hit with the song "Dancing Queen"?

5 Born Arthur Jefferson in 1890, what was this comic better known as?

6 What profession did Hillary Clinton previously practise?

7 Which character was played on TV by both Julie Walters and Lulu?

8 In which sport are there madisons and pursuits?

9 Who is the only singer to have No 1 hits in the 50s, 60s, 70s, 80s and 90s?

10 According to proverb, what does the hand that rocks the cradle do?

11 What was founded in 859 at Fez, Morocco, that is reckoned to be the oldest of its type in the world?

12 Which writer established the Three Laws of Robotics?

13 Called hood in America, what's this part of the car called in the UK?

14 Titan is a moon of which planet?

15 What is hydrophobia the fear of?

16 How many furlongs in a mile?

17 On TV, what is the name of Mavis Wilton's husband?

18 Which annual race was first held in 1829?

19 What type of animal is a Lhasa Apso?

20 Garibaldi, Nice and Ginger Nut are all types of what?

21 In the USA, which are the two main political parties?

22 Which Noel said, "Television is something you appear on: you don't watch it"?

23 What was the trade of Thomas Wolsey's father?

24 What did Siam change its name to?

25 Who recorded the album "Hold Me, Thrill Me, Kiss Me"?

26 Which Bay housed the island prison Alcatraz?

27 What colours are on the flag of Argentina?

28 In which town did Jesus grow up?

29 Who set up Biba?

30 If a triangle has an angle of 58 degrees and an angle of 77 degrees, what is the third angle?

31 Which country is Aeroflot from?

32 Who created Jimmy Porter?

33 Which instrument measures a plane's height above sea level?

34 Who recorded the album "Listen Without Prejudice"?

35 Who played the Bandit in "Smokey and The Bandit"?

100

36 Which king of England abdicated and was succeeded by his younger brother?

37 In rhyming slang what is meant by rabbit and pork?

38 How is Frederick Austerlitz better known?

39 How many players are there in a volleyball team?

40 What is the third book of the Old Testament?

41 What is the common name for the complaint bursitis?

42 In which city is La Scala opera house?

43 In the British army which rank comes between Lieutenant and Major?

44 What colour is the gem jet?

45 What is the name of the newsagent's in "Coronation Street"?

46 How many sides has a heptagon?

47 What type of creature is used for the dish Bombay duck?

48 Where on your body is your olfactory organ?

49 Which major river flows through Liverpool?

50 Which singer had a No 1 with "All Kinds Of Everything"?

A nswers to Quiz 47, HOLLYWOOD

1. Humphrey Bogart. 2. Bing Crosby. 3. Ingrid Bergman. 4. Tony. 5. Richard Gere. 6. Bette. 7. De Mille. 8. Keystone. 9. Liza Minnelli. 10. Michael Douglas. 11. Gardner. 12. Sister. 13. Hepburn. 14. Kelly. 15. Alfred Hitchcock. 16. Jane Fonda. 17. Clark Gable. 18. Walter Matthau. 19.Ginger Rogers. 20. Temple. 21. Valentino. 22. Barrymore. 23. Newman. 24. Madonna. 25. Doris Day. 26. Tom Cruise. 27. Cagney. 28. Nose. 29. Elizabeth Taylor. 30. Moore. 31. Marlon Brando. 32. Anthony Hopkins. 33. Harrison Ford. 34. Nicholson. 35. Murphy. 36. Caine. 37. Lemmon. 38. Demi Moore. 39. Hepburn. 40. Barbra Streisand. 41. Beatty. 42. Newman. 43. Australia. 44. Tom Hanks. 45. Meryl Streep. 46. 80s. 47. Scotland. 48. Pacino. 49. Tom Cruise. 50. Purple.

 Q₄₉^{UIZ} Animals

1. Where does a kangaroo keep its young?
2. Which black and white mammal lives in China's bamboo forests?
3. Where do koalas live?
4. How many legs does an adult insect have?
5. What type of creature is a black widow?
6. Which animal's nickname is 'ship of the desert'?
7. Which breed of spaniel shares its name with a king?
8. Which sea creature is known as a Portuguese man-of-war?
9. What is a female sheep called?
10. What do carnivorous animals live on?
11. Which animals are described as canine?
12. What is a fox's tail called?
13. Which saint is the heaviest breed of dog named after?
14. What is special about a guinea pig's tail?
15. What are pigs' feet called?
16. Which elephants have the smaller ears, African or Indian?
17. What are edible sturgeon eggs called?
18. What name is given to the period of winter sleep by some animals?
19. What does an invertebrate animal not have?
20. What would a billy and a nanny produce?
21. Which black and white mammal sprays a foul smelling liquid when attacked?
22. How does a boa constrictor kill its prey?
23. Why does a fish need gills?
24. What does a scorpion have at the end of its tail?
25. What does a chameleon change to camouflage itself?
26. What does an Isle of Man Manx cat not have?
27. What type of insect is a Red Admiral?
28. What is another name for an Alsatian dog?
29. What kind of animal is a Suffolk Punch?
30. A lynx is a member of which family group?
31. In mammals, the Asian elephant is second but man has the longest - what?
32. A papillon is a breed of what?
33. What is the term for a group of beavers?
34. Alphabetically, which animal always comes first?
35. Dromedary and Bactrian are types of what?
36. What is a male fox called?
37. How many teats does a cow usually have?
38. In Britain, which is the only venomous snake?

39 What type of leaves does a koala feed on?

40 The cairn terrier was originally bred in which country?

41 What type of animal is a natterjack?

42 What type of "ology" is the study of animals?

43 What colour are the markings on a skunk?

44 A jenny is a female what?

45 What is the term for a group of elephants?

46 Which monkey has a blue and red face?

47 What type of animal is an ibex?

48 Which animal lives in an earth or sett?

49 What type of animal eats meat?

50 What name is given to a baby kangaroo?

QUIZ 50 Pot Luck

1. Dr John Pemberton invented which drink in 1886?

2. Usually called by his last name, what was Steed's first name in the "Avengers"?

3. Which Fleet Street church has the tallest steeple designed by Christopher Wren?

4. Victor Barna was five times world champion in which sport?

5. What is the Welsh name for Wales?

6. How many years are celebrated by an emerald anniversary?

7. In which village is "Emmerdale" set?

8. What three colours are on the flag of Australia?

9. What number does the Roman numeral L stand for?

10. Who recorded the album "Everything Changes"?

11. In cartoons, who 'kept on walking'?

12. What do you suffer from if you have coryza?

13. What is the first name of TV cook Tovey?

14. What are the initials of comic writer Wodehouse?

15. Who directed the film "Tommy"?

16. The Haka is a dance performed by which rugby union team?

17. Which George wrote "Porgy And Bess"?

18. Snooker's Eddie Charlton comes from which country?

19. In which year were women first given the vote?

20. On what part of your body would you wear an espadrille?

21. Which of the following can vote in a general election: the mentally ill, criminals, people under 18?

22. In which country is the Curragh racecourse?

23. Which element is used in computer chips?

24. To five years either way, when was the GLC formed?

25. Which planet is 4,500 million years old?

26. What does the French word pomme mean?

27. What trees belong to the genus Quercus?

28. Which village is the setting for "Noel's House Party"?

29. Who wrote the poem "Anthem For Doomed Youth"?

30. Who scored a century in the 1996 cricket World Cup Final?

31. Which Order did Edward III found in 1350?

32. Which tavern was the favourite of Falstaff?

33. Which actor talked to a six-foot high, invisible rabbit in the film "Harvey"?

34. Which England soccer skipper was injured in both the 1986 and 1990 World Cup final stages?

35 Which Harold said, "Most of our people have never had it so good."

36 Cliff Richard and Marty Robbins had different songs that shared which title?

37 Which writer featured Jonathan Harker in his most famous novel?

38 Myosotis is more commonly known as which flower?

39 Which Tropic is further north, Capricorn or Cancer?

40 To ten years either way, when did Thomas Cook organize his first continental holiday?

41 Which orange seller became mistress of Charles II?

42 Who recorded the album "Shepherd Moons"?

43 What is the word for a group of hounds?

44 Which sport is a mixture of map reading and cross country running?

45 Which actor recorded that he "was born under a wand'rin' star"?

46 How many legs has a spider?

47 In music, name the horizontal lines around which notes are written?

48 Which New England poet had "miles to go before I sleep"?

49 Which work does Anitra's Dance come from?

50 Who made his last stand at Little Bighorn?

A nswers to Quiz 49, ANIMALS

1. In a pouch. 2. Panda. 3. Australia. 4. Six. 5. Spider. 6. Camel. 7. King Charles. 8. Jellyfish. 9. Ewe. 10. Meat. 11. Dogs. 12. Brush. 13. St Bernard. 14. It doesn't have one. 15. Trotters. 16. Indian. 17. Caviar. 18. Hibernation. 19. Backbone. 20. Kids. 21. Skunk. 22. Squeezing. 23. To breathe. 24. Sting. 25. Colour. 26. A tail. 27. Butterfly. 28. German Shepherd. 29. Horse. 30. Cat. 31. Life span. 32. Dog. 33. Colony. 34. Aardvark. 35. Camels. 36. Dog. 37. Four. 38. Adder. 39. Eucalyptus. 40. Scotland. 41. Toad. 42. Zoology. 43. Black and white. 44. Donkey. 45. Herd. 46. Mandrill. 47. Goat. 48. Badger. 49. Carnivore. 50. Joey.

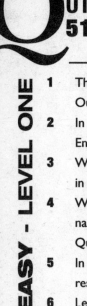

QUIZ 51 Around the UK

EASY - LEVEL ONE

1 The Severn, the Trent and the Ouse are all what?

2 In which county are all ten of England's highest peaks?

3 Which is the second largest city in England?

4 Which London station was named after a long-reigning Queen?

5 In which county are the seaside resorts of Clacton and Southend?

6 Leeds Castle is in Kent. Where is Leeds?

7 Which seaside resort is famous for its Tower and its Golden Mile?

8 What might you see at Regent's Park, Chester and Whipsnade?

9 What is the name of the famous cathedral in York?

10 Which is the largest island in England?

11 What did Sunderland become in 1992 which Manchester, Liverpool and Birmingham became in the 19th century?

12 Which river runs through London?

13 Which is further north, Southport or Northampton?

14 Which stretch of water divides England and France?

15 What do the letters NEC stand for?

16 What is the area around Stoke-on-Trent known as?

17 Which northern city is served by Ringway airport?

18 Which motorway starts south of Birmingham and goes northwest towards Scotland?

19 Which part of the country would a Geordie come from?

20 Near which large city would you find the Wirral?

21 Which two cities are the home of England's two oldest universities?

22 Which range of northern hills is called the backbone of England?

23 Which moorland area of southwest Devon is the site of a high-security prison?

24 What are Dagenham, Luton and Cowley famous for producing?

25 Where would a Manx person come from?

26 Which famous stones can be seen on Salisbury Plain?

27 Whose birthplace might you be visiting in Stratford-on-Avon?

28 In which county is the English terminal of the Channel Tunnel?

29 How many square miles is the City of London?

30 Which was England's smallest county before the 1974 changes?

31 Glasgow is the administrative centre of which Scottish region?

32 Which is further north, Liverpool or Leeds?

33 What before the 1996 reorganization was the only

Welsh county to begin with C?

34 Which motorway would you travel on from London to Leeds?

35 How is the Welsh island Ynys Mon also known?

36 In which part of the UK is Newry?

37 How many counties have a border with Cornwall?

38 In which District are Ullswater and Bassenthwaite?

39 Which resort beginning with S lies between Whitby and Bridlington?

40 In which country is Prestwick Airport?

41 On which river does Hull lie?

42 Which city's major station is New Street?

43 In which city is Princes Street a major shopping thoroughfare?

44 On which coast of Scotland is Dundee?

45 Which motorway would you travel on from London to Cambridge?

46 London Zoo is in which Park?

47 Which motorway stretches from the outskirts of London into Wales?

48 On which island are Shanklin and Sandown?

49 Which two south-coast resorts include the name Regis?

50 Which two London Boroughs begin with E?

1. Coca Cola. 2 John. 3. St Bride's. 4. Table tennis. 5. Cymru. 6. 55. 7. Beckindale. 8. Blue, red and white. 9. 50. 10. Take That. 11. Felix the Cat. 12. Common cold. 13. John. 14. P.G. 15. Ken Russell. 16. All Blacks. 17. Gershwin. 18. Australia. 19. 1918. 20. Feet. 21. None. 22. Ireland. 23. Silicon. 24. 1965. 25. Earth. 26. Apple. 27. Oaks. 28. Crinkley Bottom. 29. Wilfred Owen. 30. Aravinda de Silva. 31. Garter. 32. The Boar's Head. 33. James Stewart. 34. Bryan Robson. 35. Macmillan. 36. Devil Woman. 37. Bram Stoker. 38. Forget-me-not. 39. Cancer. 40. 1855. 41. Nell Gwyn. 42. Enya. 43. Pack. 44. Orienteering. 45. Lee Marvin. 46. 8. 47. Stave. 48. Robert Frost. 49. Peer Gynt. 50. General Custer.

Q UIZ 52 Pot Luck

EASY - LEVEL ONE

1 If it rains on St Swithin's Day, how many more days is it supposed to rain?

2 In which TV programme did Bruce Forsyth and Rosemarie Ford appear?

3 Who played Robin Hood in the original British TV series?

4 Which composer wrote "The Marriage of Figaro"?

5 What is a low, shallow basket used by gardeners called?

6 How many years are celebrated by a golden anniversary?

7 In "David Copperfield" what was the surname of Uriah?

8 What name is shared by TV presenter Zoe and singer Michael?

9 What number does the Roman numeral M stand for?

10 What sort of creature is a capercaillie?

11 In which month is Remembrance Day?

12 What type of vehicle provided a 50s hit for Nancy Whiskey?

13 How many faces has an icosahedron?

14 What are the initials of "Lady Chatterley" author Lawrence?

15 What name is given to a litter of piglets?

16 What type of dancing is associated with Margot Fonteyn?

17 Which soap pub sells Churchill Strong?

18 Who recorded the album "Both Sides"?

19 How many children did Queen Victoria have?

20 Who is the resident Lord in "Private Eye"?

21 What are paper measures called equal to 500 sheets?

22 In which country is Flushing Meadow tennis stadium?

23 What is the domed recess at the east end of a church called?

24 What is a young goat called?

25 How did master escapologist Harry Houdini die?

26 After which George was the American state of Georgia named?

27 Which viral disease is also called grippe?

28 Who said, "Anyone can get old. All you have to do is live long enough"?

29 In what game do you peg, and score for pairs and fifteens?

30 What does PYO stand for?

31 What animal-linked name describes someone who always gets blamed?

32 How many seconds in five minutes?

33 Which German side won the European Cup in 1974, 1975 and 1976?

34 Debussy appears on which

108

French bank note?

35 Which Andy said, "In the future everyone will be famous for 15 minutes?"

36 In snooker what is the score for potting a black?

37 Pb is the symbol of which chemical element?

38 Who recorded the seasonal song "Merry Xmas Everybody"?

39 Which term means dying without having made a will?

40 Who or what was the Empress of Blandings?

41 Who was Little Sure Shot according to Sitting Bull?

42 Who recorded the album "Bat Out Of Hell"?

43 What is the word for a group of bees?

44 Which musical instrument is played by Acker Bilk?

45 What is another name for the prairie wolf?

46 How many colours are there in the rainbow?

47 In music, what is a note if it is neither sharp nor flat?

48 Who was Madonna desperately seeking in her first feature film?

49 How many inches in two yards?

50 What type of fruit is dried to produce a sultana?

A nswers to Quiz 51, AROUND THE UK

1. Rivers. 2. Cumbria. 3. Birmingham. 4. Victoria. 5. Essex. 6. Yorkshire. 7. Blackpool. 8. Zoo. 9. The Minster. 10. Isle of Wight. 11. A city. 12. Thames. 13. Southport. 14. English Channel. 15. National Exhibition Centre. 16. The Potteries. 17. Manchester. 18. M6. 19. Northeast. 20. Liverpool. 21. Oxford. Cambridge. 22. Pennines. 23. Dartmoor. 24. Cars. 25. Isle of Man. 26. Stonehenge. 27. Shakespeare's. 28. Kent. 29. One. 30. Rutland. 31. Strathclyde. 32. Leeds. 33. Clwyd. 34. M1. 35. Anglesey. 36. Northern Ireland. 37. One - Devon. 38. Lake District. 39. Scarborough. 40. Scotland. 41. Humber. 42. Birmingham. 43. Edinburgh. 44. East. 45. M11. 46. Regent's Park. 47. M4. 48. Isle of Wight. 49. Bognor, Lyme. 50. Ealing, Enfield.

Q₅₃^{UIZ} Who's Who

EASY - LEVEL ONE

1   Who married Patsy Kensit in April 1997?

2   Which singer's daughter is called Lourdes Maria?

3   Who has a backing group called the Waves?

4   Who took "Wannabe" to No. 1 in 1996?

5   Who is lead singer with Wet Wet Wet?

6   Who won the Eurovision Song Contest with "Puppet on a String"?

7   Who sang "Strangers in the Night"?

8   Who is the brother of the late Karen Carpenter?

9   Who wrote "Words", a 90s hit for Boyzone?

10   Which singer/songwriter received a knighthood in January 1997?

11   Who was Bernie Taupin's most famous songwriting partner?

12   Who is Mick Jagger's second wife?

13   Who changed his name from Gordon Sumner to top the charts?

14   Who was the only female singer managed by Brian Epstein?

15   Who was the female vocalist with the Pretenders?

16   Who co-starred with Whitney Houston in "The Bodyguard"?

17   Who wrote the music for" Jesus Christ Superstar"?

18   Who were known on TV as Dave Tucker and Paddy Garvey?

19   Who sang that they were "Back For Good" in 1995?

20   Whose "new" single, "Free As A Bird", charted in 1995?

21   The title from which TV drama gave Jimmy Nail a hit in 1994?

22   Who was the subject of the biopic "What's Love Got to Do With It?"?

23   Whose first solo No. 1 was "Sacrifice/Healing Hands"?

24   Who was the British Monkee?

25   Who played Wimbledon's Centre Court without a racket in 1996?

26   Who had a hit with "Radio Ga Ga"?

27   Who was the father of the former Mrs Lisa Marie Jackson?

28   Which 80s duo included Andrew Ridgeley?

29   Who had his first UK solo No. 1 with "I Just Called To Say I Love You"?

30   Who was lead singer with Culture Club?

31   Who formed the Black Abbots and had a TV Madhouse?

32   Which Paula presented "The Tube" and "Big Breakfast"?

33   What is the profession of Miriam Stoppard?

34   What do Jilly Goolden and Oz Clarke of "Food and Drink"

sample?

35 Which Jeremy has fronted "Newsnight" and "University Challenge"?

36 Which Gaby presented the first series of "Whatever You Want"?

37 Barry Norman fronts a long-running show on which subject?

38 Which Sue co-presented ITV's 1997 "Election Night" programme?

39 What are the first names of Wood and Walters?

40 Which David presents sports programmes such as skiing and snooker?

41 Which part of the UK is GMTV's Lorraine Kelly from?

42 Which Mr Whiteley presents "Countdown"?

43 Which Alan replaced the late Geoff Hamilton on "Gardener's World"?

44 What is the surname of the actor David and his brother, the newsreader John?

45 Which Michael has been from "Pole to Pole"?

46 Which outspoken American interviewed the Duchess of York?

47 Which Eamonn spoke the first words on GMTV?

48 Who is Mrs Lenny Henry?

49 Which talented cartoonist presents "Animal Hospital"?

50 Which knight presents a breakfast programme on Sundays?

A nswers to Quiz 52, Pot Luck

1. 40. 2. The Generation Game. 3. Richard Greene. 4. Mozart. 5. Trug. 6. 50. 7. Heap. 8. Ball. 9. 1,000. 10. A bird. 11. November. 12. Freight Train. 13. 20. 14. D.H. 15. A farrow. 16. Ballet. 17. Queen Vic (EastEnders). 18. Phil Collins. 19. Nine. 20. Lord Gnome. 21. Ream. 22 .USA. 23. Apse. 24. Kid. 25. A blow to his stomach. 26. King George II. 27. Influenza. 28. Groucho Marx. 29. Cribbage. 30. Pick Your Own. 31. Scapegoat. 32. 300. 33. Bayern Munich. 34. 20 franc. 35. Warhol. 36. Eight. 37. Lead. 38. Slade. 39. Intestate. 40. A pig. 41. Annie Oakley. 42. Meatloaf. 43. Swarm. 44. Clarinet. 45. Coyote. 46. Seven. 47. Natural. 48. Susan. 49 72. 50 Grape.

Quiz 54 Pot Luck

FOR ANSWERS SEE QUIZ NO 55

EASY - LEVEL ONE

1 What colour is a peridot stone?

2 What is the zodiac sign of the Twins?

3 In which part of the body is the patella?

4 Who had a No 1 hit with the song "Bachelor Boy"?

5 What is the second letter of the Greek alphabet?

6 What is the nest of an eagle called?

7 Which film star has a statue in Leicester Square?

8 In which month is Queen Elizabeth II's official birthday?

9 Who was lead singer with Dawn?

10 What did the Rochdale Pioneers pioneer?

11 Which 1995 movie starred a wet Kevin Costner?

12 Which board game involves moving through rooms to solve a murder?

13 Called a tuxedo in America, what's this garment called in the UK?

14 What type of jewels are traditionally associated with Amsterdam?

15 What is zoophobia a fear of?

16 In which programme did Rab C. Nesbitt first appear on TV?

17 What was Charon's job?

18 Which Edith sang "Je ne regrette rien" (No Regrets)?

19 What colour is the Central Line on a London Underground map?

20 What type of food is a bagel?

21 What sits on a dolly in a television studio?

22 Who says, "You'll like this – not a lot!"?

23 Which day of the week is named after the god Woden?

24 Who recorded the album "From The Cradle"?

25 Which "Coronation Street" supermarket employed Reg and Vera?

26 What is the claw of a bird of prey called?

27 What type of sport took place in the 'Frying Pan'?

28 Dr Stephen Hawking wrote a brief history of what?

29 Which Club is concerned with pedigree in the dog world?

30 Which English king was painted by Hans Holbein?

31 Which country are All Nippon Airways from?

32 What is the currency of India?

33 On TV, what are the names of Pauline Fowler's two sons?

34 How many squares are there on a chess board?

35 James I and Charles I were members of which royal dynasty?

36 How many lanes are there in an Olympic swimming pool?

37 Who is the sister of Joey Boswell?

38 How is Gordon Sumner better known?

39 What name links singer Kate and former USA President George?

40 In the Bible, who was famous for his wisdom?

41 What was the secret state police of Nazi Germany called?

42 In which country is Schiphol airport?

43 What is Kevin Webster's job in "Coronation Street"?

44 What colour is heliotrope?

45 Which tree family includes the sycamore and maple?

46 How many sides has a dodecagon?

47 Which event did the first popular greeting card celebrate?

48 What is the home of a beaver called?

49 Who wrote of "Season of mists and mellow fruitfulness'?

50 What name is given to an extension of a stage in front of a curtain?

1. Liam Gallagher. 2. Madonna. 3. Katrina. 4. The Spice Girls. 5. Marti Pellow. 6. Sandie Shaw. 7. Frank Sinatra. 8. Richard. 9. The Bee Gees. 10. Paul McCartney. 11. Elton John. 12. Jerry Hall. 13. Sting. 14. Cilla Black. 15. Chrissie Hynde. 16. Kevin Costner. 17. Andrew Lloyd Webber. 18. Robson and Jerome. 19. Take That. 20. The Beatles. 21. "Crocodile Shoes". 22. Tina Turner. 23. Elton John. 24. Davy Jones. 25. Cliff Richard. 26. Queen. 27. Elvis Presley. 28. Wham! 29. Stevie Wonder. 30. Boy George. 31. Russ Abbot. 32. Yates. 33. Doctor. 34. Drink. 35. Paxman. 36. Roslin. 37. Films. 38. Lawley. 39. Victoria, Julie. 40. Vine. 41. Scotland. 42. Richard. 43. Titchmarsh. 44. Suchet. 45. Palin. 46. Ruby Wax. 47. Holmes. 48. Dawn French. 49. Rolf Harris. 50. Sir David Frost.

Quiz 55 Transport

EASY - LEVEL ONE

1 Which motorway runs from London to Leeds?

2 Do more countries drive on the left or on the right?

3 In which county is Stansted airport?

4 Which company made the first production-line car, the Model T?

5 What did the Mongolfier brothers fly in in 1783?

6 What was the surname of aviation pioneers Orville and Wilbur?

7 What is the full name of the QE2?

8 Which country do Renault cars come from?

9 Who produced the luxury Silver Ghost?

10 Over which ocean did Alcock and Brown fly in 1919?

11 What would you be travelling in if you were in a Pullman?

12 Under which stretch of water would you be if you were on Le Shuttle?

13 Which engine for aircraft was patented by Frank Whittle in 1930?

14 Which Anglo-French supersonic aircraft made its first flight in 1969?

15 What is the traditional colour for a London taxi?

16 Which motorway circles London?

17 Which city is served by Ringway Airport?

18 Which type of sports car is also the name of a big cat?

19 What was the Queen Elizabeth's luxury sister ship?

20 Which motorway runs from London to Cambridge?

21 Which London railway station is named after a battle with Napoleon?

22 Which country do Volkswagen cars originate in?

23 How would you be travelling if you were taking the Jubilee line?

24 In which city is Charles de Gaulle airport?

25 What type of vehicle is a juggernaut?

26 Which type of transport is George Stephenson famous for?

27 Near which Kent port is the English opening of the Channel Tunnel?

28 In which year did Nigel Mansell last race Formula 1 cars?

29 The Trans-Siberian railway runs from Vladivostock to which Russian city?

30 At which Thames crossing is there a tunnel and the Queen Elizabeth Bridge?

31 In which decade did the driving test introduce a written section?

32 What is an Eskimo canoe called?

33 Which is Germany's main

airport?

34 What name is given to a cigar-shaped airship?

35 Which musical features a song about a "surrey with a fringe on top"?

36 The Montgolfier brothers flew in what type of craft?

37 Which motor company made the first production-line car?

38 What shape is the bottom of a punt?

39 E is the international vehicle registration letter of which country?

40 Whose 60s report axed many railway lines in Britain?

41 Orly airport is in which city?

42 In which country did the Toyota Motor Corporation originate?

43 Eurostar goes from which London station?

44 In song, "my old man said follow" which vehicle?

45 A Chinook is what type of vehicle?

46 What colour is the Circle Line on a London Underground map?

47 In which century was the Suez Canal opened?

48 What is the Boeing 747 usually known as?

49 What is the international vehicle registration letter of Germany?

50 The SNFC operates in which country?

Answers to Quiz 54, POT LUCK

1. Green. 2. Gemini. 3. Knee. 4. Cliff Richard. 5. Beta. 6. Eyrie. 7. Charlie Chaplin. 8. June. 9. Tony Orlando. 10. The Co-op. 11. Waterworld. 12. Cluedo. 13. Dinner jacket. 14. Diamonds. 15. Animals. 16. Naked Video. 17. Ferryman who, in Greek mythology, takes the dead to the underworld. 18. Piaf. 19. Red. 20. Bread roll. 21. A camera. 22. Paul Daniels. 23. Wednesday. 24. Eric Clapton. 25. Bettabuys. 26 Talon. 27. Horse racing. 28. Time. 29. Kennel. 30. Henry VIII. 31 Japan. 32. Rupee. 33. Mark, Martin. 34. 64. 35. Stuarts. 36. Eight. 37. Aveline. 38. Sting. 39. Bush. 40. Solomon. 41. Gestapo. 42. Netherlands. 43. Car mechanic. 44. Mauve. 45 Acer. 46. 12. 47. St Valentine's Day. 48. Lodge. 49. John Keats. 50. Apron.

Quiz 56 Pot Luck

EASY - LEVEL ONE

1 Catherine Parr survived which royal husband?

2 Which programme features Jilly Goolden, Oz Clarke and Michael Barry?

3 What is meant by the Latin phrase *caveat emptor*?

4 Which English club did soccer TV pundit Alan Hansen play for?

5 What spirit is made from fermented sugar cane?

6 How many years are celebrated by a silver anniversary?

7 Which Phil became famous for presenting "One Man And His Dog"?

8 What is the capital of the Isle of Man?

9 How did Yetta Feldman die in "So Haunt Me"?

10 Which Tom starred in "Magnum"?

11 Which word meaning letter is in titles of books of the Bible?

12 Who recorded the album "Simply The Best"?

13 What paper is used to test acid and alkali?

14 What are the initials of English writer Priestley?

15 Who presented the first ever edition of "Mastermind"?

16 How many seconds in quarter of an hour?

17 Which special day follows Shrove Tuesday?

18 Who came first as US President, Washington or Lincoln?

19 Diana Ross, Florence Ballard and Mary Wilson formed what?

20 How is the UK golfing term albatross known in America?

21 Which social security benefit was introduced in 1909?

22 What name is adopted by Don Diego de la Vega?

23 What were the first three Eddystone lighthouses lit by?

24 What is a young hare called?

25 At what degree celsius does water freeze?

26 Which animal's name means river horse?

27 What is the first name of TV cook Carrier?

28 Which day of the week is *dimanche* in French?

29 What nickname was given to winter sportsman Eddie Edwards?

30 In "The Colbys" what is Sable short for?

31 Which soap has the pub The Malt Shovel?

32 How many minutes in two and a half hours?

33 Which country is a car from if it has the international registration letters CH?

34 In CB terminology, what is a water hole?

35 Which Harold said, "A week is a long time in politics!"?

36 In darts, what is the lowest score for three trebles?

37 N is the symbol of which chemical element ?

38 Who recorded the album "Parklife"?

39 Which actress Jane developed her fitness programmes?

40 What is the last month of the year to have exactly 31 days?

41 Which Australian bird does not fly?

42 Which veteran DJ Tony was the first voice on Radio 1?

43 In geometry, how many minutes are there in a degree?

44 What is a segment of garlic called?

45 Which Barbra sang "A Woman In Love"?

46 What is the first letter on the bottom line of a keyboard?

47 Where is the surgery of Dr Richard Locke?

48 What is 'black gold'?

49 How many feet are there in ten yards?

50 What is Edward Woodward's only hit single?

1. M1. 2. Right. 3. Essex. 4. Ford. 5. Hot Air Balloon. 6. Wright. 7. Queen Elizabeth II. 8. France. 9. Rolls Royce. 10. Atlantic. 11. Train. 12. English Channel. 13. Jet. 14. Concorde. 15. Black. 16. M25. 17. Manchester. 18. Jaguar. 19. Queen Mary. 20. M11. 21. Waterloo. 22. Germany. 23. Underground. 24. Paris. 25. Lorry. 26. Railway. 27. Folkestone. 28. 1995. 29. Moscow. 30. Dartford. 31. 1990s. 32. Kayak. 33. Frankfurt. 34. Zeppelin. 35. Oklahoma. 36. Hot-air balloon. 37. Ford. 38. Flat. 39. Spain. 40. Dr Beeching. 41. Paris. 42. Japan. 43. Waterloo. 44. Van. 45. Helicopter. 46. Yellow. 47. 19th. 48. Jumbo jet. 49. D. 50 France.

Q UIZ 57 Technology

EASY - LEVEL ONE

1 What is the difference between a mixture and a compound?

2 What are the three methods by which heat travels?

3 What force does a car have to overcome when it starts moving?

4 What do we call the point about which a lever turns?

5 Oil is used to reduce what?

6 What is an abacus?

7 What are the two ways by which nuclear energy is produced?

8 What do we call the force that pulls objects inwards?

9 Why do streamlined vehicles use less fuel?

10 What simple devices are used to change the direction of a force?

11 In the Middle Ages what use did candles have apart from illumination?

12 What was unusual about the Heinkel He 178?

13 What was notable about the Focke-Wulf 61?

14 Which time-keeping device had the most moving parts?

15 Which time-keeping device had no moving parts?

16 What is the cause of the apparent bending of a stick when it is thrust into water?

17 If three light bulbs were wired in parallel and threein series, which would be the brighter?

18 If you wire up a small torch bulb in an electrical circuit containing a fresh lemon, will the bulb light?

19 Nutcrackers are an example of what sort of mechanical device?

20 Why are drainage inspection covers usually round?

21 What device, which made use of phosphorus, was patented by Alonzo D. Phillips in 1836?

22 What improvement did John B. Dunlop make to the bicycle?

23 In 1849 Walter Hunt reinvented which device, used by ancient peoples for fastening clothes?

24 What oar-propelled craft did Dutchman Cornelius van Drebbel invent?

25 What invention did Sir John Harrington bring to the court of Queen Elizabeth I?

26 What device, still in common use, was invented by Alessandro Volta?

27 Where was the wheel invented?

28 Which city built the world's second underground railway?

29 What is the connection between Leonardo da Vinci and the bicycle?

30 Who was Laika?

31 E. G. Otis demonstrated his newly invented lift by asking a spectator to cut its cable. What happened?

32 Which household device originated in observations of the way in which ether evaporates?

33 What does the cochineal beetle

have in common with gastropods?

34 Who invented the mercury thermometer?

35 Which was invented first, the screw or the screwdriver?

36 In which country was the mechanical clock first devised?

37 Salvino degli Armati was far-sighted enough to invent what common device in about 1280?

38 What device did Jethro Tull invent to improve agriculture?

39 In the 1930s Chester Carlson carried out research on which device which became common in many offices?

40 Nicolas Appert won a prize of 12,000 francs for his invention, which would be of immense benefit to armies. What was it?

41 The Remington company produced guns and what?

42 Outside which building were the first traffic signals erected?

43 The zipper was invented by a man named Henrik Zipp. True or false?

44 The safety razor was invented by a king. True or false?

45 What did Guglielmo Marconi invent in his parents' attic?

46 How were the earliest glass windows made?

47 What was Parkesine?

48 What items were made from ivory and later from celluloid?

49 What was a Bissell Grand Rapids?

50 In 1882 Henry W. Seeley invented what device?

A nswers to Quiz 56, Pot Luck

1. Henry VIII. 2. Food and Drink. 3. Buyer beware. 4. Liverpool. 5. Rum. 6. 25. 7. Drabble. 8. Douglas. 9. Choked on a chicken bone. 10. Selleck. 11. Epistle. 12 . Tina Turner. 13. Litmus. 14. J.B. 15. Magnus Magnusson. 16. 900. 17. Ash Wednesday. 18. Washington. 19. The Supremes. 20. Double eagle. 21. Old age pension. 22. Zorro. 23. Candles. 24. Leveret. 25. 0. 26. Hippopotamus. 27. Robert. 28. Sunday. 29. The Eagle. 30. Sabelia. 31. Emmerdale. 32. 150. 33. Switzerland. 34. Pub. 35. Wilson. 36. Nine. 37. Nitrogen. 38. Blur. 39. Fonda. 40. December. 41. Emu. 42. Tony Blackburn. 43. 60. 44. Clove. 45. Streisand. 46. Z. 47. Ambridge (in the Archers). 48. Oil. 49. 30. 50. The Way You Look Tonight.

$Q^{\text{UIZ}}_{\text{58}}$ Pot Luck

EASY - LEVEL ONE

1. On which day of the week is the Budget usually presented?
2. What was the French title of "It's A Knockout"?
3. Which fictional bear is named after a London station?
4. Who did Robbie Coltrane play in "Tutti Frutti"?
5. What is the largest state of the USA?
6. How many years are celebrated by a pearl anniversary?
7. Which curly-leaved salad plant is a member of the chicory family?
8. Which armoured combat vehicle was first used in World War I?
9. Which doctor does Simon Shepherd play in "Peak Practice"?
10. In "Coronation Street" what is the name of Deirdre's daughter?
11. In which month is the shortest day?
12. Who recorded "Michael Caine"?
13. In which sport is the Thomas Cup awarded?
14. To ten years either way, when were women first allowed to take degrees at British universities?
15. Which group had a No 1 with "See My Baby Jive"?
16. Which bird is associated with Lundy Island?
17. How is Russian revolutionary Vladimir Ilyich Ulyanov better known?
18. Who played Beattie Bellman in the TV commercials?
19. What are Marc Bolan and Micky Finn better known as?
20. How do male moths find female moths in the dark?
21. Which canal had an opera written especially for its opening?
22. What type of nut is a marron glacé?
23. In which film did Elvis Presley play a double role?
24. What is a young horse called?
25. Who recorded the album "Crocodile Shoes"?
26. Who became Lord Warden of the Cinque ports in 1978?
27. Which show has featured Christopher Biggins, Bob Carolgees and Gordon Burns?
28. Which Samuel kept a famous diary in the seventeenth century?
29. What is a coley?
30. In education, what does OU stand for?
31. How did Van Gogh commit suicide?
32. What is the upper age limit for being an MP in the UK?
33. Who spent most weeks in the singles' charts in 1994?
34. Who was the first reigning British monarch to visit a Communist country?
35. Which opera features the song "Take A Pair Of Sparkling Eyes"?

36 In snooker, how many points are scored for potting the green ball?

37 S is the symbol of which chemical element?

38 Who recorded the album "Music Box"?

39 Which card game is another name for a prison van?

40 What is the second month of the year to have exactly 31 days?

41 In the Bible, who led the children of Israel to the Promised Land?

42 What goes before 'mantle', 'slipper' and 'smock' in flower names?

43 Where in Indiana was actor Gary Cooper born?

44 Who played Rowdy Yates in "Rawhide"?

45 Which horse won the English Triple Crown in 1970?

46 Timperley Early and Cawood Castle are types of what?

47 In the solar system which is the third planet from the sun?

48 What has subdivisions comprising 12, 52 and 365 units?

49 How many sides in four oblongs?

50 According to proverb, a little what is a dangerous thing?

Answers to Quiz 57, TECHNOLOGY

1. In mixtures the various substances are not bonded together chemically, as they are in a compound. 2. Conduction, convection, and radiation. 3. Inertia. 4. The fulcrum. 5. Friction. 6. A primitive counting machine. 7. Fission and fusion. 8. Centripetal force. 9. Streamlining reduces wind resistance – a form of friction. 10. Pulleys. 11. They were used for simple time-keeping. 12. It was the first jet plane. 13. It was the first successful helicopter. 14. A sand-glass. 15. The sun dial. 16. Refraction. 17. Those wired in parallel. 18. True. 19. Levers. 20. It is the only shape that cannot fall back down the hole. 21. The match. 22. He invented the pneumatic tyre. 23. The safety pin. 24. A submarine. 25. The flushing toilet. 26. The first battery. 27. Mesopotamia. 28. Budapest, in 1896. 29. Leonardo was the first person to sketch the chain drive which was later utilized on bicycles. 30. The Soviet dog that was sent into orbit. 31. The lift fell only a few feet. Otis had invented a ratchet which made lifts safe even if the cable snapped. 32. The refrigerator. 33. Both are sources of natural dye. 34. D. G. Fahrenheit. 35. The screw. At first screws were beaten home with a hammer. 36. China. 37. Spectacles. 38. The seed drill. 39. The photocopier. 40. A technique for preserving food in bottles. 41. The typewriter. 42. The Houses of Parliament in London. 43. False. The name comes from the sound the zip makes. 44. True. King Camp Gillette, an American salesman, came up with the idea. 45. Radio. 46. By blowing a large vessel and then flattening it while still hot. 47. The first plastic. 48. Billiard balls. 49. An early carpet sweeper. 50. The electric iron.

QUIZ 59 History

FOR ANSWERS SEE QUIZ NO 60

EASY - LEVEL ONE

1 Which admiral organized the German navy of World War I?

2 What was the name of William the Conqueror's book?

3 In which war did Wellington drive the French out of Spain?

4 What is King Alfred famous for?

5 What did Henry IV of France promise each of his subjects?

6 Who conquered most of the world before dying aged 33?

7 Who became first president of the Indonesian republic in 1945?

8 Name all the US presidents who have been assassinated.

9 When told the people had no bread who is reputed to have said, 'Let them eat cake.' ?

10 By what name was Thailand known prior to 1949?

11 By what name is southern Rhodesia now known?

12 Sweet William was named after the Duke of Cumberland. What do the Scots call it?

13 In which country did shoguns wield political and military power?

14 In which year did the Confederate army fire on Fort Sumter?

15 In 1890, 200 Native Americans were killed by US troops where in south west Dakota?

16 In 1520, Henry VIII and Francis I met near Calais. By what name was this site later known?

17 In 1879 140 British soldiers held off an army of 4,000 Zulus. Name the place.

18 Of which country was Brian Boru king?

19 What discovery allowed Egyptian hieroglyphs to be translated?

20 What event took place in England in the years 1642–51?

21 Clausewitz was an acknowledged authority on what subject?

22 Which line of Egyptian kings began with one of Alexander the Great's generals?

23 What was cuneiform?

24 In which country was there a Cultural Revolution in 1966–8?

25 Name the French literary character who is chiefly famous for his enormous nose.

26 What important historical documents were discovered by accident in caves near Qumran?

27 Vlad IV The Impaler inspired which fictional character?

28 Who were the murderous followers of the goddess Kali?

29 Whose early experiments with electricity included flying a kite during a thunderstorm.

30 What calendar was used in England until 1752?

31 What Georgian city is famous for being burned by General Sherman during the American Civil War?

32 In which country was Ned Kelly noted as an outlaw?

33 What do we call books printed before 1500?

34 Name the Italian who writes about China under Kublai Khan.

35 What sect was founded by George Fox in the 1640s as the Religious Society of Friends?

36 For which enterprise was Baron Paul von Reuter famous?

37 Who rode to warn Massachusetts the British were coming?

38 Who was the first woman to fly solo across the Atlantic and Pacific Oceans?

39 Who founded the Society of Jesus?

40 What institution used have the task of fighting heresy?

41 What would you expect to find in the caves of Lascaux?

42 Who was 'The Welsh Wizard' who led Britain in World War I?

43 Who was the wife of the Emperor Claudius?

44 The atom bomb was used twice in warfare. Where was it dropped?

45 On what paper-like substance did the ancient Egyptians write?

46 Of which country was Ngo Dinh Diem president?

47 What name did the victorious North Vietnamese call Saigon?

48 Which leader of the French Revolution was called 'The Incorruptible'?

49 Who headed Hitler's Gestapo?

50 Who was the first English sea captain to sail around the world?

Answers to Quiz 58, POT LUCK

1. Tuesday. 2. Jeux Sans Frontières. 3. Paddington. 4. Danny McGlone. 5. Alaska. 6. 30. 7. Endive. 8. Tank. 9. Simon Preston. 10. Tracy. 11. December. 12. Madness. 13. Badminton. 14. 1878. 15. Wizzard. 16. Puffin. 17. Lenin. 18. Maureen Lipman. 19. T. Rex. 20. By sense of smell. 21. Suez. (The opera was Aida.) 22. Chestnut. 23. Kissin' Cousins. 24. Foal. 25. Jimmy Nail. 26. The Queen Mother. 27. Surprise, Surprise. 28. Pepys. 29. Fish. 30. Open University. 31. He shot himself. 32. There isn't one. 33. Mariah Carey. 34. Elizabeth II (1972 Yugoslavia). 35. The Gondoliers. 36. Three. 37. Sulphur. 38. Mariah Carey. 39. Black Maria. 40. March. 41. Moses. 42. Lady's. 43. Gary. 44. Clint Eastwood. 45. Nijinsky. 46. Rhubarb. 47. Earth. 48. A year. 49. 16. 50. Knowledge.

QUIZ 60 The Royals

EASY - LEVEL ONE

1 In which decade did Prince Charles marry Lady Diana Spencer?

2 What was Sarah Duchess of York's maiden name?

3 Prince Michael's title is of which county?

4 Who is the elder of Prince Andrew's daughters, Beatrice or Eugenie?

5 What is Princess Anne's son's first name?

6 Which royal title do Princess Anne's children have?

7 What was the occupation of Princess Margaret's first husband?

8 What was the name of the king who abdicated in 1936?

9 What was the surname of the woman he married a year later?

10 What was the name of the first monarch of the 20th century?

11 Which Duchess comforted a weeping Jana Novotna at Wimbledon?

12 Which royal yacht will be out of service from the end of the 1990s?

13 What is the Queen's residence in Norfolk called?

14 Which school did Prince William attend in his teens?

15 Who is next in line to the throne after Prince William?

16 With which royal did Captain Peter Townsend have a romance?

17 What was the name of the king immediately before Elizabeth II?

18 Which royal has a daughter called Zara?

19 Which royal couple organized a large golden-wedding anniversary celebration in 1997?

20 Which royal highlighted the problems of landmines in Angola?

21 Who had a father called Prince Andrew and has a son called Prince Andrew?

22 In which cathedral did Charles and Diana marry?

23 In which decade did Elizabeth II come to the throne?

24 How many children did she have when she became Queen?

25 Whose country home is at Highgrove?

26 Which birthday did the Queen Mother celebrate in 1996?

27 How many grandchildren does she have?

28 Who is the Queen Mother's younger daughter?

29 Which Princess is married to Angus Ogilvy?

30 What was Lord Mountbatten's first name?

31 How many daughters does Queen Elizabeth II have?

32 Who is the father of Princes William and Harry?

33 What is the Duchess of York's

124

nickname?

34 Which member of the royal family was married to Lord Snowdon?

35 What is the Queen Mother's first name?

36 What is the Queen's residence in Scotland called?

37 Which Prince is Duke of Edinburgh?

38 Which Prince was a helicopter pilot in the Falklands War?

39 Who is the Princess Royal?

40 On which programme did the Princess of Wales give her first solo TV interview?

41 Which school did Prince William start at in 1995?

42 What is the Queen's favourite breed of dog?

43 What was the name of the woman for whom Edward VIII abdicated?

44 Which Queen was married to Prince Albert?

45 What is the name of the Queen's London residence?

46 How many English kings have been called George?

47 What was the Princess of Wales' maiden name?

48 What was Princess Anne's first husband called?

49 Who is the father of Princesses Beatrice and Eugenie?

50 Who is Queen Elizabeth II's youngest son?

A nswers to Quiz 59, History

1. Admiral Tirpitz. 2. The Domesday Book. 3. The Peninsular War. 4. He burned the cakes. 5. A chicken in every pot. 6. Alexander the Great. 7. Sukarno. 8. Lincoln, Garfield, McKinley, and Kennedy. 9. Marie Antoinette. 10. Siam. 11. Zimbabwe. 12. Stinking Billy. 13. Japan. 14. 1861. 15. Wounded Knee. 16. The Field of the Cloth of Gold. 17. Rorke's Drift. 18. Ireland. 19. The Rosetta Stone. 20. The Civil War. 21. Warfare. 22. The Ptolemies. 23. A form of writing. 24. People's Republic of China. 25. Cyrano de Bergerac. 26. The Dead Sea Scrolls. 27. Dracula. 28. The thugs. 29. Benjamin Franklin. 30. The Julian. 31. Atlanta. 32. Australia. 33. Incunabula. 34. Marco Polo. 35. The Quakers. 36. His news agency. 37. Paul Revere. 38. Amelia Earhart. 39. Ignatius Loyola. 40. The Inquisition. 41. Palaeolithic paintings. 42. David Lloyd George. 43. Messalina. 44. Hiroshima and Nagasaki. 45. Papyrus. 46. South Vietnam. 47. Ho Chi Minh City. 48. Robespierre. 49. Heinrich Himmler. 50. Sir Francis Drake.

QUIZ 61 | Pot Luck

EASY - LEVEL ONE

1. What is the name of the computer game hedgehog?
2. What is the zodiac sign of the Crab?
3. Which Alan wrote "Boys From the Blackstuff"?
4. Who had a No 1 hit with the song "Maggie May"?
5. In golf what is the term for two over par?
6. The initials TC stand for which cartoon character?
7. What were followers of John Wycliffe called?
8. Which country's national flag is a green rectangle?
9. Which group consists of twins Maurice and Robin and older brother Barry?
10. Who said - though not in English - "I think therefore I am"?
11. In education, what does GCSE stand for?
12. Which rock superstar is a former chairman of Watford football club?
13. Called a trailer in America, what's the name of this vehicle in the UK?
14. In which month is Royal Ascot horse-racing season?
15. What is agoraphobia a fear of?
16. What do the initials RAM stand for in computing?
17. Which village does Jane Marple live in?
18. How many kilogrammes make one metric ton?
19. Which comedian uses the catchphrase, "Rock on, Tommy"?
20. What type of food is dill?
21. Which Scottish soccer team are known as 'The Dons'?
22. Who says, "Hi-Yo Silver!"?
23. Which day of the week is named after the Anglo-Saxon god Tiw?
24. On what date is American Independence Day?
25. What kind of animal is a seahorse?
26. The failure to produce enough insulin leads to which medical condition?
27. Which soccer side play at a Cottage?
28. Which insect transmits malaria?
29. In the fable, what did the boy cry to trick the villagers?
30. What does Norman Painting write and appear in?
31. Which country is Lufthansa from?
32. What is the currency of Greece?
33. What is another word for nacre?
34. Who recorded the album "Stars"?
35. In "EastEnders" what is the name of Carol's red-haired daughter?
36. In Morse Code what letter is represented by three dashes?
37. In rhyming slang what are mince pies?

38 How is Frances Gumm better known?

39 What are Trinity and Hilary?

40 In the Bible, who was betrayed by Delilah?

41 In which branch of the arts is the metronome used?

42 Which musical instrument featured in the theme of "The Third Man"?

43 What type of whale is the largest?

44 What colour is vermilion?

45 Which Desmond wrote "The Naked Ape"?

46 How many sides has a decagon?

47 What is the fourth book of the Old Testament ?

48 Which night is April 30th?

49 "Spycatcher" was the controversial memoirs of which former intelligence officer?

50 A cob is a male of which creature?

Answers to Quiz 60, The Royals

1. 1980s. 2. Ferguson. 3. Kent. 4. Beatrice. 5. Peter. 6. None. 7. Photographer. 8. Edward (VIII). 9. Simpson. 10. Victoria. 11. Kent. 12. Britannia. 13. Sandringham. 14. Eton. 15. Prince Harry. 16. Princess Margaret. 17. George (VI). 18. Princess Anne. 19. The Queen and Prince Philip. 20. Diana, Princess of Wales. 21. Prince Philip. 22. St Paul's. 23. 1950s. 24. Two. 25. Prince Charles. 26. 96th. 27. Six. 28. Princess Margaret. 29. Alexandra. 30. Louis. 31. One. 32. Prince Charles. 33. Fergie. 34. Princess Margaret. 35. Elizabeth. 36. Balmoral. 37. Philip. 38. Prince Andrew. 39. Princess Anne. 40. Panorama. 41. Eton. 42. Corgi. 43. Mrs Wallis Simpson. 44. Victoria. 45. Buckingham Palace. 46. Six. 47. Spencer. 48. Mark Phillips. 49. Prince Andrew, Duke of York. 50. Prince Edward.

QUIZ 62 Musicals

EASY - LEVEL ONE

1 Which musical is based on the story of Romeo and Juliet?

2 Who wrote the long-running play "The Mousetrap"?

3 Complete the title of the comedy: "No Sex Please _____"

4 In "Starlight Express" what do the cast wear on their feet?

5 What was Jesus Christ according to Tim Rice and Andrew Lloyd Webber?

6 According to the comedy, There's a what in My Soup?

7 Where is the Fiddler in the musical which starred Topol?

8 Which London theatre's motto was, "We never closed"?

9 Which New York street is famous for its theatres?

10 Which musical about Professor Higgins and Eliza Doolittle is based on "Pygmalion"?

11 Who wrote the music in the comic operas for which Gilbert wrote the words?

12 What do the initials RSC stand for?

13 Which musical is based on T. S. Eliot's poems?

14 Who first played the title role in "Evita" in the West End?

15 Which musical is the name of a US state?

16 Which show includes "Climb Ev'ry Mountain"?

17 Which musical is the name of a fairground ride?

18 Which musical is about a circus impresario?

19 In which musical does Fagin appear?

20 Which Boulevard is the title of a musical?

21 Which part of the Pacific is the setting for a popular musical?

22 Which class of Society is a musical based on "The Philadelphia Story"?

23 Oh which Indian city appears in the title of a controversial show?

24 The Importance of Being what is the name of an Oscar Wilde play?

25 Who are with the Guys in the show about gangsters?

26 Which girl is the lecturer Educating in the play by Willy Russell?

27 Which Miss is a musical set in Vietnam?

28 What is the full name of the show often just referred to as Les Mis?

29 What do you say to Dolly in the title of the show?

30 Aspects of what are the theme of which Lloyd Webber musical?

31 The song "Memory" comes from which musical?

32 Which John starred in the film of "Grease"?

33 Which Michael had a hit with

"Music Of The Night"?

34 Who sang with Elaine Paige on the single "I Know Him So Well"?

35 Which musical did the song in question 34 come from?

36 Which Captain had an unlikely No. I with "Happy Talk"?

37 The song "You'll Never Walk Alone" comes from which musical?

38 In the film "Evita", who sang "You Must Love Me"?

39 Phillip Schofield and Jason Donovan have played which biblical character?

40 In which song are the words, "I kept my promise, Don't keep your distance"?

41 Which musical features Danny and Sandy in the rock 'n' roll 50s?

42 Tim Rice and writers from which supergroup wrote "Chess"?

43 Which Antonio featured in the film "Evita"?

44 Who starred in the 60s film "Summer Holiday"?

45 Who wrote the music for "Cats"?

46 Which Pete wrote the rock/opera "Tommy"?

47 Who wrote the lyrics for "Jesus Christ Superstar"?

48 What word describes Joseph's Dreamcoat?

49 Which character did Jimmy Nail play in "Evita"?

50 Which Victor Hugo novel became a musical?

A nswers to Quiz 61, Pot Luck

1. Sonic. 2. Cancer. 3. Bleasdale. 4. Rod Stewart. 5. Double bogey. 6. Top Cat. 7. Lollards. 8. Libya. 9. The Bee Gees. 10. René Descartes. 11. General Certificate of Secondary Education. 12 Elton John. 13 Caravan. 14 June. 15. Open spaces. 16. Random Access Memory. 17. St Mary Mead. 18. One thousand. 19. Bobby Ball. 20. Herb. 21. Aberdeen. 22. The Lone Ranger. 23. Tuesday. 24. 4th July. 25. Fish. 26. Diabetes. 27. Fulham. 28. Mosquito. 29. Wolf. 30. The Archers. 31. Germany. 32. Drachma. 33. Mother of Pearl. 34. Simply Red. 35. Bianca. 36. 0. 37 Eyes. 38. Judy Garland. 39. Terms at Oxford. 40. Samson. 41. Music. 42. Zither. 43. Blue Whale. 44. Red. 45. Morris. 46. Ten. 47. Numbers. 48. Walpurgis. 49. Peter Wright. 50. Swan.

Quiz 63 Pot Luck

EASY - LEVEL ONE

1. On which day are hot cross buns traditionally eaten?
2. How many signs of the zodiac are there?
3. In which decade of the 20th century was Muhammad Ali born?
4. What word can go after "hobby" and before "radish"?
5. How is Maurice Cole better known?
6. Which soccer club has had Royal and Woolwich as part of its name?
7. Who wrote the novel "Lucky Jim"?
8. On a Monopoly board, what colour is Old Kent Road?
9. Who invented Braille?
10. In song, who was born "on a mountain top in Tennessee"?
11. What is Kampuchea now called?
12. Which Richard starred in "The Good Life"?
13. Lance Cairns played cricket for which country?
14. What word can go before "draft", "flow" and "shadow"?
15. Traditionally, what colour is willow pattern?
16. In which country is the city of Addis Ababa?
17. Which Boys recorded "Barbara Ann" in the 60s?
18. Which cartoon character has an anchor tattooed on his arm?
19. What is the square root of 4?
20. Iceberg and Dorothy Perkins are examples of what?
21. Ivor Allchurch is associated with which sport?
22. Which film ends with "tomorrow is another day"?
23. A revolving firework is named after which saint?
24. Who murdered Abel?
25. In 1974, parts of Somerset and Gloucestershire made which new county?
26. Which Italian phrase used in English means in the fresh or cool air?
27. In which TV series did the characters Edina and Saffron appear?
28. Which Ben won an Oscar for Best Actor in "Gandhi"?
29. How many degrees in a right angle?
30. Which group had a No. 1 with "Hey Jude"?
31. Which UK car manufacturer produced the Cambridge?
32. Which Welsh comedian was a member of the Goons?
33. Gubby Allen is associated with which sport?
34. What word can go after "roller" and before "board"?
35. In which country is the city of Acapulco?
36. How many millimetres in three

centimetres?

37 Who wrote the novel "Jane Eyre"?

38 The character Elsie Tanner appeared in which TV soap?

39 Who had an 80s No. I with "You Win Again"?

40 In which decade of the 20th century was Woody Allen born?

41 Al is the chemical symbol for which element?

42 In which TV series did the characters James, Siegfried and Tristan appear?

43 What title did the eldest son of the king of France hold?

44 Ben Gurion airport is in which country?

45 How is Sophia Scicoloni better known?

46 Which Tim became Britain's most expensive soccer keeper in 1993?

47 Bob Cratchit appears in which Charles Dickens novel?

48 What does the C stand for in ACAS?

49 What is the administrative centre for the county of Avon?

50 Which quizmaster says, "I've started so I'll finish"?

A nswers to Quiz 62, MUSICALS

1. West Side Story. 2. Agatha Christie. 3. We're British. 4. Skates. 5. Superstar. 6. Girl. 7. On the Roof. 8. The Windmill. 9. Broadway. 10. My Fair Lady. 11. Sullivan. 12. Royal Shakespeare Company. 13. Cats. 14. Elaine Paige. 15. Oklahoma. 16. The Sound of Music. 17. Carousel. 18. Barnum. 19. Oliver. 20. Sunset. 21. South. 22. High. 23. Calcutta. 24. Earnest. 25. Dolls. 26. Rita. 27. Saigon. 28. Les Misérables. 29. Hello. 30. Love. 31. Cats. 32. Travolta. 33. Crawford. 34. Barbara Dickson. 35. Chess. 36. Sensible. 37. Carousel. 38. Madonna. 39. Joseph. 40. "Don't Cry For Me, Argentina". 41. Grease. 42. Abba. 43. Banderas. 44. Cliff Richard. 45. Andrew Lloyd Webber. 46. Townshend. 47. Tim Rice. 48. Technicolor. 49. Magaldi. 50. Les Miserables.

FOR ANSWERS SEE QUIZ NO 65

Food and Drink

EASY - LEVEL ONE

1 What meat is used to make Moussaka?

2 Which animal does venison come from?

3 Which garden herb is made into a sauce often eaten with lamb?

4 In which country did the word biscuit originate?

5 What is traditionally eaten on Shrove Tuesday?

6 What is another name for French fries?

7 What is a slice of bacon called?

8 Which edible sugary substance do bees make?

9 What is done to a herring to make it into a kipper?

10 Which vegetable can be King Edward or Desirée?

11 Which country does Edam cheese originate from?

12 What do you add to milk to make porridge?

13 What is minestrone?

14 What is bottled tomato sauce called?

15 What colour is vodka?

16 Where did the dish *paella* originate?

17 Which fruit is covered with toffee at a fairground?

18 Which nuts are used to make marzipan?

19 Is a Spotted Dick usually eaten hot or cold?

20 What meat dish is Cumberland famous for?

21 Which pudding is eaten with roast beef?

22 Which vegetables can be French, runner or baked?

23 What colour is piccalilli?

24 What sort of food is a rollmop?

25 Is wholemeal bread brown or white?

26 If something is cooked 'au gratin' what must it contain?

27 Petits pois are small what?

28 In which country is Peroni beer bottled?

29 What are the two main ingredients of a shandy?

30 Who hosts "Masterchef" on TV?

31 What colour is crème de menthe?

32 Which county does Wensleydale cheese traditionally come from?

33 What type of vegetable is a Maris Piper?

34 What are the two main ingredients of a vinaigrette dressing?

35 What is the fruit flavour of Cointreau?

36 What type of food is coley?

37 What is basmati?

38 Which food accompaniment is Dijon famous for?

39 What is a small segment of garlic called?

40 What is the main ingredient of a traditional fondue?

41	What type of food is pitta?
42	Are giant pandas herbivores?
42	Which shellfish are in Moules Marinière?
43	What is the top layer of a Queen of Puddings made from?
44	What type of meat is brisket?
45	What colour is paprika?
46	What is the chief vegetable ingredient of coleslaw?
47	At which stage of a meal would you have an hors d'oeuvre?
48	What type of drink is Darjeeling?
49	If a coffee was drunk au lait, what would it have added to it?
50	What is a tortilla?

A nswers to Quiz 63, Pot Luck

1. Good Friday. 2. 12. 3. 40s. 4. "Horse". 5. Kenny Everett. 6. Arsenal. 7. Kingsley Amis. 8. Brown. 9. Louis Braille. 10. Davy Crockett. 11. Cambodia. 12. Briers. 13. New Zealand. 14. "Over". 15. Blue. 16. Ethiopia. 17. The Beach Boys. 18. Popeye. 19. 2. 20. Rose. 21.Football. 22. Gone With The Wind. 23. Catherine. 24. Cain. 25. Avon. 26. Al fresco. 27. "Absolutely Fabulous". 28. Kingsley. 29. 90. 30. The Beatles. 31. Austin. 32. Harry Secombe. 33. Cricket. 34. "Skate". 35. Mexico. 36. 30. 37. Charlotte Brontë. 38. "Coronation Street". 39 .Bee Gees. 40. 30s. 41. Aluminium. 42. "All Creatures Great And Small". 43. Dauphin. 44. Israel. 45. Sophia Loren. 46. Tim Flowers. 47. A Christmas Carol. 48. Conciliation. 49. Bristol. 50. Magnus Magnusson.

QUIZ 65 | Pot Luck

EASY - LEVEL ONE

1 In Greek mythology, who married Eurydice?

2 Through which film did Paul Hogan come to fame?

3 Which country does the island of Crete belong to?

4 In which of the following countries are you most likely to come across a synagogue: Egypt, China, or Israel?

5 In computer language, what does MB stand for?

6 What do you call an optical instrument through which you look at pieces of colored glass that form numerous symmetrical patterns when rotated?

7 In which country are you most likely to hear the bagpipes being played?

8 What does a seismograph record?

9 What type of organism is a sea anemone?

10 What do you call the tall posts, carved and painted by Native Americans?

11 According to legend, by which animal were Romulus and Remus nourished?

12 Which of the following languages is not written from left to right: (a) Arabic, (b) Russian, (c) Greek?

13 What do you call a pupa of a butterfly, enclosed in a cocoon?

14 What type of stories is Aesop famous for?

15 What is a facsimile machine commonly known as?

16 Which machine preceded the record player?

17 Which is the largest ape?

18 What could you do with a magic lantern?

19 What do you call a device in which two small telescopes are joined together and looked through simultaneously with both eyes?

20 What does a flint do when struck with a piece of steel?

21 In which country would you buy a stamp with the word Hellas on it?

22 In which country is the Sea of Galilee?

23 What would you make on a spinning wheel?

24 What is the title of the last Indiana Jones film?

25 What were catacombs used as?

26 What do fleas live on?

27 Which Greek philosopher lived in a tub?

28 What is measured on the Beaufort scale?

29 In which country is The Hague situated?

30 Which group brought out the album "Invisible Touch"?

31 What do you call the part of a river where it meets the sea?

32 With which organ do fish breathe?

33 Which part of a ship is the stern?

34

34 What name is given to troops that fight on horseback?

35 In computer terms, what does VDU stand for?

36 How many squares are there on a chessboard?

37 What is a loom used for?

38 Can you name the three kinds of honeybee?

39 What do you call a person who studies plants scientifically?

40 A quintet is made up of how many musicians?

41 In which European city would you find Tower Bridge?

42 A sphinx has a body of what animal?

43 Can you name the four oceans?

44 What do you call a shape whose two halves are mirror images of each other?

45 With which TV series do you associate Mr Spock?

46 Which nationality was Peter the Great?

47 Which street in New York is famous for its theatres?

48 What do you call a person who dies for his religious beliefs?

49 Which country does Camembert cheese come from?

50 Which animal is associated with being lazy?

A nswers to Quiz 64, FOOD AND DRINK

1. Lamb. 2. Deer. 3. Mint. 4. France. 5. Pancakes. 6. Chips. 7. Rasher. 8. Honey. 9. Smoked. 10. Potato. 11. Holland. 12. Oats. 13. Soup. 14. Ketchup. 15. Colourless. 16. Spain. 17. Apples. 18. Almonds. 19. Hot. 20. Sausage. 21. Yorkshire. 22. Beans. 23. Yellow. 24. Fish. 25. Brown. 26. Cheese. 27. Peas. 28. Italy. 29. Beer and lemonade. 30. Lloyd Grossman. 31. Green. 32. Yorkshire. 33. Potato. 34. Oil, vinegar. 35. Orange. 36. Fish. 37. Rice. 38. Mustard. 39. Clove. 40. Cheese. 41. Bread. 42. Mussels. 43. Meringue. 44. Beef. 45. Red. 46. Cabbage. 47. Beginning. 48. Tea. 49. Milk. 50. Pancake.

QUIZ 66 | The Arts

EASY - LEVEL ONE

1 What was unusual about the gangster movie "Bugsy Malone"?

2 On which book by Shaw was "My Fair Lady" based?

3 What was the name of Leonard Bernstein's musical based on Shakespeare's "Romeo and Juliet"?

4 In which film did Gregory Peck play the part of Atticus Finch?

5 Apart from John, Paul, George, and Ringo, name two other Beatles.

6 Who made the film "Fantasia"?

7 Which detective story became the UK's longest-running stage play?

8 What was the name of Smokey Robinson's group?

9 Which film actor sounded less scary by his real name of William Henry Pratt?

10 Which film, directed by David Lynch, concerned a hideously deformed Victorian man?

11 Which film, starring Richard Attenborough, told the story of the murderer John Christie?

12 What were the Beatles first top-30 singles in both the UK and US?

13 Which Canadian singer wrote the novel "Beautiful Losers"?

14 Who said, 'Extraordinary how potent cheap music is'?

15 With which group was Sid Vicious associated?

16 Who made the album "Sweet Baby James"?

17 Which US singer was killed in a car crash on April 17, 1960?

18 Who played the female lead in the 1976 version of "A Star is Born"?

19 Who directed the 1956 version of "The Ten Commandments"?

20 Which classic John Ford western of 1939 was remade in 1966?

21 Who played Zorba the Greek in the 1964 film?

22 Who wrote the play "The Importance of Being Earnest"?

23 In which Edward Albee play did Virginia Woolf feature?

24 Who wrote the poem "If"?

25 In which film did Charlotte Rampling and Dirk Bogarde resurrect a relationship that began in a concentration camp?

26 Who was the first actor to talk in the film "The Jazz Singe"r?

27 Which Shakespeare play is unlucky to mention by name?

28 Why did Gore Vidal fall out with Charlton Heston over "Ben Hur" years after it was made?

29 Who painted "The Sun of Venice Going to Sea"?

30 Which US state starred in a Rodgers and Hammerstein musical?

31 Who composed "Rhapsody in Blue"?

32 Who wrote "Take Five"?

33 Who in 1986 wrote the music for

"Phantom of the Opera"?

34 Who played the 1964 part of Eliza Doolittle in "My Fair Lady"?

35 Which Margaret Mitchell novel became one of the greatest movies of all time?

36 Which poem by Tennyson reads: 'Theirs not to reason why, Theirs but to do and die'?

37 Who painted "The Laughing Cavalier"?

38 What name connects Phil Collins with a book of the Bible?

39 By what name is Cherilyn Sarkasian LaPierre better known?

40 Which singer, famed for his large nose, sang "The Man Who Found the Lost Chord"?

41 Which family group recorded the hit album "3+3" in 1973?

42 Where did the band Men at Work come from?

43 Who was best known for her rendering of "There's No Business Like Show Business"?

44 Who appeared naked on the cover of the album "Unfinished Music No 1: Two Virgins"?

45 Which member of the Rolling Stones died in his swimming pool?

46 Kismet was based on the work of which Russian composer?

47 Where in London were most of Shakespeare's plays presented.

48 By what nickname was the actress Lillie Langtry known?

49 For what theatrical entertainment was William Cody responsible?

50 What does 'opera' mean?

A nswers to Quiz 65, POT LUCK

1. Orpheus. 2. Crocodile Dundee. 3. Greece. 4. Israel. 5. Megabyte. 6. Kaleidoscope. 7. Scotland. 8. Earth tremors. 9. It is an animal. 10. Totem poles. 11. A wolf. 12. (a) Arabic. 13. A chrysalis. 14. Fables. 15. A fax. 16. The gramophone. 17. The gorilla. 18. Project an enlarged picture on a wall. 19. Binoculars. 20. It produces a spark. 21. Greece. 22. Israel. 23. Yarn or thread. 24. Indiana Jones and the Last Crusade. 25. Burial grounds. 26. Blood. 27. Diogenes. 28. Wind speed. 29. The Netherlands. 30. Genesis. 31. The estuary. 32. Gills. 33. The rear part. 34. Cavalry. 35. Visual display unit. 36. Sixty-four. 37. Weaving cloth. 38. Workers, drones, and queens. 39. A botanist. 40. Five. 41. London. 42. A lion. 43. Atlantic, Pacific, Indian, and Arctic Oceans. 44. Symmetrical. 45. Star Trek. 46. Russian. 47. Broadway. 48. A martyr. 49. France. 50. A sloth.

Quiz 67 | Pot Luck

EASY - LEVEL ONE

1 What is the seventh commandment?

2 What sport takes place in a velodrome?

3 In TV comedy, where did Uncle Martin come from?

4 Who sang the theme song for "The Man With The Golden Gun"?

5 Who said, "I shall hear in heaven"?

6 In which card game do you 'peg out'?

7 Which bingo number is clickety click?

8 What was Ivan Lendl's first Wimbledon tournament win?

9 What is another name for Lady's Fingers?

10 Which member of The Monkees appeared in "Coronation Street"?

11 What colour is ebony?

12 What do you have at the bottom of a colander?

13 Who wrote the TV musical drama "Lipstick On Your Collar"?

14 Which magazine called itself the junior TV Times?

15 In which track event do you get wet even when it's not raining?

16 On which track at Pennsylvania Station did the Chattanonnga Choo Choo leave?

17 What colour are French post boxes?

18 What is the nationality of Formula I driver Schumacher?

19 Who played Len Fairclough?

20 When during a meal would you have an hors d'oeuvre?

21 Which team did Alf Garnett support?

22 What is the US military academy called?

23 Over what food did Edwina Currie resign a ministerial post?

24 Which classical composer did Richard Chamberlain play in "The Music Lovers"?

25 What is the name of the cat which dips its paw in the food tin?

26 Which programme featuring Prunella Scales and Joan Sanderson transferred from radio to TV?

27 What name is given to the style of riding when both the rider's legs are on the same side of the horse?

28 Who tragically died while appearing on Live at Her Majesty's?

29 Where might you find a breeze block?

30 Whose motto is "Nation shall speak unto nation"?

31 What sort of Circle do conjurers join?

32 Which UK coin has a diameter of 3cms?

33 Which football club does Jasper

Carrott support?

34 Which musical includes the characters Sky Masterson and Nathan Detroit?

35 What can be the name of a hat and a member of a cricket team?

36 Which sign of the zodiac follows Capricorn?

37 Which game might you be watching if you were at The Belfry?

38 Variola is more commonly called what?

39 Who wrote the play "An Inspector Calls"?

40 What is Diana Prince's other identity?

41 Which Scottish group took their name from a Scritti Politti lyric?

42 Which section do you look for in the newspaper to read what the stars have in store for you?

43 Which musical instrument does Nigel Kennedy play ?

44 Which residence of the Queen's was opened to the public in 1993?

45 In which month is the Le Mans 24 hour race held?

46 Who wrote the theme song to "Harry's Game"?

47 After what is London's Fleet Street named?

48 Which "Knight Rider" travelled to "Baywatch"?

49 Who did Frank Bruno beat to become WBC heavyweight champion in 1995?

50 What is a cassoulet?

A nswers to Quiz 66, THE ARTS

1. The cast were all children. 2. Pygmalion. 3. West Side Story. 4. To Kill a Mocking Bird. 5. Stuart Sutcliffe and Pete Best. 6. Walt Disney. 7. The Mousetrap. 8. The Miracles. 9. Boris Karloff. 10. The Elephant Man. 11. 10 Rillington Place. 12. 'I Wanna Hold Your Hand' in the US; . . 'Love Me Do' in the UK. 13. Leonard Cohen. 14. Noel Coward. 15. The Sex Pistols. 16. James Taylor. 17. Eddie Cochran. 18. Barbra Streisand. 19. Cecil B. DeMille. 20. Stagecoach. 21. Anthony Quinn. 22. Oscar Wilde. 23. Who's Afraid of Virginia Woolf. 24. Rudyard Kipling. 25. The Great Plague. 26. Al Jolson. 27. Macbeth. 28. Over an alleged homosexual relationship . between characters in the film. 29. J.M.W. Turner. 30. Oklahoma! 31. George Gershwin. 32. Dave Brubeck. 33. Andrew Lloyd Webber. 34. Audrey Hepburn. 35. Gone With the Wind. 36. 'The Charge of the Light Brigade'. 37. Frans Hals. 38. Genesis. 39. Cher. 40. Jimmy Durante. 41. The Isley Brothers. 42. Australia. 43. Ethel Merman. 44. John Lennon and Yoko Ono. 45. Brian Jones. 46. Borodin. 47. The Globe. 48. The Jersey Lily. 49. The Buffalo Bill Wild West Show. 50. Works; from the Latin opus.

QUIZ 68 History

MEDIUM - LEVEL TWO

1 Who was the first Roman emperor?

2 Where did the last battle of the Napoleonic Wars take place, resulting in a defeat for the French army?

3 Who was beaten in the Battle at Gettysburg?

4 What was the name of the British ship sunk by a German submarine on May 7, 1915?

5 What was the name of the wars between Rome and Carthage?

6 What does Hadrian's Wall mark??

7 Where was Joan of Arc burned?

8 Who discovered Botany Bay in Australia?

9 Who was Charles I fighting against in the English Civil War?

10 Who succeeded Peter the Great as czar?

11 Who was president of the Weimar Republic?

12 Which two countries sided with Franco's Nationalists in the Spanish Civil War?

13 Which empire did Hammurabi found?

14 Mount Vernon is the estate of which American president?

15 Who sailed to the USA on the Mayflower?

16 What was the name of the people of the Bronze Age civilization on the island of Crete?

17 Who was the leader of the Jacobins in the French Revolution?

18 Where did the Black Death first strike?

19 Who was the last czar of Russia?

20 Who published the Communist Manifesto?

21 Which country was the Spanish Armada set to invade?

22 From which area did the Mayan tribes originate?

23 Who was the first Englishman to sail around the world?

24 The peoples of which civilization invented the alphabet?

25 Which animals did Hannibal take with him for the invasion of Italy?

26 Which North American state did the Americans purchase from Napoleon in 1803?

27 Who was the longest-reigning British monarch?

28 Who was crowned emperor by the Pope in ad 800?

29 Which French Monarch was known as the Sun King?

30 What was the purpose of the Crusades?

31 Who was fighting the Peloponnesian War?

32 Which Roman emperor was regarded as the founder of the Christian Empire?

33 What was the name of Lenin's party during the Russian Revolution?

34 Who was American president at

140

the start of the Great
Depression?

35 Which important British
document was issued in the year
1215?

36 During the reign of which king did
the French Revolution start?

37 Which countries formed the
Central Powers at the outbreak of
World War I?

38 What was the name of the inter
national conference held in order
to redraw the map of Europe
after Napoleon's downfall?

39 What did Martin Luther post on
the church door at Wittenberg?

40 Who was Stalin's main opponent
as Lenin's successor?

41 Which important waterway was
opened in 1914?

42 What was the name of the French
protestants during the 16th and
17th centuries?

43 Which incident started the Thirty
Years' War?

44 Who was Henry VIII's first wife?

45 Which country did Frederick the
Great rule?

46 Which Royal Family ruled England
from 1485 to 1603?

47 In which year did William the
Conqueror invade England?

48 Who was the wife of Louis XVI
who was later guillotined?

49 Where was Napoleon exiled in
1815?

50 What was the name of the
German king and emperor who
led the Third Crusade?

Answers to Quiz 133, MOVIES: WHO'S WHO

1. O.J. Simpson. 2. Glenn Close. 3. Dustin Hoffman. 4. Miriam Margolyes, Joanna Lumley. 5. Oliver Stone. 6. Val Kilmer. 7. Ralph Fiennes. 8. John Cleese. 9. John Hurt. 10. Ava Gardner. 11. 20th Century Fox, Betty Grable. 12. Fay Wray. 13. Cher. 14. Sheriff of Nottingham. 15. Hugh Grant. 16. Mick Jagger. 17. George Clooney. 18. Grace Kelly. 19. Tina Turner. 20. Richard Gere. 21. Arthur Miller. 22. The Odd Couple (Walter Matthau and Jack Lemmon). 23. Sally Field. 24. Quentin Tarantino. 25. John Travolta. 26. Sean Connery. 27. Bruce Willis - he was the baby's voice in Look Who's Talking. 28. Barbra Streisand. 29. Sam. 30. Liz Hurley. 31. Jack Nicholson. 32. Harrison Ford. 33. Meg Ryan. 34. Clint Eastwood. 35. Sean Connery. 36. Clark Gable. 37. Katharine Hepburn. 38. Fletcher Christian. 39. Cary Grant. 40. Lawyer. 41. Tom Cruise. 42. Michael Douglas. 43. Michelle Pfeiffer. 44. Humphrey Bogart. 45. Scent of a Woman. 46. Spencer Tracy. 47. "Thanks For the Memory". 48. Fred Astaire and Ginger Rogers. 49. Joan Crawford. 50. Arnold Schwarzenegger.

Q UIZ 69 Pot Luck

MEDIUM – LEVEL TWO

1 Who joined forces with The Pogues on "Jack's Heroes"?

2 What is the zodiac sign of the Lion?

3 Who recorded the album "Spark To A Flame"?

4 Which duo created "Birds Of A Feather"?

5 In the Bible, what part of John the Baptist's anatomy did Salome demand as a reward for her dancing?

6 Which comedian talked about "Loadsamoney"?

7 Which radio show was originally called "Crazy People"?

8 Which two TV comedians say "It's goodnight from me..." "...And it's goodnight from him"?

9 Who did Tony Robinson play in the "Blackadder" series?

10 According to proverb, how do still waters run?

11 In the broadcasting sector, what does ITN stand for?

12 Which exotic bird stands on one leg?

13 The Americans call it vaudeville, what is it called in Britain?

14 Which actor plays the title role in "Lovejoy"?

15 What is hippophobia a fear of?

16 Which musical does "Hey Big Spender" come from?

17 Which Great breed of dog sounds like it comes from Scandinavia?

18 What is the first name of TV cook Mott?

19 Which singer's name is Ciccone?

20 What type of food is a bloomer?

21 Chukkas are the playing periods in which sport?

22 Who says, "All wight?"?

23 Which day of the week is named after the goddess Frigg?

24 Which Anne kept a diary while in hiding during the Second World War?

25 What was Ceylon renamed as?

26 What is Fiona's job in "Coronation Street"?

27 Which record producer Phil produced a 'wall of sound' in the 1960s?

28 What is ikebana?

29 Who headed the report into the 1981 Brixton riots?

30 Who is Hale's comic partner?

31 Which country are KLM from?

32 What is the currency of the Netherlands?

33 What is the first name of TV cook Dimbleby?

34 Which birds congregate in a gaggle?

35 On TV, what is the first name of Alf Roberts' wife?

36 What was Tony Hancock's address in East Cheam?

37 In rhyming slang what is the Sweeney Todd?

38 How is Robert Zimmermann better known?

39 Who punched Russell Harty during a chat show?

40 In the Bible, what was the name of the first garden?

41 How many minutes in four and three quarter hours?

42 What is the name of 'She Who Must Be Obeyed'?

43 Which cartoon character says, "Smarter than the average bear"?

44 What colour do you get if you mix red and yellow?

45 Which sport does Sam Torrance play?

46 How many sides has a rhombus?

47 In which children's TV show did Bungle, George and Zippy appear?

48 What colour was the Pimpernel in Baroness Orczy's novel?

49 Which major river flows through Vienna?

50 Which song was a hit for both Buddy Holly and Mud?

Answers to Quiz 68, HISTORY

1. Augustus. 2. Waterloo. 3. The Confederate army in the American Civil War. 4. Lusitania. 5. The Punic Wars. 6. The northern boundary of Roman Britain. 7. Rouen. 8. Captain Cook. 9. Oliver Cromwell's Parliamentarians. 10. Catherine the Great. 11. Paul von Hindenburg. 12. The Germans and Italians. 13. The Babylonian Empire. 14. George Washington. 15. The Pilgrims. 16. The Minoans. 17. Robespierre. 18. China. 19. Nicholas II. 20. Karl Marx and Friedrich Engels. 21. England. 22. Central America. 23. Francis Drake. 24. The Phoenicians. 25. Elephants. 26. Louisiana. 27. Queen Victoria. 28. Charlemagne. 29. Louis XIV. 30. European Christians wanted to conquer the Holy Land from the Muslims. 31. Athens against Sparta. 32. Constantine the Great. 33. The Bolsheviks. 34. Herbert Hoover. 35. The Magna Carta. 36. Louis XVI. 37. Germany, Austria-Hungary, and Turkey. 38. The Vienna Congress. 39. The 95 theses. 40. Trotsky. 41. The Panama Canal. 42. The Huguenots. 43. The Defenestration of Prague. 44. Catherine of Aragon. 45. Prussia. 46. The Tudors. 47. 1066. 48. Marie Antoinette. 49. St. Helena. 50. Frederick Barbarossa.

Quiz 70 — Food and Drink

MEDIUM – LEVEL TWO

1 Which vegetable is used for making tzatziki?

2 From which French region does Muscadet originate?

3 What type of meat is used for osso buco?

4 Which is the main spice found in goulash?

5 What type of stew is a bouillabaisse?

6 Which country does Tokaj wine come from?

7 What is the name of a Greek dish with layers of minced lamb or beef and aubergines (eggplant), topped with a cheese sauce?

8 Which vegetable does the dish choucroute contain?

9 What type of meat is haggis made of?

10 What type of cheese is used for tiramisú?

11 What is couscous made of?

12 What is borscht?

13 What is a crêpe?

14 What type of meat is used for making ratatouille?

15 What type of cheese is gorgonzola?

16 What is ouzo flavored with?

17 What does kedgeree consist of?

18 What do you call nut kernels (freaquently almonds), cooked in boiling sugar syrup until crisp and brown?

19 In crème fraîche, what has the crème been thickened with?

20 What is the type of brandy which is made in north-western France from apples?

21 In dolmades, what type of leaf is stuffed with meat and other ingredients?

22 What do you call the spicy sauce eaten with Mexican food, especially tortillas, that is made of tomatoes, chilli, and onions?

23 What type of meat is used for châteaubriand?

24 What is wan tun?

25 What sort of fruit is shiraz?

26 What is claret?

27 What gives a bloody Mary its spicy flavor?

28 What are calamari?

29 With what is kirschwasser flavored?

30 What sort of ice-cream is Neopolitan?

31 What is special about a glass of sambuca?

32 What is the Angler fish often called when served as a food?

33 Amazonian Indians eat the giant tarantula baked. True or false?

34 What sort of meat would you expect to find in kleftico?

35 What does the word 'spaghetti' literally mean?

36 What do anthropophagi eat?

37 What fungus is associated with

the production of alcohol?

38 From what is taramasalata made?

39 What do you call the type of ribbon noodles that are about a third as thick as spaghetti?

40 What sort of dish is mulligatawny?

41 What is baklava?

42 What is zabaglione made of?

43 What part of the cow is a T-bone steak taken from?

44 What is the name of the soft, white, Italian cheese which is similar to cottage cheese?

45 Which family does the caraway seed come from?

46 What is turnip cabbage also called?

47 What sort of dish is julienne?

48 What is the name for a confection which consists of jelly-like cubes dusted in icing sugar?

49 What is minestrone?

50 What are gnocchi?

1. The Dubliners. 2. Leo. 3. Chris de Burgh. 4. Marks and Gran. 5. Head. 6. Harry Enfield. 7. The Goon Show. 8. Ronnie Barker, Ronnie Corbett. 9. Baldrick. 10. Deep. 11. Independent Television News. 12. Flamingo. 13. Music hall. 14. Ian McShane. 15. Horses. 16. Sweet Charity. 17. Dane. 18. Ruth. 19. Madonna. 20. Loaf of bread. 21. Polo. 22. Michael Barrymore. 23. Friday. 24. Frank. 25. Sri Lanka. 26. Hairdresser. 27. Spector. 28. Japanese flower arranging. 29. Lord Scarman. 30. Pace. 31. Netherlands. 32. Guilder. 33. Josceline. 34. Geese. 35. Audrey. 36. 23 Railway Cuttings. 37. Flying Squad. 38. Bob Dylan. 39. Grace Jones. 40. Eden. 41. 285. 42. Hilda Rumpole. 43. Yogi Bear. 44 .Orange. 45. Golf. 46. Four. 47. Rainbow. 48. Scarlet. 49. Danube. 50. Oh Boy.

Pot Luck

QUIZ 71

MEDIUM - LEVEL TWO

1 How many packs of cards are needed for a game of Canasta?

2 What is the zodiac sign of the Virgin?

3 Which character did Harrison Ford play in "Star Wars"?

4 What is a sabot?

5 Bill Gates founded which computer corporation?

6 Which Clark was a journalist on "The Daily Planet"?

7 Where would you see fog called the Tablecloth?

8 Carol Hersey is reckoned to be the most seen person on British television. Where does she appear?

9 What is the first name of TV cook Stein?

10 Who recorded the album "Once Upon A Time"?

11 Who did Sirhan Sirhan assassinate?

12 In 1995 which political party leadership was contested by two Johns?

13 What is ruled by the House of Grimaldi?

14 In "Coronation Street" what is Maureen Holdsworth's mother called?

15 What are the two main ingredients of a Bloody Mary?

16 In the rhyme, who killed Cock Robin?

17 What is a world sport, an American vegetable and a British soft drink?

18 Who recorded the album "The Colour Of My Love"?

19 Who jumped off the Tallahatchee Bridge?

20 What type of food is consommé?

21 The 'Silver Ghost' was what type of car?

22 Who says, "Not many people know that!"?

23 Which day of the week is named after the god Saturn?

24 What was Sam asked to play by Rick in "Casablanca"?

25 Where would you eat if you were eating al fresco?

26 How is Norma Jean Baker better known?

27 What colour features in the title of George Gershwin's Rhapsody?

28 What is the lowest weight in boxing?

29 How many sheets of paper are there in a ream?

30 Who was Sonny's singing partner?

31 Which country are Qantas airlines from?

32 What is the currency of Russia?

33 What type of plant grows from seed, flowers and dies in a year?

34 Helen Sharman was the first Briton to go where?

35 What is Andy Capp's wife called?

36 Which British monarch was the

husband of Queen Elizabeth the Queen Mother?

37 In rhyming slang what is Barnet Fair?

38 How is Declan McManus better known?

39 What animal is shown in the painting "The Monarch Of The Glen"?

40 Where would you look to discover the Mount of the Moon and the Girdle of Venus?

41 Which insect might be used by a snooker player?

42 In Roman numerals what is MD + MD?

43 What is the first name of Polish film director Polanski?

44 What colour is saffron?

45 What was Al short for in Al Capone's name?

46 How many sides has a trapezium?

47 In which Olympic event would the competitor use ribbons and hoops?

48 Which metal is an alloy of copper and zinc?

49 Which major river flows through Cairo?

50 What is a Blenheim Orange?

Answers to Quiz 70, FOOD AND DRINK

1. Cucumber. 2. The Loire Valley. 3. Veal. 4. Paprika. 5. A fish stew. 6. Hungary. 7. Moussaka. 8. Sauerkraut. 9. Minced heart, lungs, and liver of a sheep or calf. 10. Mascarpone. 11. Semolina. 12. A beet soup, usually served with sour cream. 13. A thin, small pancake. 14. No meat. It is a vegetable stew. 15. A blue-veined, Italian cheese made from cow's milk. 16. Aniseed. 17. Rice, flaked fish, and hard-boiled eggs. 18. Praline. 19. Lactic acid. 20. Calvados. 21. A vine leaf. 22. Salsa. 23. Beef. 24. A small, Chinese dumpling. 25. A type of grape. 26. The red wine of Bordeaux. 27. Worcester sauce. 28. Squid. 29. Cherries. 30. Multi-flavored. 31. It is usually set alight before being served. 32. Monk fish. 33. True. 34. Lamb. 35. Little strings. 36. Humans – they are cannibals. 37. Yeast. 38. A paste of fish roe. 39. Vermicelli. 40. An Indian curry soup. 41. A cake made of thin layers of pastry, nuts, and honey. 42. Egg yolks, sugar, and wine. 43. The small end of the loin. 44. Ricotta. 45. The carrot family. 46. Kohlrabi. 47. A broth flavored with thin strips of vegetables. 48. Turkish delight. 49. A thick soup containing vegetables, pasta, and broth. 50. Shaped pasta dumplings made from semolina or potato flour.

QUIZ 72 Sport

MEDIUM - LEVEL TWO

1 Which countries played in the in the 1990 soccer World Cup final?

2 Who won the ladies' singles tennis championship at Wimbledon in 1978?

3 Who is the American swimmer who won seven gold medals in the 1972 Olympics?

4 In which discipline was Ben Johnson stripped of his gold medal in the 1988 Olympics?

5 What is the name of the British ice dancing couple who won gold at the 1984 Winter Olympics?

6 Where were the Los Angeles Raiders formerly based?

7 Who won the Masters Golf Tournament in 1988?

8 Which American athlete set a new record in the 100 meters in 1991?

9 How many holes does a golf course consist of?

10 How many titles did Bjorn Borg win at Wimbledon?

11 In which sport would you use a foil, épée, and sabre?

12 With which sport do you associate Charles Daniels?

13 How many in a cricket team?

14 Which Soviet gymnast won three gold medals in the '72 Olympics?

15 The Corbillon Cup is associated with which sport?

16 With which sport is Pete Rose associated?

17 Which female American sprinter won three gold medals at the 1988 Olympics?

18 Which American boxer won the world heavyweight title in 1964, 1974, and 1978?

19 Which country did West Germany defeat in the final of the 1974 soccer World Cup?

20 Which black American athlete won four gold medals in the 1936 Olympics in Berlin?

21 Who won the 1988 men's singles championship at Wimbledon?

22 In which sport could you win a Drysdale Cup as an award?

23 Which American swimmer won five gold medals at the 1988 Olympics?

24 With which sport is Byron Nelson associated?

25 Which American long jumper set a new world record in 1968?

26 With which sport is Jack Dempsey associated?

27 Who became the ladies' French Open Singles Champion from 1990 to 1992?

28 How many players are there in a soccer team?

29 Who won the Masters Golf Tournament in 1993?

30 With which sport do you associate the Calcutta Cup?

31 Who became the youngest ever heavyweight champion in 1986?

32 Where was the first Super Bowl?

148

33 In which city did the first modern Olympic Games take place?

34 Which Romanian gymnast won six medals in the 1976 Olympics and four in the 1980 Olympics?

35 Which male tennis player won the US Open Championship in 1994?

36 With with sport is the Ryder Cup associated?

37 What was unusual about the 1980 Olympic Games held at Moscow?

38 What is the Indianapolis 500?

39 What popular name was given to the American boxer Joe Louis?

40 How many players are there in a handball team?

41 Who came first in the Tour de France for the fourth consecutive year in 1994?

42 Who beat Bjorn Borg in the men's singles tennis championships at Wimbledon in 1981?

43 Which golf player won the British Open in 1987, 1990, and 1992?

44 What name is given to the umpire at a football game?

45 With which sport is the Davis Cup associated?

46 What was the location of the Summer Oympics in 1988?

47 Which team lost the Super Bowl four times during the 1970s?

48 Which American tennis player won the Women's Singles at Wimbledon in 1974, 76 and 81?

49 What do the symbols on the Olympic flag stand for?

50 In the Olympics, which five events make up the modern pentathlon?

A nswers to
Quiz 71, POT LUCK

1. Two. 2. Virgo. 3. Han Solo. 4. Clog. 5. Microsoft. 6. Kent. 7. Table Mountain. 8. On the BBC colour test card. 9. Rick. 10. Simple Minds. 11. Robert Kennedy. 12. Conservative. 13. Monaco. 14. Maud Grimes. 15. Vodka and tomato juice. 16 Sparrow. 17 Squash. 18 Celine Dion. 19. Billy Joe McAllister. 20. Soup. 21. Rolls Royce. 22. Michael Caine. 23. Saturday. 24. As Time Goes By. 25. Outside. 26. Marilyn Monroe. 27. Blue. 28. Light flyweight. 29. 500. 30. Cher. 31. Australia. 32. Rouble. 33. Annual. 34. Space. 35. Flo. 36. George VI. 37. Hair. 38. Elvis Costello. 39. A red deer stag. 40. In the palm of your hand. 41. Spider. 42. MMM. 43. Roman. 44. Yellow. 45. Alphonse. 46. Four. 47. Rhythmic gymnastics. 48. Brass. 49. Nile. 50. An apple.

QUIZ 73 Pot Luck

1   In which English county are Taunton and Wells?

2   Which fictional detective wrote "The Corpse Danced At Midnight"?

3   On the London Underground, on which line is Knightsbridge station?

4   What is the name of Frank Sinatra's daughter?

5   What is the name of Phil's brother in "EastEnders"?

6   In which Ian Fleming novel did James Bond first appear?

7   Who did 1975 Miss World Wilnelia Merced marry in the 1980s?

8   What type of entertainment is the musical "Barnum" about?

9   In which year did "Dr Who" first appear on BBC?

10 Over how many days is an Olympic decathlon held?

11 What did Maureen Lipman, aka Beattie, encourage us to use in the TV advertising campaign?

12 In June 1980, which coin ceased to be legal tender?

13 Who is actress Sandra Dickinson married to?

14 Which magician presents TV's "Wipeout"?

15 Who was the first British monarch to visit America?

16 What is the first name of comedian Dee?

17 0161 is the dialling code for which city?

18 Which husband and wife team were together in "Upstairs, Downstairs" and "Forever Green"?

19 What is Alec Gilroy's relationship to Vicky in "Coronation Street"?

20 Which member of "Dad's Army" had a chart topping hit?

21 At which game has Omar Sharif represented his country?

22 Which group features the children of 50s and 60s folk singer Ian Campbell?

23 What does Tenko mean in English?

24 C.Day Lewis and John Betjeman have both held which title?

25 In which real state is the fictitious town of Knots Landing?

26 On which Street is the New York Stock Exchange?

27 How many times do you sing "Happy Birthday" if you sing two verses of the song?

28 Who left Channel 4 to become Director of the Royal Opera House?

29 Sunderland lies at the mouth of which river?

30 Of which union was Ray Buckton once a leader?

31 What is the capital city of Hawaii?

32 What is the mint with the hole?

33 What boat is found on the canals of Venice?

34 What is a misanthrope?

35 Where would you find a *kibbutz*?

36 Where are the Quantocks

37 Which England football manager was dubbed a turnip by The Sun?

38 Which London underground station was named after a football club?

39 Who uncrossed their legs to much ado in "Basic Instinct"?

40 Who played the female lead in a sexual harrassment case in the film "Disclosure"?

41 Who founded the Microsoft Corporation?

42 Who wrote the novel "Trainspotting"?

43 Who won the Nobel Prize for Literature in 1995?

44 Where are the Shankly Gates ?

45 In which city did Molly Malone wheel her wheelbarrow?

46 What is the name of the badger's residence?

47 Which office block is located at the junction of Charing Cross Road and Tottenham Court Road?

48 What is the collective noun for Geese?

49 Who is the only cricketer to score 501 in first class cricket?

50 What have Tunbridge Wells, Windsor and Kensington & Chelsea got in common?

1. Germany and Argentina. 2. Martina Navratilova. 3. Mark Spitz. 4. 100 meters. 5. Jayne Torvill and Christopher Dean. 6. Oakland. 7. Sandy Lyle. 8. Carl Lewis. 9. Eighteen. 10. Five. 11. Fencing. 12. Swimming. 13. Eleven. 14. Olga Korbut. 15. Table tennis. 16. Baseball. 17. Florence Griffith Joyner. 18. Muhammad Ali. 19. The Netherlands. 20. Jesse Owens. 21. Stefan Edberg. 22. Squash. 23. Matt Biondi. 24. Golf. 25. Bob Beamon. 26. Boxing. 27. Monica Seles. 28. Eleven. 29. Bernhard Langer. 30. Rugby. 31. Mike Tyson. 32. Los Angeles. 33. Athens. 34. Nadia Comaneci. 35. Andre Agassi. 36. Golf. 37. The USA together with 57 other nations boycotted the games. 38. A motor race. 39. The Brown Bomber. 40. Seven. 41. Miguel Indurain. 42. John McEnroe. 43. Nick Faldo. 44. The zebra. 45. Tennis. 46. Seoul, Korea. 47. Minnesota Vikings. 48. Chris Evert. 49. The five continents. 50. Swimming, cross-country running, fencing, riding, and shooting.

QUIZ 74 | Seas

MEDIUM - LEVEL TWO

1 In which ocean would you find Tristan da Cunha?

2 Where would you find the Weddell Sea?

3 In which ocean are the Seychelles?

4 In which ocean would you find the Canary Islands?

5 Which sea separates Egypt and the Arabian Peninsula?

6 In which sea would you find the Dardanelles?

7 Which sea separates the Aegean and the Black Sea?

8 In which sea would you find Corsica and Sardinia?

9 What does Mediterranean literally mean?

10 What name is given to the arm of the Atlantic Ocean that separates Ireland from Great Britain?

11 What is the French name for the English Channel?

12 Which stretch of water separates Spain from Africa?

13 Which sea lies to the west of Korea?

14 Into which body of water does the River Ganges flow?

15 Which sea lies east of Kamchatka?

16 Where would you find Palk Strait?

17 What body of water separates the Persian Gulf from the Arabian Sea?

18 Which sea separates Australia and New Zealand?

19 In which sea do the West Indies lie?

20 Which is the world's largest ocean?

21 What is the sea between Java and Borneo called?

22 The sea between New Ireland and New Britain bears the name of a German statesman. What is it?

23 In which sea would you find the Great Barrier Reef?

24 In which sea would you find Christmas Island?

25 What body of water separates Borneo from the Malay Peninsula?

26 To the south of Timor lies the Timor Sea. What lies to the north?

27 What body of water separates Borneo from the Celebes?

28 Which sea is contained within the Philippines?

29 Where would you find the Gulf of Carpentaria?

30 Where would you find the Flores Sea?

31 The two halves of which country are separated by the Cook Strait?

32 The Tasman Sea lies to the west of New Zealand. What lies to the east?

33 Which basin would you find off the west coast of South America?

34 Which basin would you find to the north of the North Sea?

35 Which sea would you find to the north of Norway and Finland?

36 Seas lie to the west and east of

the Republic of Georgia. What are they?

37 What gulf lies between North Vietnam and China?

38 Which body of water lies to the west of Cuba?

39 What is the name of the passage south of Cape Horn?

40 What is the large body of water between Quebec and the Northwest Territories?

41 Name two of the large bodies of water surrounding Baffin Island.

42 In which sea would you find the Dogger Bank?

43 What body of water is found to the west of Newfoundland?

44 Near which sea would you find Mecca?

45 Near which body of water, after which a city is named, would you find Brigham City, Utah?

46 Into which body of water does the Mississippi flow?

47 Where, in the Pacific Ocean, would you find the Channel Islands?

48 Which two US cities border the Gulf of Santa Catalina?

49 What water lies between the Gulf of Mexico and the Atlantic Ocean?

50 What body of water separates Long Island from Connecticut?

A nswers to Quiz 73, Pot Luck

1. Somerset. 2. Jessica Fletcher. 3. Piccadilly. 4. Nancy. 5. Grant. 6. Casino Royale. 7. Bruce Forsyth. 8. Circus. 9. 1963. 10. Two. 11. The telephone. 12. Sixpence. 13. Peter Davison. 14. Paul Daniels. 15. George VI. 16. Jack. 17. Manchester. 18. Pauline Collins and John Alderton. 19 .Grandfather. 20. Clive Dunn. 21. Bridge. 22. UB40. 23. Roll call. 24. Poet Laureate. 25. California. 26. Wall Street. 27. Eight. 28. Jeremy Isaacs. 29. Wear. 30. ASLEF. 31. Honolulu. 32. Polo. 33. Gondola. 34. A hater of mankind. 35. Israel. 36. Somerset. 37. Graham Taylor. 38. Arsenal. 39. Sharon Stone. 40. Demi Moore. 41. Bill Gates. 42. Irvine Welsh. 43. Shamus Heaney. 44. Anfield, Liverpool. 45. Dublin. 46. Sett. 47. Centrepoint. 48. gaggle. 49. Brian Lara. 50. They are all royal boroughs.

Q UIZ 75 | Cities

FOR ANSWERS SEE QUIZ NO 76

MEDIUM - LEVEL TWO

1 Which city in the world has the largest populations?

2 Which city in Europe has the largest population?

3 Name the city with the largest population in the USA.

4 What is the capital of Cambodia?

5 Istanbul is the capital of Turkey. True or false?

6 By what name is Baile Atha Cliath better known?

7 Thai people seldom call their capital Bangkok. What is its local name?

8 If you visited the city of Tallinn, which country would you be in?

9 Of which country is Ulan Bator the capital?

10 If you landed at O'Hare airport, which city would you be in?

11 Is Jerusalem or Tel Aviv the capital of Israel?

12 Where would you find Chang Kai Shek airport?

13 Which city, according to Oscar Wilde, is an expensive place to die?

14 'If a man is tired of ... he is tired of life.' Of which city was this said?

15 There are two monuments called Cleopatra's Needle. In which cities are they?

16 Which large Kenyan city lies to the east of Lake Victoria?

17 What is the state capital of Georgia?

18 What is the capital of Florida?

19 Which city, known for its gambling, is found in Nevada?

20 What does the name 'Philadelphia' mean?

21 Which city is also known as Motown?

22 In which state would you find Sioux Falls?

23 Which was the 'rose red city half as old as time'?

24 Which European city relies entirely on its waterways for transport?

25 Which city was often called Blighty by its inhabitants?

26 Which city is called The Big Apple?

27 In which city would you find the cemetery of Père Lachaise?

28 In which city would you find the Paseo del Prado?

29 Tiananmen Square is found in Beijing. What does the name mean?

30 St. Petersburg was known by what name until recently?

31 Why are there two Kansas Cities?

32 Who described London as 'a modern Babylon'?

33 What new name did the British give to the settlement known as New Amsterdam?

34 Which Indian city was infamous for the 'Black Hole' incident?

154

35 Which city was Japan's capital from AD 794 to 1868?

36 Which city boasted a street called Unter den Linden?

37 In which city was King Wenceslas, of Christmas carol fame, murdered?

38 In which cathedral city did Thomas à Becket meet his death?

39 What do the Cambridges of England and the USA have in common?

40 Where in England would you find one of the largest cathedrals in one of the smallest cities?

41 Which city of ancient Palestine was, according to the Bible, to be the site of the Armageddon?

42 Why was the town of Cairo, Illinois, given its name?

43 In which city would you find the Lido?

44 Which European city is built on a system of semi-circular canals?

45 Which German city lends its name to a smoked sausage?

46 Which city is found beside Botany Bay?

47 Which city gave its name to a doughnut?

48 Which city was known as Auld Reekie?

49 What is the capital of Sweden?

50 Which German city gives its name to a perfume?

Answers to Quiz 74, SEAS

1. South Atlantic. 2. Near Antarctica. 3. The Indian Ocean. 4. The North Atlantic. 5. The Red Sea. 6. The Aegean. 7. The Sea of Marmara. 8. The Mediterranean. 9. In the middle of the land. 10. The Irish Sea. 11. La Manche. 12. The Strait of Gibraltar. 13. The Yellow Sea. 14. The Bay of Bengal. 15. The Bering Sea. 16. Between India and Sri Lanka. 17. The Gulf of Oman. 18. The Tasman Sea. 19. The Caribbean. 20. The Pacific. 21. The Java Sea. 22. Bismarck Sea. 23. The Coral Sea. 24. The Indian Ocean. 25. The South China Sea. 26. The Banda Sea. 27. The Makassar Strait. 28. The Sulu Sea. 29. North Australia. 30. Indonesia. 31. New Zealand. 32. The Pacific Ocean. 33. The Peru Basin. 34. The Norwegian Basin. 35. Barents Sea. 36. The Black and the Caspian seas. 37. The Gulf of Tongkin. 38. The Gulf of Mexico. 39. Drake Passage. 40. Hudson Bay. 41. Baffin Bay, Foxe Basin, Hudson Strait, Davis Strait. 42. The North Sea. 43. The Gulf of St. Lawrence. 44. The Red Sea. 45. Salt Lake. 46. The Gulf of Mexico. 47. Just off the coast of California near Los Angeles. 48. Los Angeles and San Diego. 49. The Straits of Florida. 50. Long Island Sound.

Q^{UIZ}_{76} Pot Luck

MEDIUM - LEVEL TWO

1   Which instrument did Franz Liszt play?

2   By what name is Betty Jean Persice better known?

3   In which republic of the former USSR is Chernobyl?

4   In which year were East and West Germany unified?

5   Where was the treaty signed that established the EEC?

6   Who won the first Rugby Union World Cup, held in 1987?

7   On which circuit is motor racing's Grand Prix d'Endurance run?

8   Which two South American countries produce the most coffee?

9   What is the capital of Ecuador?

10 Helium belongs to which group of elements?

11 Where in the cell is DNA stored?

12 Who was the author of "Spycatcher" in 1987?

13 Who wrote the play "Waiting For Godot"?

14 Which Australian city is named after William IV's queen?

15 Which Greenpeace ship was sunk in Auckland harbour in 1985?

16 In "Emmerdale" what did Annie Sugden's name change to?

17 What is Del Boy's local?

18 Who was the first director of Britain's National Theatre Company?

19 Which song features the line "I bet you think this song is about you"?

20 Who painted "The Nightwatch?"

21 Which German brothers collected such stories as "Hansel and Gretel"?

22 What nationality was Hans Christian Andersen?

23 Who said, "A Scout smiles and whistles under all circumstances"?

24 Who first urged Beethoven to "roll over" in 1956?

25 What name was given to the practice which tried to turn lead into silver and gold?

26 Who shared a Nobel Prize for physics with his son?

27 What is a chinook?

28 In which country was Rudyard Kipling born?

29 Which poet drowned while sailing off the coast of Italy in 1822?

30 Which British prime minister wrote "Coningsby" and "Sybil"?

31 What is Terry Wogan's real first name?

32 What name was given to the 19th-century group who wrecked machines?

33 What is the name of Orson Welles' first film, made when he

156

was 26?

34 Who wrote the television series "The Singing Detective"?

35 Which river runs through the Grand Canyon?

36 Name the geological fault that runs the length of California?

37 Which bandmaster composed "The Stars and Stripes Forever"?

38 Which drug is derived from the willow, *Salix alba*?

39 Where was Captain Cook killed?

40 Where was the Royal Mint until 1810?

41 Which drink did Leonard Rossiter and Joan Collins advertise?

42 What is the full name for DNA?

43 Other than the "Odyssey", which work is Homer famed for?

44 Name the art of making decorative lacework with knotted threads?

45 To which family does the chive belong?

46 Which indoor game was invented by British Army Officers in India in 1875?

47 Which microbe is the basis of the brewing and baking industry?

48 Who wrote the novel "The Van"?

49 In bluegrass music who is Flatt's partner?

50 Philip Glass wrote an opera about which scientist?

1. São Paolo. 2. Moscow. 3. New York. 4. Phnom Penh. 5. False. The capital is Ankara. 6. Dublin. 7. Khrung Thep. 8. Estonia. 9. Mongolia. 10. Chicago. 11. Jerusalem. 12. Taiwan. 13. Paris. 14. London. 15. London and New York. 16. Nairobi. 17. Atlanta. 18. Miami. 19. Las Vegas. 20. Brotherly love. 21. Detroit. 22. South Dakota. 23. Petra. 24. Venice. 25. London. 26. New York. 27. Paris. 28. Madrid. 29. The Gate of Heavenly Peace. 30. Leningrad. 31. One is in Kansas and the other adjacent to it in Missouri. 32. Benjamin Disraeli. 33. New York. 34. Calcutta. 35. Kyoto. 36. Berlin. 37. Prague. 38. Canterbury. 39. They are both university towns. 40. Ely. 41. Megiddo. 42. It is situated on a delta like the Egyptian city after which it is named. 43. Venice. 44. Amsterdam. 45. Frankfurt. 46. Sydney. 47. Berlin. 48. Edinburgh. 49. Stockholm. 50. Cologne.

QUIZ 77 | The Arts

MEDIUM - LEVEL TWO

1 Which of the duo Laurel and Hardy was British by birth?

2 In which year did "South Pacific" first appear on Broadway?

3 Which American comedy actress was noted for her 1946 appearance in "Annie Get Your""Gun?

4 For what catchphrase was Bugs Bunny famous?

5 In which year did Mickey Mouse first appear as a comic figure?

6 Who were the owners of the fictional Fresh-Air Taxicab Co.?

7 When did Sergeant Pepper's Lonely Hearts Club Band appear?

8 Which artist portrayed the music halls of Montmartre?

9 On which island did Gauguin paint some of his finest works?

10 Which musical celebrated an Argentine president's wife?

11 Who played the female lead in "One Hundred Men and a Girl"?

12 In which film did Greta Garbo say "I want to be alone"?

13 Who was the female lead in "Jezebel" in 1938?

14 Who said: 'If Mr Vincent Price were to be co-starred with Miss Bette Davis in a story by Mr Edgar Allan Poe directed by Mr Roger Corman, it could not fully express the pent-up violence and depravity of a single day in the life of the average family'?

15 Which British actor made his

name playing villains such as Dracula and Dr Fu Manchu?

16 Who is often regarded as the national poet of Scotland?

17 Who did Leonard Nimoy play?

18 Who wrote "Under Milk Wood"?

19 Which 60s youth hero and singer said: 'I'm glad I'm not me'?

20 What was the name of the Music and Art Fair held in the Catskill Mountains at Bethel, N.Y. in 1969?

21 Which instrument is Yehudin Menuhin famous for playing?

22 Who is reputed to be the greatest maker of violins?

23 Why is a 'jews harp' so called?

24 What does the 1812 Overture celebrate?

25 Who painted "Le Déjeuner sur l'Herbe"?

26 'April is the cruellest month, breeding lilac out of the dead land...' comes from which poem?

27 Who wrote: 'Do not go gentle into that good night... Rage, rage, against the dying of the light'?

28 Who wrote "Gormenghast"?

29 In which book was the future said to be like 'a boot stamping on a human face – forever'?

30 Who said, 'The only end of writing is to enable the readers better to enjoy life, or better to endure it'?

31 Who wrote "The Red Badge of Courage"?

32 Who played the lead role in "The

158

Bridge on the River Kwai"?

33 Which film, starring Hugh Grant, concerned rites of passage?

34 Daniel Day Lewis starred in "The Last of the . . ."?

35 Who played the young female lead in "A Room With a View"?

36 Which creature, invented by Tove Jansson, featured in her series of children's novels.

37 Who was the wizard who befriended dwarves and hobbits?

38 What was the name of the evil lord in Lord of the Rings?

39 Name two boys whose evidence saved Muff Potter from hanging?

40 Gulliver visited a land of giants. What was it called?

41 What Anthony Burgess novel of featured Alex and his droogs?

42 In the film "Bringing up Baby", who was Baby?

43 Who says of his creator: 'There were things which he stretched, but mainly he told the truth'?

44 In which book does a crocodile swallow an alarm clock?

45 Which jungle-dweller appears in the film Greystoke?

46 Which murderous British barber became the subject of a musical?

47 Who from a Swedish children's story is famous for her strength?

48 Which crime writer was played by Vanessa Redgrave in a film about a mysterious part of her life?

49 Who was the sister in the Osmonds?

50 What is Meat Loaf's real name?

Answers to Quiz 76, Pot Luck

1. Piano. 2. Lauren Bacall. 3. Ukraine. 4. 1990. 5. Rome. 6. New Zealand. 7. Le Mans. 8. Brazil and Colombia. 9. Quito. 10. Inert gases. 11. Nucleus. 12. Peter Wright. 13. Samuel Beckett. 14. Adelaide. 15. Rainbow Warrior. 16. Annie Kempinski. 17. The Nag's Head. 18. Laurence Olivier. 19. You're So Vain. 20. Rembrandt. 21. The Brothers Grimm. 22. Danish. 23. Robert Baden-Powell. 24. Chuck Berry. 25. Alchemy. 26. William Bragg. 27. Helicopter. 28. India. 29. Shelley. 30. Disraeli. 31. Michael . 32. Luddites. 33. Citizen Kane. 34. Dennis Potter. 35. Colorado. 36. San Andreas fault. 37. John Philip Sousa. 38. Aspirin. 39. Hawaii. 40. The Tower of London. 41. Cinzano. 42. Deoxyribonucleic acid. 43. The Iliad. 44. Macramé. 45. Onion. 46. Snooker. 47. Yeast. 48. Roddy Doyle. 49. Scruggs. 50. Albert Einstein.

QUIZ 78 People

FOR ANSWERS SEE QUIZ NO 79

MEDIUM - LEVEL TWO

1 When was JFK assassinated?
2 Which movie mogul said: 'That's the trouble with directors. Always biting the hand that lays the golden egg'?
3 Which cartoon character had a girlfriend called Olive Oyl?
4 Whose face reputedly 'launched a thousand ships'?
5 Which name connects Woody Allen with Bob Dylan?
6 Who was Russia's 'Mad Monk'?
7 Name a sergeant whose band was made famous by the Beatles.
8 By what name was Marion Morrison better known?
9 Under what name did Samuel Langhorne Clemens find fame?
10 Name the outlaw couple immortalized on film by Faye Dunaway and Warren Beatty.
11 Which Indian political leader was known as 'Mahatma'?
12 Who was the first US president?
13 Which marooned character had a companion called Man Friday?
14 Name the Three Musketeers and their constant companion.
15 Who did Scout, Jem, and Dill want to tempt out of his house?
16 Which Black civil rights leader said, 'I have a dream'?
17 Which boxer was formerly known as Cassius Clay?
18 Which king died at the Battle of Hastings by being shot in the eye?

19 Which Soviet leader took a name which meant 'steel'?
20 Which 18th-century British explorer was killed by the natives of Hawaii in 1779?
21 Which jungle-dweller was created by Edgar Rice Burroughs?
22 With which security organization was J. Edgar Hoover associated?
23 Who is notorious for plotting to blow up the UK Houses of Parliament with gunpowder?
24 Which Polish–French woman scientist discovered radium?
25 Who was the constant companion of Tom Sawyer?
26 Which American politician was known as LBJ?
27 Which Mexican General did Davy Crockett and Jim Bowie face at the Alamo?
28 What machine was first manufactured by the gunsmith Philo Remington in 1874?
29 What is O. J. Simpson's full name?
30 Who was the leader of the Free French in World War II?
31 Name the American whose detective agency was famous for spying behind Confederate lines and strike breaking?
32 What was Henry Deringer famous for inventing?
33 Charles Lutwidge Dodgson was a mathematician. For what was he better known?

34 Which film star was famous for the phrase 'You dirty rat!', even though he never actually said it?

35 Which Hunkpapa Sioux leader is given principal credit for defeating General Custer?

36 Who was the pirate, Bluebeard or Blackbeard?

37 By what name was William H. Bonney better known?

38 On which vessel would you expect to find William Shatner?

39 Which British author wrote gloomily about the year 1984?

40 Which fictional heroine lived in a house with green gables?

41 Who was treated as a giant by the Lilliputians?

42 When a lady told him, 'Sir, you smell!' he replied, 'No, Madam, you smell, I stink'. Who was he?

43 Which name links a South African statesman with the Battle of Trafalgar?

44 Which French heroine was burned as a witch by the English?

45 Which Scottish king defeated the English at Bannockburn?

46 Which Italian dictator was known as 'Il Duce'?

47 Sir Edmund Hillary climbed Everest in 1953. Who was his Sherpa companion?

48 Which fictional hero came from the planet Krypton?

49 Which outlaw lived with his Merry Men in Sherwood Forest?

50 Which scientist discovered gravity with the help of an apple?

1. Stan Laurel. 2. 1949. 3. Ethel Merman. 4. 'What's up, Doc?' 5. 1931. 6. Amos 'n' Andy. 7. 1967. 8. Toulouse Lautrec. 9. Tahiti. 10. Evita. 11. Deanna Durbin. 12. Grand Hotel. 13. Bette Davis. 14. Quentin Crisp. 15. Christopher Lee. 16. Robert Burns. 17. Mr Spock. 18. Dylan Thomas. 19. Bob Dylan. 20. Woodstock. 21. The violin. 22. Stradivari. 23. It is a corruption of 'jaws harp', the instrument being held between the teeth. 24. Napoleon Bonaparte. 25. Manet. 26. The Wasteland by T.S. Eliot. 27. Dylan Thomas. 28. Mervyn Peake. 29. 1984 by George Orwell. 30. Samuel Johnson. 31. Stephen Crane. 32. Alec Guinness. 33. Four Weddings and a Funeral. 34. The Last of the Mohicans. 35. Helena Bonham-Carter. 36. Moomins. 37. Gandalf. 38. Sauron. 39. Tom Sawyer and Huckleberry Finn. 40. Brobdingnag. 41. A Clockwork Orange. 42. A leopard. 43. Mark Twain (according to Huck Finn). 44. Peter Pan. 45. Tarzan of the Apes. 46. Sweeney Todd. 47. Pippi Longstocking. 48. Agatha Christie. 49. Marie. 50. Marvin Lee Aday.

Quiz 79 | 80s & 90s

MEDIUM - LEVEL TWO

1 Which controversial BBC Falklands film was broadcast in May 1988?

2 In which month was the marriage of Prince Charles and Lady Diana?

3 The SAS stormed which embassy in Knightsbridge?

4 Where were the 1980 Olympics?

5 Where did the Polish Solidarity movement start its strikes?

6 In August 1980 unemployment in Britain reached what figure?

7 Which US President ordered the aborted rescue of US hostages in Tehran?

8 Which Lord prepared a report following the Brixton riots?

9 Who did Pat Cash beat in the final when he won Wimbledon?

10 Who became the first Pope to visit Britain in 400 years?

11 Which charity record was the last to reach No.1 in the 80s?

12 Who were Liverpool's opponents in the Hillsborough disaster?

13 Who "got on his bike and looked for work"?

14 What did Prince Edward resign?

15 How did Princess Grace die?

16 Which Tory MP Keith was involved in dodgy applications for shares?

17 In which month of 1982 did Argentine forces invade the Falkland Islands?

18 Greenham Common is in which county?

19 Which police officer was shot outside the Libyan embassy?

20 How old was Bjorn Borg when he retired from tennis?

21 What was Reagan's Strategic Defence Initative known as?

22 What did Monday, October 19th, 1987 become known as?

23 Which North Sea oil rig exploded with the loss of over 150 lives?

24 Which former MI5 man wrote "Spycatcher"?

25 Which American politician made the famous "watch my lips" speech?

26 How old was Tony Blair when he became Prime Minister?

27 Who first won the US Amateur Championship in 1994?

28 The invasion of which country sparked off the Gulf War?

29 Who was third in the 1997 Tory leadership election?

30 Which 25-year-old recording was 1990's best-selling single?

31 What is Bill Clinton's middle name?

32 Anthea Turner became the first female presenter of which live weekly event?

33 Who shared the 1993 Nobel Peace Prize with Nelson Mandela?

34 Paul Stewart scored an FA Cup Final goal for which team?

35 On TV, who were the Long Johns?

36 Which English fast bowler took the first wicket in the 1997 Ashes?

37 Jonathan Aitken withdrew his court case against which paper?

38 Which royal financial advisor used toes for more than counting on?

39 In the 90s, who was Education Secretary, Home Secretary and Chancellor?

40 Which city hosted the 1992 Olympic Games?

41 Who succeeded Robert Runcie as Archbishop of Canterbury?

42 Andy Thomson became world indoor champion at what?

43 Which journalist helped write "Diana: Her True Story"?

44 Who made his last trip on the yacht "Lady Ghislaine"?

45 Who was the first man to win two Oscars in the 90s?

46 What is the S in BSE?

47 Which sport's world series was cancelled due to the players' strike in 1994?

48 Who was No. I when Michael Jackson was No. 2 for five weeks with "Heal the World"?

49 Who stood against Margaret Thatcher for the Tory leadership?

50 Who did 22-year-old model Rachel Hunter marry in 1990?

Answers to Quiz 78, PEOPLE

1. 1963. 2. Samuel Goldwyn. 3. Popeye. 4. Helen of Troy's. 5. Allen. Bob Dylan was born Robert Allen Zimmerman and Woody Allen was Allen Stewart Konigsberg. 6. Grigori Yefimovich Rasputin. 7. Sergeant Pepper. 8. John Wayne. 9. Mark Twain. 10. Bonnie and Clyde. 11. Mohandas Karamchand Gandhi. 12. George Washington. 13. Robinson Crusoe. 14. Athos, Porthos, Aramis, and D'Artagnan. 15. Boo Radley. 16. Martin Luther King, Jr. 17. Muhammad Ali. 18. King Harold II. 19. Stalin. 20. Captain James Cook. 21. Tarzan. 22. The FBI. 23. Guy Fawkes. 24. Marie Curie. 25. Huckleberry Finn. 26. Lyndon Baines Johnson. 27. Santa Anna. 28. The typewriter. 29. Orenthal James. 30. General de Gaulle. 31. Allan Pinkerton. 32. A short-barreled pistol that had a large bore and was small enough to be carried in a pocket. 33. He wrote Alice in Wonderland under the name of Lewis Carroll. 34. James Cagney. 35. Sitting Bull. 36. Blackbeard. 37. Billy the Kid. 38. The Starship Enterprise. 39. George Orwell. 40. Anne. 41. Gulliver. 42. Dr Samuel Johnson. 43. Nelson. 44. Joan of Arc. 45. Robert the Bruce. 46. Benito Mussolini. 47. Tenzing Norgay. 48. Superman. 49. Robin Hood. 50. Sir Isaac Newton.

Q^{UIZ}_{80} Nature

MEDIUM - LEVEL TWO

1 Under what other name is a blue berry also known?

2 Which family does the honeysuckle belong to?

3 Where does the labrador retriever originate?

4 What is a black leopard better known as?

5 What does the fly agaric look like?

6 What type of plant is a bladder wort?

7 Where do dragonflies lay their eggs?

8 How do lampreys eat their food?

9 What type of animal is a gharial?

10 Under what name is woodbine also known?

11 What age can a parrot live to?

12 What distinguishes the tenrec from the hedgehog in appearance?

13 What types of tree would you find in the tundra?

14 What do the roots of the scammony plant yield?

15 How many pairs of legs does a centipede have on average?

16 Where do walrusses live?

17 In which position do sloths spend the majority of their time?

18 In what type of habitat do gentians grow?

19 What type of animal is an ibex?

20 What do wild pigs use their upturned canines for?

21 Which domesticated animal is the guanaco related to?

22 What sort of animal is the flying fox?

23 How does a chipmunk carry his food?

24 Where do tapirs live?

25 Which is the world's largest land animal after the elephant?

26 What sort of animal is a caribou?

27 What type of vegetation can you find in the taiga?

28 What is a Painted Lady?

29 Which family does the crocus belong to?

30 Which is the largest bird of prey?

31 How does a cheetah bring down its prey?

32 On what type of plant do kiwis grow?

33 What is a syringa also known as?

34 What sort of animal is a marmoset?

35 How does a python kill its prey?

36 Which order does the kangaroo belong to?

37 Where do giraffes live?

38 What sort of animal is a wilde beest?

39 To which family do salamanders belong?

40 What is the name of the insect that transmits malaria?

41 Which type of bear is also called silvertip?

42 The adult male of which monkey has a brightly colored face and

buttocks?

43 Where does the emu live?

44 Which is the largest freshwater fish?

45 What do koalas feed on?

46 What is the name of the insect that transmits sleeping sickness?

47 Do pumas have a spotted skin?

48 Which animal does the okapi resemble?

49 What does a tick feed on?

50 What kind of animal is a chinchilla?

Answers to Quiz 79, 80s & 90s

1. Tumbledown. 2. July. 3. Iranian. 4. Moscow. 5. Gdansk. 6. Two million. 7. Jimmy Carter. 8. Scarman. 9. Ivan Lendl. 10. John Paul II. 11. "Do They Know It's Christmas?". 12. Nottingham Forest. 13. Norman Tebbit's father. 14. Commission in the Royal Marines. 15. In a car crash. 16. Best. 17. April. 18. Berkshire. 19. Yvonne Fletcher. 20. 26. 21. Star Wars. 22. Black Monday (Stock Market crash). 23. Piper Alpha. 24. Peter Wright. 25. George Bush. 26. 43. 27. Tiger Woods. 28. Kuwait. 29. John Redwood. 30. "Unchained Melody" (Righteous Brothers). 31. Jefferson. 32. National Lottery. 33. President F.W. de Klerk. 34. Spurs. 35. John Bird and John Fortune. 36. Darren Gough. 37. The Guardian. 38. John Bryan. 39. Kenneth Clarke. 40. Barcelona. 41. George Carey. 42. Bowls. 43. Andrew Morton. 44. Robert Maxwell. 45. Tom Hanks. 46. Spongiform. 47. Baseball. 48. Whitney Houston. 49. Michael Heseltine. 50. Rod Stewart.

Q^{UIZ}₈₁ Costume

MEDIUM - LEVEL TWO

1 Which people invented the parka?

2 What name is given to the small cap often worn by Jewish men?

3 What is the Mexican name for a blanket with a hole in the centre which is used as a cloak?

4 What is a toupee?

5 What is the name for a wide length of cotton wrapped around the waist, with the end pulled up and tucked between the legs?

6 What is the chequered scarf worn by Palestinians called?

7 What is the traditional skirt worn by Indonesians?

8 Sarongs are often dyed by a process that utilizes hot wax. What is this process called?

9 What is the name of the traditional black robe worn by women in Iran?

10 What color are the robes of a Buddhist monk in Thailand?

11 What is the traditional costume of Japanese women called?

12 What name is given to the decorative sash worn with a kimono?

13 What is the name given to the protective leather coverings worn by cowboys over their trousers?

14 Western men in evening dress often add what around the waist?

15 What head covering do Sikh men wear?

16 What is the name of the furry pocket hung at the front of a kilt?

17 What encouraged women to adopt the wearing of bloomers?

18 What was a bustle?

19 What name is given to the tall bearskin hats worn by members of the British guards regiments?

20 What is the name of the flowing robe worn by Indian women?

21 What is a ballerina's dress called?

22 What was the robe of the ancient Romans called?

23 What was Beau Brummell's connection with clothes?

24 What women's fashion was created by Christian Dior just after the Second World War?

25 Which British men in the 1950s wore drape coats, drainpipe trousers, and crêpe-soled shoes?

26 What were the two tunic-like garments worn in ancient Greece?

27 What did the double crown worn by the Pharaohs of Egypt signify?

28 Which garment did the ancient Greeks regard as the infallible mark of a barbarian?

29 On what part of the body is a snood worn?

30 What adornment did the Romans award to those who deserved public praise?

31 What distinguishing mark could Roman patricians add to togas?

32 The soldiers of which country (excluding Scotland) wear a skirt as part of their ceremonial dress?

33 What leg covering was worn with a doublet?

34 What hat was once regarded as the distinguishing mark of British businessmen?

35 Witches are popularly supposed to have a worn a high, pointed hat. What was it called?

36 What is the name given to an eye glass held in one eye?

37 For what footwear are the Dutch best known?

38 Which British nobleman invented waterproof boots?

39 What metallic addition did Levi Strauss make to blue jeans?

40 What colour clothes are worn at Eastern funerals?

41 In China what color were the Emperor's clothes?

42 The coats used for fox hunting appear to be red. What is the official name for this color?

43 What name is given to the soft leather shoes traditionally worn by Native Americans?

44 What is a bolero?

45 What was a goose-belly?

46 Why were wigs made from horse hair?

47 Where did the word bikini originate?

48 What jacket would a British Victorian gentleman wear?

49 What surprising feature did top hats worn for the opera have?

50 Golfers in the 1920s often wore wide knickerbockers. What were they called?

Answers to Quiz 80, NATURE

1. Bilberry. 2. Caorifoliaceae. 3. Newfoundland. 4. Panther. 5. It is a fungus with a red cap with white patches. 6. Carnivorous. 7. In water. 8. They suck the blood from other fish. 9. A crocodile. 10. Virginia creeper. 11. Captive parrots can live to more than 80 years. 12. It has a long pointed snout and often no tail. 13. No trees: only stunted shrubs, mosses, and lichens can survive. 14. Resin. 15. 35. 16. The Arctic. 17. They hang upside down from branches. 18. Alpine regions. 19. A wild goat. 20. To intimidate other animals. 21. The llama. 22. A bat. 23. In his cheek pouches, which are expandable. 24. In Central and South America and South-east Asia. 25. The white rhinoceros. 26. A wild reindeer. 27. Coniferous forests. 28. A type of butterfly. 29. The iris family. 30. The condor. 31. It trips it up. 32. On a vine. 33. Mock orange. 34. A small monkey. 35. By squeezing it. 36. Marsupials. 37. In the open savanna south of the Sahara. 38. An antilope. 39. Amphibians. 40. The anopheles mosquito. 41. The grizzly bear. 42. The mandrill. 43. Australia. 44. The sturgeon. 45. Eucalyptus leaves. 46. The tsetse fly. 47. Only young ones do: the spots disappear when they get older. 48. A small short-necked giraffe, but it has zebra-like stripes on his buttocks and legs. 49. Blood. 50. A South American rodent.

Q UIZ 82 Places

MEDIUM - LEVEL TWO

1 Which country would you reach if you crossed the Strait of Gibraltar due south from Spain?

2 On which border is Lake Geneva?

3 What is the name of the Australian island south of Victoria?

4 In which state would you find the Grand Canyon?

5 What was Rock Island used for during the American Civil War?

6 Which country has the world's second largest population?

7 What is South West Africa now called?

8 What is the predominant religion in Mexico?

9 What is the most northerly town in Europe?

10 In which country would you pay in Schilling?

11 Which is the most southerly point of the UK?

12 Which is New York's largest borough?

13 In which country does the Danube rise?

14 In which city is the Hagia Sofia situated?

15 Which is the only predominantly Moslem state in India?

16 Which country do the Faeroe Islands belong to?

17 In which sea is the Crimea situated?

18 What is the name of the mountain overlooking Capetown?

19 In which Australian state is Sydney?

20 Which three countries form the Baltic states?

21 In which mountain range is Andorra situated?

22 What is the capital of Indonesia?

23 What is the name of the group of islands off the southern tip of South America?

24 Which is the highest mountain in Japan?

25 On which river is Rome situated?

26 In which city can you find St Basil's cathedral?

27 Which town is further north – Oslo or St. Petersburg?

28 Which is China's largest city?

29 Can you name the three Balearic Islands?

30 In which city can you find the statue of the Little Mermaid?

31 On which border lies the Principality of Liechtenstein?

32 Which Scottish island group do Skye and Iona belong to?

33 What is the name of the strait between the European and Asian part of Turkey, connecting the Sea of Marmara with the Black Sea?

34 What is the capital of Morocco?

35 In which country is the ancient city of Carthage?

36 Which is the most northerly of the Great Lakes in North America?

37 In which city would you find the Taj Mahal?

38 Which is the largest province in Canada?

39 Which is the most sparsely populated state in the USA?

40 Which is the most northerly county in England?

41 In which mountain range would you find the Matterhorn?

42 On which island is Tokyo situated?

43 Which two former African countries formed Tanzania?

44 Where would you find the Prado?

45 What is the capital of Colorado?

46 What island group do Cuba and Jamaica belong to?

47 In which Italian region is Florence situated?

48 Which of the following countries is not in the northern hemisphere: Thailand, Ethiopia, Venezuela, Philippines, Zambia?

49 On which river is Cologne situated?

50 Which country do the Azores belong to?

A nswers to Quiz 81, COSTUME

1. The Inuit. 2. A yarmulke (or kippah). 3. A poncho. 4. A partial wig. 5. A dhoti. 6. Keffiyeh. 7. Sarong. 8. Batik. 9. Chador. 10. Saffron (orange). 11. Kimono. 12. Obi. 13. Chaps. 14. A cummerbund. 15. A turban. 16. A sporran. 17. The desire to ride bicycles. 18. A small frame worn by a women to make their skirt stand out at the rear. 19. Busbies. 20. Sari. 21. A tutu. 22. A toga. 23. He was a famous dandy and leader of fashion who spent huge sums of money on clothes. Whatever he wore was considered good taste. 24. The New Look. 25. Teddy boys. 26. The peplos which was gradually replaced by the chiton. 27. Sovereignty over both Upper and Lower Egypt. 28. Trousers. 29. The hair. 30. A laurel wreath. 31. A purple border. 32. Greece. 33. Hose. 34. The bowler. 35. A steeple hat. 36. A monocle. 37. Wooden clogs. 38. The Duke of Wellington. 39. He added copper rivets 40. White. 41. Yellow. 42. Hunting pink. 43. Moccasins. 44. A very short tight-fitting jacket. 45. An artificial paunch, originating in Spain, made from padding stuffed into the front of a doublet. 46. They were much cheaper and did not uncurl when they became wet. 47. From Bikini Atoll, where nuclear bombs were tested. 48. A frock coat. 49. They could be flattened for storage under one's seat. 50. Plus fours. Shorter versions were called plus twos.

QUIZ 83 | Medicine

MEDIUM - LEVEL TWO

1 Which eye disorder is caused by inadequate drainage of excess fluid?

2 Why do human beings not develop an immunity against the common cold?

3 What disease does a person suffer from who has the protein factor VIII missing from the plasma?

4 What are people with agoraphobia frightened of?

5 In a person with periodontal disease, what is inflamed?

6 In a person suffering from Down's syndrome, how do the body cells differ from those of normal people?

7 What type of cancer is malignant melanoma?

8 What are people with anemia lacking?

9 What is thrombosis?

10 In which allergic disease do the muscles of the bronchi and bronchioles contract, resulting in the narrowing of the air passages?

11 The disease rickets implies that there is a bone defiency in what?

12 Mammography is used for screening for which disease?

13 What is the cause of angina pectoris?

14 What is a person with osteoporosis suffering from?

15 What does AIDS stand for?

16 What type of disease is psoriasis?

17 What does 'grand mal' mean?

18 Which widespread viral infection has been eradicated since 1979 due to a worldwide vaccination programme?

19 In a person suffering from emphysema, which organ is affected?

20 What does ECG stand for?

21 Which disease does the ades mosquito transmit?

22 In leukemia, which cells are affected?

23 If a person is short-sighted, what type of lens would he need to correct this?

24 Which virus causes chicken pox?

25 In a person suffering from hepatitis, which organ is affected?

26 What permanent condition can an infection of poliomyelitis lead to?

27 What are the main symptons of a tetanus infection?

28 In encephalitis, which part of the body is inflamed??

29 Which serious condition can be caused by a burst appendix?

30 Which are the main glands affected by an attack of mumps?

31 Which part of the body does the bacterium vibrio cholerae affect?

32 In tuberculosis, which are the main organs affected?

33 What is German measles also called?

34 Which virus causes a cold sore?

35 Which infectious disease is caused

170

by the spirochete Treponema pallidum?

36 Which condition describes the lesion of the mucous membrane of the stomach accompanied by inflammation?

37 What is infectious mononucleosis also called?

38 Which degenerative nervous disease is associated with the destruction of brain cells that produce dopamine?

39 Which serious contagious disease is caused by the bacterium Bordetella pertussis?

40 What type of infection is ringworm?

41 In which part of the body does gout usually start?

42 What is the purpose of a vagotomy?

43 How is a stroke caused?

44 What condition describes the inflammation of the membranes of the cavities in the skull?

45 By what other name are hemorrhoids also known?

46 What is a sty caused by?

47 Spondylitis is an inflammation of which part of the body?

48 What is icterus also called?

49 What do doctors examine by use of an angiography?

50 What is the effect of a cataract?

QUIZ 84 | Sport

MEDIUM - LEVEL TWO

1 What was the location of the 1994 Winter Olympics?

2 Which male tennis player won the Australian Open Singles Championship in 1989 and 1990?

3 With which sport is Max Schmeling associated?

4 Who was the first woman to swim the English Channel?

5 For which football team did 'Red' Grange play?

6 What is the main difference between the decathlon and the modern pentathlon?

7 What type of sport is aikido?

8 Who became the first British golfer in 50 years to win the US Open in 1970?

9 Where is the Longchamp race course situated?

10 What sport do you associate with Damon Hill?

11 With which sport is Peggy Fleming associated?

12 In which sport would you find the James Norris Trophy?

13 Which golfer won the British Open in 1979, 1984, and 1988?

14 With which sport is Anita Lonsbrough associated?

15 Who founded the modern Olympic Games?

16 Which British runner became the first person to run a mile in under four minutes in 1954?

17 How long is a marathon race?

18 Which country won soccer's World Cup in 1966?

19 How many singles titles did Navratilova win at Wimbledon?

20 Which US soccer team did Pelè play for from 1975 to 1977?

21 Who was the first black American major-league baseball player?

22 Which American swimmer won gold medals in the Olympics and became a film actor?

23 With which sport is Bobby Jones associated?

24 Which British athlete won gold in the decathlon in the 1980s?

25 Which US speed skater won all five men's gold medals at the 1980 Winter Olympics?

26 What does the biathlon winter event consist of?

27 With which sport is Wilt Chamberlain associated?

28 At which modern Olympic Games was the torch first introduced?

29 In which city would you find a football team called the Steelers?

30 Which US World War II general represented his country in the Olympic Games?

31 Which female tennis player became the French Open Singles Champion in 1993?

32 Which stadium was built in honor of baseball player Babe Ruth?

33 With which sport is Gene Tunney associated?

34 Why did 32 black countries boycott the 1976 Olympic Games?

35 Which team did Babe Ruth play for during his record-breaking season in 1927?

36 Which are the two events in international gymnastics in which both men and women take part?

37 In which Olympic event did Abebe Bikila gain a medal?

38 In which sport would you be awarded the Dunhill Cup?

39 Which tennis player won the men's singles at Wimbledon in 1993 and 1994?

40 Who won the 1988 World Snooker Championship?

41 Which sport is associated with the Uber Cup?

42 Which athlete was referred to as 'The Flying Finn'?

43 With which sport would you associate the term 'wicket'?

44 For which event did David Hemery win a gold medal at the 1968 Olympics?

45 With which sport would you associate Willie Shoemaker?

46 Which sport is Franz Klammer associated with?

47 What was the location of the 1968 Summer Olympics?

48 Which female tennis player became the US Open Champion in 1990?

49 Which two players fought for the World Chess Championship in Rejkavik in 1972?

50 What is Le Mans famous for?

A nswers to Quiz 83, MEDICINE

1. Glaucoma. 2. The cold virus keeps changing and therefore the immune system cannot recognize it. 3. Haemophilia. 4. Public places. 5. The gums. 6. They consist of 47 instead of 46 chromosomes. 7. Skin cancer. 8. Red blood cells. 9. The creation of blood clots in the arteries. 10. Asthma. 11. Vitamin D. 12. Breast cancer. 13. The narrowing of the arteries, restricting the flow of blood. 14. The thinning and weakening of the bones. 15. Acquired Immune Deficiency Syndrome. 16. A kind of dermatitis. 17. A severe seizure in someone suffering from epilepsy. 18. Small pox. 19. The lungs. 20. Electrocardiograph. 21. Yellow fever. 22. White blood cells. 23. A concave lens. 24. The herpes zoster virus. 25. The liver. 26. Paralysis. 27. Muscle spasms. 28. The brain cells. 29. Peritonitis. 30. The salivary glands. 31. The intestines. 32. The lungs. 33. Rubella. 34. The herpes simplex virus. 35. Syphilis. 36. Gastric ulcer. 37. Glandular fever. 38. Parkinson's disease. 39. Whooping cough. 40. A fungal infection of the skin. 41. The big toe. 42. To reduce the acid secretion of the stomach. 43. The blood supply to the brain is disrupted. 44. Sinusitis. 45. Piles. 46. The inflammation of one or more sebaceous glands on the eyelid. 47. The vertebrae. 48. Jaundice. 49. Blood vessels in the form of X-rays. 50. The clouding of the lens in the eye, which can eventually lead to blindness.

Q UIZ 85 | Places

1 Where is the world's coldest town?

2 Which country is the odd one out: Mexico, Brazil, Argentina, Venezuela or Chile?

3 Which of the following cities is furthest south: Madrid, New York, San Francisco, Cairo or Tokyo?

4 In which country would you pay in escudos?

5 Which is the main religion in Brazil?

6 With which of the following countries does Germany not form a border: Belgium, Switzerland, Hungary or Denmark?

7 What is the capital city of New Zealand?

8 In which country would you find Cork, Waterford, and Galway?

9 In which state is the city of New Orleans?

10 Which Chinese city has the highest population?

11 Which of the following states is the odd one out: Manchuria, Estonia or Ukraine?

12 What is the capital of Massachusetts?

13 Name the independent principality in south-eastern France?

14 Which Pacific islands are famous for their giant tortoises?

15 Where is the largest cave system in the world and what is it called?

16 Which is the largest coral reef in the world?

17 What is the capital of Zimbabwe?

18 Which street in London was famous for its association with newspaper publishing?

19 Which of the following countries is the odd one out: Pakistan, India, Iraq or Egypt?

20 Which is the largest active volcano in the world?

21 In which city would you find Madison Square Garden?

22 The Strait of Messina separates Italy from which island?

23 In which country would you find Stavanger, Bergen, and Trondheim?

24 In which city would you find The Spanish Steps?

25 In which country would you hear Catalan spoken?

26 Which country is referred to as the Emerald Isle?

27 With which of the following states does Florida not have a border: Georgia, Alabama or Tennessee?

28 What is the capital of Peru?

29 Where is The Giant's Causeway?

30 With which cloth is the French town of Chantilly associated?

31 Which city is further south – Buenos Aires or Brisbane?

32 On which river would you find the Victoria Falls?

33 In which country is the shekel the official currency?

34 Which Australian state lies to the

north-east of the country?

35 What is the name of the large area of wetlands in Florida?

36 Which of these countries does not have a coastline on the Mediterranean: Israel, Greece or Saudia Arabia?

37 Which city is commonly known as the The Big Apple?

38 What other West Indian island did Trinidad join to form a state?

39 Havana is the capital of which country?

40 Which state lies to the west of Colorado: Utah, Wyoming or Arizona?

41 Which Canadian province borders Hudson Bay, Ontario, and the Gulf of St. Lawrence?

42 In which city would you find the Capitol?

43 What is the capital of the Philippines?

44 Which of the following countries does not have a coastline on the North Sea: Great Britain, The Netherlands or Poland?

45 Which European country is divided into 23 cantons?

46 In which European city would you find St. Peter's Square?

47 In which Italian city would you find the Uffizi Gallery?

48 In which city would you find Carnaby Street?

49 Which state is commonly known as 'The Sunshine State'?

50 Orange Free State is a province of which country?

Answers to Quiz 84, SPORT

1. Lillehammer, Norway. 2. Ivan Lendl. 3. Boxing. 4. Gertrude Ederle. 5. The Chicago Bears. 6. The decathlon consists of ten events, the modern pentathlon of only five. 7. A Japanese art of self-defence. 8. Tony Jacklin. 9. In the Bois de Bologne in Paris. 10. Motor racing. 11. Figure skating. 12. Ice hockey. 13. Seve Ballesteros. 14. Swimming. 15. Pierre de Coubertin. 16. Roger Bannister. 17. Twenty-six miles. 18. England. 19. Nine. 20. The New York Cosmos. 21. Jackie Robinson. 22. Johnny Weissmuller. 23. Golf. 24. Daley Thompson. 25. Eric Heiden. 26. A combination of cross-country skiing and target shooting. 27. Basketball. 28. The 1936 Games in Berlin. 29. Pittsburgh. 30. George Patton. He was a pentathlete at the 1912 Olympic Games in Stockholm. 31. Steffi Graf. 32. Yankee Stadium. 33. Boxing. 34. Because of New Zealand's sporting links with South Africa. 35. New York Yankees. 36. Vault and floor exercises. 37. The marathon. 38. Golf. 39. Pete Sampras. 40. Steve Davis. 41. Badminton. 42. Paavo Nurmi. 43. Cricket. 44. The 400m hurdles. 45. Horse Racing. 46. Skiing. 47. Mexico City. 48. Gabriela Sabatini. 49. Bobby Fischer and Boris Spassky. 50. Its annual 24-hour car race.

60s & 70s

MEDIUM - LEVEL TWO

1 What did widow Jackie K. become?

2 What was ITV's first live pop programme?

3 Where did the record-breaking runner Peter Snell come from?

4 Who was premier of Rhodesia when UDI was declared?

5 In what year was the death penalty abolished in Britain?

6 What did the L stand for in Mary Whitehouse's NVLA?

7 Who was best man at the wedding of David Bailey and Catherine Deneuve?

8 Which No. I started "The taxman's taken all my dough"?

9 Which group did away with the "magic circle" process of choosing a leader?

10 Which former boxing champion was shot dead in Soho?

11 Jan Palach set himself alight to protest against the Russian invasion of which country?

12 Who did Lulu marry on February 18 1969?

13 What was the nickname of the East End murder victim Jack McVitie?

14 What was the BBC's longest-running radio show until 1969?

15 Which line on the Underground was opened in 1969?

16 In which city did John and Yoko hold their honeymoon bed-in?

17 Which senator was involved in the car crash at Chappaquiddick?

18 Who did Ann Jones beat in the 1969 Wimbledon singles?

19 Where did the Stones give a free concert after Brian Jones's death?

20 The Queen dedicated an acre of land in Runnymede to whom?

21 What did Dr Michael Ramsay become in June 1961?

22 Who phoned Neil Armstrong on his first moon walk?

23 Barbara Hulanicki founded which store?

24 How old was Prince Charles when he was invested as Prince of Wales?

25 On which course did Tony Jacklin win the British Open in 1969?

26 Which veteran feline star of the Kattomeat adverts died in 1976?

27 Which outstanding female runner died of cancer at the age of 22?

28 What free item to schools did Education Secretary Thatcher cancel?

29 Who was Arsenal's double winning captain?

30 Who led the Madison Square Garden concert for Bangladesh?

31 Which team bought Bob Latchford from Birmingham making him Britain's costliest player?

32 Who was Randolph Hearst's

kidnapped daughter?

33   Who did Ruby Flipper replace?

34   What was Lord Mountbatten doing when he was murdered?

35   What was Gail's last name before her marriage to Brian Tilsley?

36   What did Brighton Council agree to on a section of the beach?

37   In which month did Princess Anne marry Captain Mark Phillips?

38   Singers Lyn Paul and Eve Graham went solo to break up which group?

39   What did Rolls-Royce declare in February 1971?

40   Which northern town was advertised for the vodka it produced?

41   Who was British prime minister during the Winter of Discontent?

42   Who did Virginia Wade beat in the ladies singles at Wimbledon?

43   Who wrote *Roots*, adapted as a TV blockbuster?

44   In 1978 Pope John Paul I died after roughly how long in office?

45   Who were Jilly, Kelly and Sabrina?

46   What was Saigon renamed after the North Vietnamese take over?

47   Percy Shaw passed what on to road users?

48   Where was cricket's first World Cup Final held?

49   Where was vanishing Labour MP John Stonehouse arrested?

50   What was the name of Edward Heath's Admiral's Cup yacht?

Answers to Quiz 85, Places

1. Oimyakon in Siberia. 2. Brazil, where the spoken language is Portuguese. All the others are Spanish-speaking countries. 3. Cairo. 4. Portugal. 5. Roman Catholic. 6. Hungary. 7. Wellington. 8. Ireland. 9. Louisiana. 10. Shanghai. 11. Manchuria, which is part of China. All the other states formed part of the USSR. 12. Boston. 13. Monaco. 14. The Galapagos Islands. 15. Mammoth Cave in Kentucky. 16. The Great Barrier Reef. 17. Harare. 18. Fleet Street. 19. India; the others are predominantly Moslem, whereas India is mainly Hindu. 20. Mauna Loa on Hawaii. 21. New York. 22. Sicily. 23. Norway. 24. Rome. 25. Spain. 26. Ireland. 27. Tennessee. 28. Lima. 29. Northern Ireland. 30. Lace. 31. Buenos Aires. 32. The Zambezi river. 33. Israel. 34. Queensland. 35. The Everglades. 36. Saudi Arabia. 37. New York. 38. Tobago. 39. Cuba. 40. Utah. 41. Quebec. 42. Washington D.C. 43. Manila. 44. Poland. 45. Switzerland. 46. Rome. 47. Florence. 48. London. 49. Florida. 50. South Africa

Q₈₇UIZ Costume

MEDIUM - LEVEL TWO

1 The tie originated from neckties worn by 17th-century Croatian soldiers. What were they called?

2 Name the set of petticoats worn in the 19th century under a woman's full skirt.

3 In which region would you see people wearing a kaftan?

4 What were men's hose replaced with in the 17th century?

5 In which decade did women wear shorter skirts for the first time?

6 What is the name of the scarf worn by American cowboys over their nose and mouth?

7 Name the sleeveless garment, similar to an apron, which is usually worn as an overdress?

8 What traditional headcovering did Muslim men wear?

9 Which garment of the 1920s became known as 'Oxford Bags'?

10 What was the shape of a 1920s woman's dress in the West?

11 What is the name given to long drawers for men, originating in the 1920s, which are still worn today in cold weather?

12 Name the undergarment worn by women in the late 19th and early 20th centuries to support their waistline, hips, and bust?

13 What type of hat is a sou'wester?

14 What is the name of the traditional skirt made from woven flax which is worn by the Maoris?

15 What type of skirt do the hula dancers of Hawaii wear?

16 What does an aloha shirt, a less traditional garment worn by Hawaiians, look like?

17 What are leder hosen?

18 What were pantaloons?

19 What material is a kilt usually made from?

20 What is the name given to women's trousers cut to resemble a skirt?

21 What do you call the traditional full-skirted dress from Bavaria and Austria?

22 What did the farthingale, worn by women in the 16th and 17th centuries, try to achieve?

23 What is a jumpsuit?

24 What was the purpose of wearing pattens as footwear?

25 What special feature distinguished lorgnettes from other eyeglasses?

26 What do you call the elasticated band worn around the leg to hold up a stocking?

27 How long are Bermuda shorts?

28 The arrival of which material in the 1940s made stockings much cheaper and more hard-wearing than silk?

29 Which type of shoe featuring high heels and thick soles became fashionable in the 1970s?

30 What type of footwear was a solleret?

31 What do you call a stiff, starched, circular collar, worn in the 16th and 17th centuries?

32 What sort of people wear a cassock?

33 What is the name of the rectangular linen or woollen cloak worn in Ancient Greece?

34 What colour biretta would a bishop wear?

35 Which round, rimless cap is often worn angled to one side?

36 What sort of hat is a trilby?

37 Which decade saw the introduction of the mini–skirt?

38 What is a tuxedo also called?

39 What colour tie would you normally wear with a tuxedo?

40 What type of person wears a dog collar?

41 What color is a Panama hat?

42 What is the name for a water proof overshoe?

43 What is the upper part of an espadrille usually made from?

44 In which country would a sarafan be worn?

45 What sort of dress is a chemise?

46 What type of clothing is a dashiki?

47 What is the name for a tight-fitting permeable suit worn in order to retain body heat?

48 What is a boater made from?

49 What do you call the protective glove worn with medieval armor?

50 What do you call a roll made of cloth with an opening at each end for warming your hands?

Answers to Quiz 86, 60s & 70s

1. Jackie O. (Onassis). 2. "Ready, Steady, Go!". 3. New Zealand. 4. Ian Smith. 5. 1965. 6. Listeners. 7. Mick Jagger. 8. "Sunny Afternoon" (The Kinks). 9. Conservatives. 10. Freddie Mills. 11. Czechoslovakia. 12. Maurice Gibb. 13. "The Hat". 14. "The Dales". 15. The Victoria Line. 16. Amsterdam. 17. Edward Kennedy. 18. Billie Jean King. 19. Hyde Park. 20. President Kennedy. 21. Archbishop of Canterbury. 22. Richard Nixon. 23. Biba. 24. 20. 25. Lytham St Annes. 26. Arthur. 27. Lillian Board. 28. Milk. 29. Frank McClintock. 30. George Harrison. 31. Everton. 32. Patricia Hearst. 33. Pan's People (on "Top of The Pops"). 34. Fishing. 35. Potter. 36. Naturist bathing. 37. November. 38. New Seekers. 39. It was bankrupt. 40. Warrington. 41. Jim Callaghan. 42. Betty Stove. 43. Alex Haley. 44. One month (33 days). 45. Charlie's Angels. 46. Ho Chi Minh City. 47. Invented cat's-eyes. 48. Lord's. 49. Australia. 50. Morning Cloud.

Q^{UIZ}_{88} Mountains

FOR ANSWERS SEE QUIZ NO 89

MEDIUM - LEVEL TWO

1 In which country are the Southern Alps?

2 Which is the highest mountain in the US?

3 In which mountain range is the Yosemite National Park situated?

4 Which is the highest peak of the Caucasus?

5 Mount Everest is situated on the border of which two countries?

6 Rock Creek Butte is the highest peak of which mountain range?

7 Which of the following States do the Rocky Mountains NOT cross: (a) Wyoming, (b) Montana, (c) Nebraska?

8 In which country is Kilimanjaro situated?

9 Which mountain range lies to the south of Brisbane?

10 In which country would you find the Grampian Mountains?

11 Which mountain range is situated to the south of Stuttgart in Germany?

12 Which plateau extends through South East Belgium, Luxembourg, and northern France?

13 Which is the highest peak of the Austrian Alps?

14 In which country are the Transylvanian Alps?

15 Which mountain ranges do the Carpathian Mountains link?

16 In which country is Table Mountain situated?

17 Where in Africa would you find the Ahagger mountain massif?

18 Through which countries do the Alps not extend: (a) The Czech Republic, (b) Germany, (c) Italy?

19 Jebel Toubkal is the highest peak of which mountain range?

20 The Jura Mountains extend along which border?

21 Which mountain range lies to the south of Strasbourg?

22 Which mountain range lies along the northern border of Czechoslovakia and Germany?

23 In which mountain range is the Annapurna massif situated?

24 What is Mount Godwin Austen also called?

25 In which country is Nanga Parbat situated?

26 Which is the highest mountain in Canada?

27 The Kanchenjunga is situated on the border between which two countries?

28 The Dolomites are part of which mountain range?

29 The Brenner Pass links which two countries?

30 In which part of Great Britain are the Cambrian Mountains situated?

31 Which is the second highest mountain in Africa, after Kilimanjaro?

32 Between which seas are the Caucasus mountains situated?

33 Through which of the following countries do the Himalayas not extend: (a) Pakistan, (b) Afghanistan, (c) Nepal?

34 Which is the highest mountain in Great Britain?

35 The Tatra Mountains are part of which larger mountain range?

36 Lake Geneva lies on the border of which two mountain ranges?

37 Which mountain is said to be the landing place of Noah's ark?

38 Which is the highest peak in the Americas?

39 On which continent would you find the Vinson Massif?

40 Which is the highest peak in Australia?

41 The Blue Ridge is part of which mountain range?

42 In which country does the Sierra Madre Oriental rise?

43 In which US National Park is Mount Whitney situated?

44 The Matterhorn is situated on the border of which two countries?

45 In which part of the Alps is Monte Rosa situated?

46 Which is the highest peak in Hawaii?

47 Krakatoa is situated between which two islands?

48 Which is the highest peak in Japan?

49 Lourdes, known as a place of pil grimage, is situated on the slopes of which mountain range?

50 Mount Corno is situated in which mountain range?

Answers to Quiz 87, COSTUME

1. A cravat. 2. A crinoline. 3. In North Africa and the Middle East. 4. Breeches. 5. The 1920s. 6. A bandana. 7. A pinafore. 8. A fez. 9. The wide-legged, baggy trousers which were first worn by Oxford undergraduates. 10. Long and straight with a belt lowered to the hip. 11. Long johns. 12. A corset. 13. A waterproof hat with a broad rim at the back to protect the neck. 14. A piupi. 15. A grass skirt. 16. It is short-sleeved and brightly colored and usually has a motif such as palm-trees or parrots. 17. Leather shorts, often with suspenders. 18. Long drawers worn in the 19th century. 19. A tartan wool. 20. Culottes. 21. A dirndl. 22. It tried to extend the skirt horizontally from the waist. 23. A one-piece garment consisting of a blouse with trousers attached to it. 24. To raise one's height in order to keep the feet clean in muddy streets. 25. They could be folded up. 26. A garter. 27. They end slightly above the knee. 28. Nylon. 29. Platforms. 30. None. 31. A ruff. 32. The clergy. 33. A himation. 34. Purple. 35. A beret. 36. A soft felt hat with a creased crown. 37. The 1960s. 38. A dinner jacket. 39. A black bow tie. 40. The clergy. 41. Natural. 42. A galosh. 43. Fabric. 44. Russia. 45. A loose-fitting, straight-cut dress, sometimes worn with a belt. 46. A loose, brightly-colored African garment. 47. A wet suit. 48. Straw. 49. A gauntlet. 50. A muff.

Q^{UIZ} 89 Pop Music

MEDIUM - LEVEL TWO

1 What was the first album Michael Jackson released after his million-seller "Thriller"?

2 Who wrote "South Pacific"?

3 Which singer released the album "No Jacket Required"?

4 Which English group derived their name from a Muddy Waters song?

5 With which group was Jim Morrison associated?

6 What were Jefferson Starship formerly known as?

7 Who sang the title song to the film 'Waiting to Exhale"?

8 In which musical is the song "Sixteen Going On Seventeen"?

9 With which group was Jerry Garcia associated?

10 Which group released the album "Achtung Baby"?

11 Which female singer sang the theme tune to the Bond film "GoldenEye"?

12 Who recorded the hit album "Aja"?

13 Together with which female singer did James Taylor record the song "Mockingbird"?

14 Which group released the album "Breakfast in America"?

15 In 1983 Irene Cara had a hit with "What a Feeling". From which film does the song come?

16 Who wrote the song "Raindrops Keep Falling On My Head"?

182 17 With which instrument do you

associate Jack Bruce?

18 Which film features the song "How Deep Is Your Love"?

19 Who wrote the music to "The Good, the Bad and the Ugly"?

20 Who had hits with"Him Or Me – What's It Gonna Be?", "Hungry" and "Good Thing"?

21 Which singer released the album "Born in the USA"?

22 On which original Simon & Garfunkel album would you find "The Boxer"?

23 From which musical is the song "Pick a Pocket or Two"?

24 Who wrote the songs to the film "Toy Story"?

25 Which singer released the album "Mercury Falling"?

26 Which group features Steven Tyler and Joe Perry?

27 When did the Rolling Stones have a hit with "Satisfaction"?

28 With which instrument do you associate Gheorge Zamfir?

29 Together with which male singer did Barbra Streisand record "You Don't Bring Me Flowers"?

30 Who had a hit in 1965 with"Got To Get You Off My Mind"?

31 Who wrote the song "Ev'ry Time We Say Goodbye"?

32 Which French female singer became known as the "Little Sparrow"?

33 Who had hits with "L-O-V-E Love'

and "Let's Stay Together"?

34 Which female soul singer brought out the album "I Feel For You"?

35 With which group is Beth Gibbons associated?

36 Which musical featured the songs "Summer Nights" and "You're the One That I Want"?

37 Which Walt Disney film contains the song "The Bare Necessities"?

38 Which Canadian group had a hit with "American Woman"?

39 What was the name of David Cassidy's 'family'?

40 Who was the lead singer of the Commodores?

41 Who pleaded Don't Shoot Me, I'm Only The Piano Player?

42 Who was Richard Wayne Penniman?

43 When did Dire Straits record their album "Brothers In Arms"?

44 Which female singer brought out the album "It's A Man's World"?

45 Which original Bon Jovi album contains the song "Livin' on a Prayer"?

46 What was the title of Kate Bush's debut album?

47 On which original Queen album would you find the song "Who Wants to Live Forever"?

48 Which group did Marc Almond sing with before going solo?

49 Which original Beatles Album contains the song "Strawberry Fields Forever"?

50 Which female singer released the album "Boys For Pele"?

Answers to
Quiz 88, MOUNTAINS

1. New Zealand. 2. Mount McKinley. 3. The Sierra Nevada. 4. Mount Elbrus. 5. Tibet and Nepal. 6. The Blue Mountains. 7. (c) Nebraska. 8. Tanzania. 9. The Great Dividing Range. 10. Scotland. 11. The Black Forest. 12. The Ardennes. 13. The Grossglockner. 14. Romania. 15. The Alps and the Balkans. 16. South Africa. 17. The Sahara. 18. (a) Czechoslovakia. 19. The Atlas Mountains. 20. The French–Swiss border. 21. The Vosges. 22. The Erzgebirge. 23. The Himalayas. 24. K2. 25. India (Kashmir). 26. Mount Logan. 27. India and Nepal. 28. The Alps. 29. Austria and Italy. 30. Wales. 31. Mount Kenya. 32. The Black Sea and the Caspian Sea. 33. (b) Afghanistan. 34. Ben Nevis. 35. The Carpathian Mountains. 36. The Alps and Jura Mountains. 37. Mount Ararat. 38. The Aconcagua. 39. Antarctica. 40. Mount Kosciusko. 41. The Appalachian Mountains. 42. Mexico. 43. The Sequoia National Park. 44. Italy and Switzerland. 45. The Pennine Alps. 46. Mouna Kea. 47. Java and Sumatra. 48. Fujiyama. 49. The Pyrenees. 50. The Apennines.

QUIZ 90 Science

MEDIUM - LEVEL TWO

1 Which gas is the major constituent of ordinary air?

2 At what speed do freely falling bodies descend under the influence of gravity?

3 It's said that Archimedes shouted 'Eureka!' upon discovering which scientific principle?

4 What is the popular name for an acid mixture capable of dissolving gold?

5 What does TNT stand for?

6 From what expression was the word radar derived?

7 Which Frenchman is regarded as the founder of modern chemistry?

8 What is litmus?

9 What approximate percentage of the atmosphere is oxygen?

10 What metal is found in both brass and bronze?

11 What is used to galvanize iron?

12 Which gas is well known for its smell of rotten eggs?

13 What does RAM stand for?

14 What property does cobalt have in common with iron?

15 What is thunder?

16 Of which creature are there most species on Earth?

17 What is the substance that makes plants green?

18 What is a metal composed of two or more others called?

19 The gene for having six fingers is dominant over the gene for having five fingers. True or false?

20 Are there land tides as well as sea tides?

21 What is meant by 'Panspermia'?

22 What is the name for a protein that functions as a biological catalyst?

23 What is another name for the star Polaris?

24 What is the closest spiral galaxy to the Milky Way?

25 Which is the farthest planet visible to the unaided eye?

26 Which is the largest planet?

27 Which planet is nearest the Sun?

28 Which is the most widely used of all solvents?

29 Amalthea and Io are satellites of which planet?

30 Which metal, used for jewelry, is more valuable than gold?

31 What is the speed of light?

32 How far is the Sun from Earth?

33 Is the Moon's diameter 3,327.50 km (5,324 miles), 552 km (345 miles), or 3,456 km (2,160 miles)?

34 What, in modern physics, is the name applied to an abrupt change from one energy level to another?

35 What name is given to the treat ment of food with heat to destroy disease-causing organisms?

36 What is the name given to the partial or complete obscuring, relative to a designated observer,

of one celestial body by another?

37 What is the scientific term for a state of complete emptiness?

38 In 1938 a revolutionary writing device was invented. What was it?

39 Which machine, invented by J. Murray Spangler in the early 1900s, has become a household word under another name?

40 What name is given to an artificial device used to replace a missing body part?

41 What is prophylaxis?

42 What name is given to the field of study devoted to processes that behave in a complex, apparently random way?

43 What is the process by which plants create food using sunlight as an energy source?

44 What is the process by which plants develop without chlorophyll through lack sunlight?

45 What is the material used as a base for bacterial culture media?

46 What basic laboratory tool was invented at Heidelberg University in 1850?

47 By what common name do we call a unit of power equal to 108,900 m-pounds/minute (33,000 foot-pounds/minute)?

48 What is the freezing point of water on the Celsius scale?

49 What is the freezing point of water on the Fahrenheit scale?

50 With what science do you associate the Austrian monk Gregor Mendel?

A nswers to Quiz 89, POP MUSIC

1. Bad. 2. Rodgers and Hammerstein. 3. Phil Collins. 4. The Rolling Stones. 5. The Doors. 6. Jefferson Airplane. 7. Whitney Houston. 8. The Sound of Music. 9. The Grateful Dead. 10. U2. 11. Tina Turner. 12. Steely Dan. 13. Carly Simon. 14. Supertramp. 15. Flashdance. 16. Burt Bacharach. 17. Bass. 18. Saturday Night Fever. 19. Ennio Morricone. 20. Paul Revere and the Raiders. 21. Bruce Springsteen. 22. Bridge Over Troubled Water. 23. Oliver! 24. Randy Newman. 25. Sting. 26. Stars. 27. 1965. 28. Panpipes. 29. Neil Diamond. 30. Solomon Burke. 31. Cole Porter. 32. Edith Piaf. 33. Al Green. 34. Chaka Khan. 35. Portishead. 36. Grease. 37. The Jungle Book. 38. Guess Who. 39. The Partridge Family. 40. Lionel Richie. 41. Elton John. 42. Little Richard. 43. 1985. 44. Cher. 45. Slippery When Wet. 46. The Kick Inside. 47. A Kind of Magic. 48. Soft Cell. 49. Magical Mystery Tour. 50. Tori Amos.

Q^{UIZ}_{91} Food and Drink

MEDIUM - LEVEL TWO

1 What is an essential ingredient of pilaf?

2 What is a croquette?

3 Which family does the herb angelica come from?

4 With which herb is saltimbocca flavored with?

5 What is polenta made with?

6 Which vegetables would you find in gazpacho?

7 What do you call the Spanish drink made from wine mixed with brandy, fruit juice, and sugar?

8 Which country does the wine retsina come from?

9 What type of meat would you use for Irish stew?

10 Which spice is used to flavor cevapcici?

11 What is a roulade?

12 What do you call the fatty tissues which are located around the kidneys of cattle or sheep and often used as cooking fat?

13 What part of the animal does hock come from?

14 Which fish does caviar usually come from?

15 Which vegetable is used in humus?

16 What is a profiterole filled with?

17 Where does shortbread originate?

18 What drink is a carbonade flavored with?

19 What is a tandoor used for?

20 What sort of sauce is a remoulade?

21 In which area of France are truffles grown?

22 What type of drink is stout?

23 What is a Screwdriver made with?

24 What do you call large tubes of pasta, filled with meat or cheese, and cooked in a tomato sauce?

25 What sort of tortilla is a taco?

26 What is the name of the Creole rice dish containing chicken, ham or shrimps with added herbs and spices?

27 What do you call an espresso coffee mixed or topped with frothy cream or milk?

28 What sort of fruit is an ugli?

29 Which region of France does chardonnay come from?

30 What is a gimlet made with?

31 What type of meat is prosciutto?

32 What vegetable family does calabrese (broccoli) come from?

33 Which herb is used for making pesto sauce?

34 Which country does the dish biryani come from?

35 What type of fish is a rollmop?

36 What would you make with an endive?

37 What is tofu made from?

38 Which fruit is slivovitz made from?

39 What is zwieback?

40 What is made from pinot noir and pinot blanc?

41 What is naan?

42 Which country does the chorizo sausage come from?

43 What grain is pumpernickel made from?

44 Which is the main vegetable in a spanakopita?

45 What is a brioche?

46 What sort of cake is a devil's food cake?

47 What is amaretto flavored with?

48 What type of dish is a chowder?

49 What part of the animal is a tournedos cut from?

50 What type of dish is shashlik?

A nswers to Quiz 90, Science

1. Nitrogen. 2. 9.81 m/second (32 feet/second). 3. Displacement. 4. Aqua regia. 5. Trinitrotoluene. 6. Radio detecting and ranging. 7. Antoine Lavoisier. 8. An organic dye usually used as an indicator of acidity or alkalinity. 9. 21%. 10. Copper. 11. Zinc. 12. Hydrogen sylphide. 13. Random Access Memory. 14. They can both be magnetized. 15. The crashing or booming sound produced by rapidly expanding air along the path of the electrical discharge of lightning. 16. Beetles. 17. Chlorophyll. 18. An alloy. 19. True. 20. Yes, the moon has the effect of causing movement in so-called 'solid' land. 21. The notion that life arrived on Earth from elsewhere in the universe. 22. An enzyme. 23. Polestar, North star, or polar star. 24. Andromeda. 25. Saturn. 26. Jupiter. 27. Mercury. 28. Water. 29. Jupiter. 30. Platinum. 31. A little over 297,600 km/sec (186,000 miles/sec). 32. 148,800,000 km (93,000,000 miles). 33. 3,456 km (2,160 miles). 34. A quantum leap. 35. Pasteurization. 36. An eclipse. 37. A vacuum. 38. The ball-point pen. 39. The Hoover vacuum cleaner. 40. A prosthesis. 41. Prevention of or protective treatment for disease. 42. Chaos theory. 43. Photosynthesis. 44. Etiolation. 45. Agar. 46. The Bunsen burner. 47. Horsepower. 48. 0°C. 49. 32°F. 50. Genetics.

QUIZ 92 | The Bible

MEDIUM - LEVEL TWO

1 What does the word 'Bible' actually mean?

2 What is the Pentateuch?

3 How many books are there in the Old Testament?

4 How many books are there in the Old and New Testaments together?

5 What is the name given to the 15 books which were not accepted into the Hebrew Bible?

6 What name was given to the Greek translation of the Five Books of Moses?

7 Why was the Septuagint so called?

8 Which are the oldest manuscripts of the Bible now in existence?

9 What name is given to a manuscript in the form of a modern book with writing on both sides of the page?

10 What is the Hebrew name for the Pentateuch?

11 Which two books tell the story of King David?

12 What did the writing on the wall at Belshazzar's feast say?

13 Why did Abraham lead the Hebrews into Egypt?

14 Who were the first two sons of Abraham?

15 Which is the world's oldest city?

16 Name the sons of Noah.

17 Who were the sons of Isaac and Rebekah?

18 Which prophet was cast into a den of lions?

19 Which son of David and Bathsheba was renowned for his wisdom?

20 Who had Samson's hair cut while he slept?

21 Who was the Philistine giant from Gath?

22 When the Jewish kingdom was split in two, what was the south ern part called?

23 Which two seas are connected by the River Jordan?

24 Which Babylonian king captured Jerusalem in 597 bc?

25 What was the name of the priestly sect who lived at Qumran and wrote the Dead Sea Scrolls?

26 Who led the children of Israel out of Egypt?

27 Who occupied the promised land when the Israelites arrived?

28 Deliverance from what is com memorated by the Passover?

29 Which queen came to test the wisdom of Solomon?

30 Of which nation was Sargon king?

31 Which Persian conqueror of Babylon allowed the Israelites to return home?

32 What name is given to the land between the rivers Tigris and Euphrates?

33 Who was king when Jesus was born?

34 Where is Nazareth?

35 What was the other name for the Sea of Galilee?

36 Who is regarded as the founder of Christianity?

37 Who was the first Christian martyr?

38 Name the four gospels of the New Testament.

39 What is the full name of the book often wrongly called The Book of Revelations?

40 What is the biblical significance of the number 666?

41 On which hill did the crucifixion take place?

42 Who were the magi?

43 Who lived on locusts and honey?

44 Who danced for John the Baptist's head?

45 Who were the Four Horsemen of the Apocalypse?

46 What are the gospels of Matthew, Mark, and Luke called?

47 Name three of Paul's letters.

48 What is strange about the census mentioned in the story of the nativity?

49 Which book comes after the three books of John?

50 Who was chosen to take Judas Iscariot's place amongst the Apostles?

Answers to Quiz 91, FOOD AND DRINK

1. Rice. 2. A small cake of minced food which is usually coated in breadcrumbs and fried. 3. The parsley family. 4. Sage. 5. Cornmeal. 6. Cucumbers, tomatoes, onions, and peppers. 7. Sangria. 8. Greece. 9. Lamb. 10. Paprika. 11. A slice of meat rolled around a filling. 12. Suet. 13. From the leg directly above the foot. 14. Sturgeon. 15. Chickpeas. 16. Cream. 17. Scotland. 18. Beer. 19. It is an Indian clay oven used for cooking meat and baking bread. 20. It is made of mayonnaise, chopped pickles, capers, and anchovies, and eaten cold. 21. Périgord. 22. A very dark, strong beer. 23. Vodka and orange juice. 24. Cannelloni. 25. A corn tortilla wrapped around a filling usually consisting of meat and cheese. 26. Jambalaya. 27. Cappuccino. 28. It is a cross between a grapefruit, an orange, and a tangerine. 29. Burgundy. 30. Vodka or gin and sweetened lime juice. 31. Ham. 32. The cabbage family. 33. Basil. 34. India. 35. A herring. 36. It is normally used for making salads. 37. An extract from soy beans. 38. Plums. 39. A sweetened bread which, after baking, is cut into slices and toasted. 40. Wine. 41. A type of Indian bread. 42. Spain. 43. Rye. 44. Spinach. 45. A type of bun. 46. A rich chocolate cake. 47. Almonds. 48. A soup. 49. The tenderloin. 50. Pieces of grilled meat on a skewer, often alternated with vegetables.

QUIZ 93 The USA

1 Which state is known as the 'Bluegrass State'?

2 Which is the smallest state?

3 Which river does the Ohio flow into?

4 In which year was the Constitution drawn up?

5 Which is the legislative branch of the federal government?

6 How many colonies declared their independence from Britain in 1776?

7 Which state has the highest population?

8 Which was the first permanent European settlement in the present USA?

9 Who was the seventh president?

10 Which two houses make up the Congress?

11 Which are the three largest cities in the country?

12 What is the capital of Florida?

13 Which war took place between 1835 and 1842?

14 In which part of the country do Apaches now live?

15 Which event precipitated the Mexican War?

16 What is the name given to the 11 southern states that seceded from the USA in 1860?

17 Which political party did Theodore Roosevelt stand for?

18 What is the maximum term for a US president?

19 What is the minimum age for someone to become president?

20 What is the capital of Maine?

21 Who succeeded President John F. Kennedy?

22 Which west-coast state forms its northern border with Canada?

23 What was the name of the independent candidate in the 1992 presidential election?

24 What is the name given to the domestic reform program of President Roosevelt during the Great Depression?

25 On which river is Washington D.C. situated?

26 Which festival is celebrated in New Orleans on Shrove Tuesday?

27 What is the name of the national anthem?

28 What is the capital of Alaska?

29 Geronimo was the leader of which tribe?

30 On which river is Memphis situated?

31 Where in the country can you find Creoles?

32 In which city is the John Hancock Tower?

33 What did the Volsted Act, passed in 1919, prohibit?

34 Beverly Hills and Santa Monica are part of which city?

35 Which is the principal river flowing through New Mexico?

36 Which island is situated to the

south-east of New York and contains two boroughs of New York City?

37 Which island served as the main entry station for US immigrants from 1892 to 1943?

38 Which two native American tribes were involved in The Battle of Little Bighorn?

39 What is the capital of Arkansas?

40 Which canal links New York with the Great Lakes?

41 Which holiday is celebrated on 12 October?

42 Who was president at the out break of World War II?

43 Where is the most southerly point of the USA?

44 Which is the oldest American college?

45 Which city was originally called Yerba Buena?

46 What is the name of the historical overland route from the Missouri river to the north-west?

47 Which state does Louisiana bor der on to the west?

48 What is the capital of New Mexico?

49 New York City is situated on the mouth of which river?

50 Which division of the US Department of Justice is responsible for dealing with all violations of federal law?

Answers to Quiz 92, THE BIBLE

1. It is from the Greek word for books. 2. The Five Books of Moses. 3. Thirty-six. 4. Sixty-three. 5. The Apocrypha. 6. The Septuagint. 7. Because it was the work of 70 translators. 8. Those found among the Dead Sea Scrolls. 9. A codex. 10. The Torah. 11. The First and Second Books of Samuel. 12. MENE MENE TEKEL UPHARSIN. 13. Because they were suffering from famine. 14. Ishmael and Isaac. 15. Jericho. 16. Ham, Shem, and Japheth. 17. Jacob and Esau. 18. Daniel. 19. Solomon. 20. Delilah. 21. Goliath. 22. Judah. 23. The Sea of Galilee and the Dead Sea. 24. Nebuchadnezzar II. 25. The Essenes. 26. Moses. 27. The Canaanites. 28. Death of the first born. 29. The Queen of Sheba. 30. Assyria. 31. Cyrus. 32. Mesopotamia. 33. Herod the Great. 34. Lower Galilee. 35. The Sea of Tiberias. 36. St. Paul. 37. St. Stephen. 38. Matthew, Mark, Luke, John. 39. The Revelation of St. John the Divine. 40. It is the Number of the Beast. 41. Golgotha. 42. Caspar, Balthazar, Melchior. 43. John the Baptist. 44. Salome. 45. Conquest, War, Famine, Death. 46. The Synoptic Gospels. 47. Romans, Corinthians, Galtaians, Ephesians, Philippians, Colossians, Thessalonians, Timothy, Titus, Philemon. 48. There is no mention of it in Roman records. 49. Jude. 50. Matthias.

QUIZ 94 | Recreation

MEDIUM – LEVEL TWO

1 Which side moves first in chess?

2 By what name is Hsiang Ch'i known in the west?

3 What is the casino game of Black Jack called when played for fun?

4 What feature do American foot ball, rugby, and Australian Rules football have in common?

5 Which boxer boasted he could 'float like a butterfly and sting like a bee'?

6 In which game can you 'huff'?

7 In which game might you capture a piece 'en passant'?

8 Which cousin of snooker and pool uses only three balls?

9 In which game might you play a 'full house'?

10 In which sport might you occupy the position of 'silly mid on'?

11 In which sport would you hope to score a strike?

12 In which sport would you try to avoid three strikes?

13 What name is given an American football is pitch?

14 In which game is the ball thrown with the aid of a large wicker scoop worn on the hand?

15 Where might you use ashi-waza?

16 In American football, how many men can play for each team during a single match?

17 What is the name of the 'human spider' that forms such an important part of a rugby match?

18 Rugby balls used to be made of camelskin. True or false?

19 Which very dangerous Native American game, once known as 'the little brother of war', is now played mainly by women?

20 Which is the fastest team sport?

21 What is the popular name for the place where ice hockey players are sent for breaking the rules?

22 Which popular game was invented by a Canadian clergyman using two peach baskets?

23 How many players are there in a netball team?

24 In which sport is a ball knocked across a net by hand?

25 Joe DiMaggio was a legendary player of which sport?

26 Are aluminium bats allowed in Major League baseball?

27 In baseball, spiked boots are not allowed. What are used instead?

28 In cricket, what is a sequence of six or eight balls called?

29 From what wood are cricket bats traditionally made?

30 What form of tennis was once the sport of kings?

31 Jeu de Paume was the precursor of what modern sport?

32 In which century was lawn tennis first played?

33 Which top-class tennis players now use wooden rackets?

34 Which game began with

Cambridge students using cigar boxes and champagne corks?

35 Is it true that the Chinese name for table tennis is 'ping pong'?

36 What do the tinted dots on squash balls denote?

37 In which sport do you 'tee off'?

38 By what other name is Association Football known?

39 By what geometrical-sounding name is fishing sometimes known?

40 Which ancient games were revived in Athens in 1896?

41 The Persian game 'As Nas' was combined with the French game 'Poque'. What was the resulting game called?

42 'Players bet on which slot of a rotating disk a small ball will come to rest in.' Of which game is this a definition?

43 By what other name is 'petanque' known?

44 What is the Irish game that resembles lacrosse?

45 In which Scottish game would you slide large 'stones' across ice?

46 Which Chinese game swept America as a craze in 1922?

47 Name a card game that sounds like two alcoholic drinks.

48 Which word game was originally called Criss-Cross?

49 Which popular type of puzzle first appeared in the USA in New York World?

50 Which village lying north-east of Athens gave its name to a battle and a famous race?

A nswers to Quiz 93, THE USA

1. Kentucky. 2. Rhode Island. 3. The Mississippi. 4. 1787. 5. The Congress. 6. Thirteen. 7. California. 8. St. Augustine, Florida. 9. Andrew Jackson. 10. The Senate and The House of . Representatives. 11. New York, Los Angeles and Chicago. 12. Tallahassee. 13. The Seminole War. 14. In the south-west, in particular New . Mexico and Arizona. 15. The annexation of Texas by the USA . in 1845. 16. The Confederacy. 17. The Republicans. 18. Two four-year terms. 19. Thirty-five. 20. Augusta. 21. Lyndon B. Johnson. 22. Washington. 23. Ross Perot. 24. New Deal. 25. The Potomac. 26. Mardi Gras. 27. The Star-spangled Banner. 28. Juneau. 29. The Apaches. 30. The Mississippi. 31. In the southern states, especially Louisiana. 32. Chicago. 33. The sale, manufacture and transportation of all alcoholic drinks. 34. Los Angeles. 35. The Rio Grande. 36. Long Island. 37. Ellis Island. 38. The Cheyennes and Sioux. 39. Little Rock. 40. The Erie Canal. 41. Columbus Day. 42. Franklin D. Roosevelt. 43. Death Valley, in California. 44. Harvard University. 45. San Francisco. 46. The Oregon Trail. 47. Texas. 48. Santa Fé. 49. The Hudson River. 50. The FBI (Federal Bureau of Investigation).

Q<small>UIZ</small> 95 | Food and Drink

1 What is an aubergine (eggplant) parmigiana be topped with?

2 What type of vegetable is a capsicum?

3 What is rutabaga also known as?

4 What is sushi traditionally wrapped in?

5 What type of fish is scampi?

6 Where does marsala originate from?

7 What type of food is Monterey Jack?

8 Name the cold dessert of stewed or puréed fruit mixed with cream or custard.

9 What is sake made from?

10 Which type of pepper is used as a stuffing for green olives?

11 What do you call a dish of ice-cream, with a topping of nuts, sauce or whipped cream?

12 What is a vol-au-vent usually filled with?

13 What is mayonnaise made of?

14 What is a blancmange?

15 What type of sauce would a chicken à la king be cooked in?

16 What is an alligator pear also known as?

17 What is whisky made from?

18 Which spice is sambal seasoned with?

19 What type of alcohol does a pink lady contain?

20 What type of dairy product does beef stroganoff contain?

21 What type of food is a shiitake?

22 What type of fruit is mace made from?

23 To make a Scotch egg, what is the egg wrapped in?

24 What is a meringue made of?

25 What is aquavit flavoured with?

26 What type of food is a madeleine?

27 To make beef Wellington, what is the beef covered with?

28 What type of cake is a strudel?

29 If you sauté potatoes, how do you cook them?

30 What is the main ingredient of a guacamole?

31 What is a curaçao flavoured with?

32 What type of food is a pirog?

33 What is the name for a white sauce made with butter, flour, and milk or cream?

34 What is piccalilli?

35 What is a pina colada made of?

36 Which country does Limburger cheese come from?

37 What do you call the fragrance of a wine or liqueur?

38 What does the word 'florentine' after a dish imply?

39 Which herbs is Béarnaise sauce flavoured with?

40 What type of dish is chicken jal frezi?

41 What is carob used as a substitute for?

42 What is crème de cassis made from?

43 Where does the dish teriyaki come from?

44 Which sauce are eggs Benedict topped with?

45 What do you call a mixture of flour and fat cooked together, usually as a base for sauces?

46 What sort of drink is manzanilla?

47 What part of the animal does sweetbread come from?

48 In what type of cooking would you use hoisin sauce?

49 What type of sauce is a satay usually dipped in?

50 Which part of the pig are chitterlings?

A nswers to Quiz 94, RECREATION

1. White. 2. Chinese chess. 3. Pontoon. 4. The shape of the ball. 5. Mohammad Ali. 6. Draughts or checkers. 7. Chess. 8. Billiards. 9. Poker. 10. Cricket. 11. Ten-pin bowling. 12. Baseball. 13. A gridiron. 14. Jai alai or pelota. 15. Judo. 16. 40. 17. A scrum. 18. True. 19. Lacrosse. 20. Ice hockey. 21. The sin bin. 22. Basketball. 23. Seven. 24. Volleyball. 25. Baseball. 26. No, only wooden ones. 27. Toe and heel plates screwed to the soles of their boots. 28. An over. 29. Willow. 30. Real tennis. 31. Tennis. 32. The 19th century. 33. None. 34. Table tennis. 35. Yes. 36. The speed of the ball. 37. Golf. 38. Soccer. 39. Angling. 40. The Olympics. 41. Poker. 42. Roulette. 43. Boules. 44. Hurling. 45. Curling. 46. Mah jongg. 47. Gin rummy. 48. Scrabble. 49. The crossword. 50. Marathon.

QUIZ 96 | Human Body

MEDIUM - LEVEL TWO

1 Which part of the eye controls the amount of light entering it?

2 In which organ would you find the following three bones: hammer, anvil and, stirrup?

3 Which blood vessels carry the blood away from the heart?

4 What are neurons?

5 What is the name of the membranes surrounding the brain?

6 What is the name of the nervous tissue linking the two halves of the brain?

7 Which muscle controls the bending of the arm?

8 What is the purpose of cartilage?

9 What is the name of the fluid in which the red and white blood cells are suspended?

10 What exactly do the two figures in measuring blood pressure refer to?

11 By what are muscles attached to the skeleton?

12 Which blood vessels allow blood to flow between the arteries and veins?

13 What is the main purpose of the lymphocytes?

14 What does the atrial septum divide?

15 Which hormone maintains the blood sugar level?

16 How much blood does the average person have?

17 Where is the pituitary gland situated?

18 In which part of the body would you find the phalanges?

19 In which tissue are the red blood cells produced?

20 Which is the longest bone in the body and where is it situated?

21 Which two sets of muscles are used for breathing in air?

22 What is the name of the membranes surrounding the lungs?

23 What is the windpipe also called?

24 Which muscle flexes the knee joint?

25 Which enzyme in the stomach is responsible for breaking down proteins?

26 Which organ has the function to store the bile produced by the liver?

27 Why is bile essential for the functioning of the digestive system?

28 Which organ controls the amount of sugar in the body?

29 The small intestine is made up of which three parts?

30 Which is the largest organ of the body?

31 What function does the appendix have?

32 What are the fluid contents of the small intestine called?

33 Of what smaller chemical units are proteins made up?

34 In which organ are the hepatocytes situated?

35 What is the name of the organelles responsible for cell metabolism, for example converting food into energy?

36 Which organ produces urine?

37 What do the letters DNA stand for?

38 What substance do the sebaceous glands produce?

39 How many teeth are in an adult full set?

40 Which parts of the body contain keratin?

41 What is the name of the tubes leading from the kidneys to the bladder?

42 Against what does the pigment melanin protect the skin?

43 What is the cranium?

44 What is the white part of the eye called?

45 What is the cochlea responsible for?

46 What is joined together by the corpus callosum?

47 What happens if melanocytes in the skin are clumped together?

48 In which part of the body would you find the calcaneus?

49 Which mechanism are the platelets responsible for?

50 What is the voice-box also called?

A nswers to Quiz 95, FOOD AND DRINK

1. Parmesan cheese. 2. A pepper. 3. Swede. 4. Seaweed. 5. A large shrimp. 6. Sicily. 7. A cheese. 8. A fool. 9. Fermented rice. 10. Pimento. 11. Sundae. 12. A ragout of meat or fish. 13. Egg yolk, oil, and lemon juice or vinegar. 14. A thick, sweetened and flavored milk pudding. 15. A cream sauce with peppers and mushrooms. 16. Avocado. 17. Barley. 18. Chilli. 19. Brandy and gin. 20. Sour cream. 21. A mushroom, grown in eastern Asia. 22. Nutmeg. 23. Sausagemeat and breadcrumbs. 24. Egg whites and sugar. 25. Caraway seed. 26. A cake. 27. Pâté and pastry. 28. Stewed fruit or cheese rolled up in a thin layer of pastry and baked. 29. You fry them lightly in an open pan, tossing them occasionally. 30. Avocado. 31. Orange peel. 32. A savory pastry. 33. Béchamel sauce. 34. A sort of relish. 35. Rum, creamed coconut and pineapple juice. 36. Belgium. 37. The bouquet. 38. It contains spinach. 39. Tarragon and chervil. 40. A curry. 41. Chocolate. 42. Blackcurrants. 43. Japan. 44. Hollandaise sauce. 45. A roux. 46. A sherry. 47. The pancreas. 48. Chinese cooking. 49. Peanut sauce. 50. The small intestines.

Quiz 97 Pot Luck

MEDIUM - LEVEL TWO

1 Who wrote the novel "From Russia With Love"?

2 What is the name of Rome's air port?

3 Which US political party has the donkey as its symbol?

4 In Rome, which flight of 137 stairs leads from Piazza di Spagne to the Church of the Trinita dei Monti?

5 With which sport do you associate Imran Khan?

6 Name the woman who has been prime minister of Pakistan twice.

7 Of which political party was Zhou Enlai a leader?

8 How, in olden days, did the Chinese most commonly refer to their country?

9 The name of the Australian airline QANTAS is an acronym. What does it stand for?

10 Which is the largest lake in Africa?

11 To which country does the word Singhalese refer?

12 In Asian countries, the word 'singh' is commonly used. What does it mean?

13 In which subcontinent would you hear Urdu, Hindi, and Bengali spoken as native languages?

14 Which English university city stands on the river Cam?

15 Cellist Jacqueline du Pré died of which illness?

16 Who wrote "Far From the Madding Crowd"?

17 Which organs of the body pro duce urine?

18 What substance is produced by the gall bladder?

19 What boon to gardeners was invented by Mr Budding and Mr Ferrabee?

20 Why is a mausoleum so-called?

21 What were the pre-communist rulers of Russia called?

22 What, in military terms, is a SAM?

23 Which country is the home of the Sony electronics company?

24 Which US poet broadcast Fascist propaganda during World War II?

25 What is the more formal name of London's Old Bailey?

26 Who shot John Lennon?

27 Who tried to assassinate President Ford in Sacramento?

28 Which US president withdrew US forces from Vietnam?

29 What is a locum?

30 What is the charleston?

31 Edward VIII of England abdicated to marry an American divorcee. What was her name?

32 Of which country is Vientiane the capital?

33 In which country would you find political parties called Fianna Fail and Fine Gael?

34 Which literary character made famous the phrase, 'Tomorrow is another day'?

35 What other name is used for the

Erse language?

36 Who wrote "Catch-22"?

37 In which year did the Six Day War take place?

38 Was Munich in East or West Germany?

39 Which fictional character would have made you an offer you could not refuse?

40 Whose house was moved by Pooh and Piglet?

41 What is an obsequy?

42 Who was the last woman to be hanged in Britain?

43 In which year was the Panama Canal completed?

44 What sort of music do you associate with Nashville, Tennessee?

45 Who wrote "For Whom the Bell Tolls"?

46 What is the connection between Truman Capote, Audrey Hepburn, and a morning meal?

47 How often are the Olympic Games held?

48 A funeral director is called different things in British and American English. Can you give both versions?

49 In English, we use the French phrase cul de sac to mean a street closed at one end. Why is the phrase not used in France?

50 What was tennis star Evonne Cawley's maiden name?

1. The iris. 2. The middle ear. 3. Arteries. 4. Nerve cells. 5. Meninges. 6. Corpus callosum. 7. The biceps. 8. It prevents the bones from rubbing and pressing against each other and thus wearing away. 9. Plasma. 10. The higher figure is the systolic pressure (the peak of the contraction of the heart). The second figure measures the diastolic pressure (the heart during relaxation). 11. Tendons. 12. Capillaries. 13. To fight infection. 14. The two pumps of the heart. 15. Insulin. 16. About 5 litres (10 pints). 17. At the base of the brain. 18. In the toes. 19. Bone marrow. 20. The femur, situated in the thigh. 21. The intercostal muscles in the ribs, and the diaphragm. 22. The pleura. 23. Trachea. 24. The hamstring. 25. Pepsin. 26. The gall bladder. 27. It emulsifies fat so that it can then enter the bloodstream. 28. The pancreas. 29. The duodenum, jejunum, and ileum. 30. The liver. 31. It has no function at all. 32. Chyme. 33. Amino acids. 34. The liver. 35. Mitochondria. 36. The kidneys. 37. Deoxyribonucleic acid. 38. Sebum. 39. Thirty-two. 40. Hair and nails. 41. The ureters. 42. Excessive ultraviolet radiation in the . . sunlight. 43. Eight pieces of bone that surround and protect the brain. 44. Sclera. 45. It is a part of the inner ear, responsible for hearing. 46. The two halves of the brain. 47. They show as freckles. 48. The heel. 49. The blood clotting mechanism. 50. The larynx.

QUIZ 98 80s Films

MEDIUM - LEVEL TWO

1 What relation was Danny de Vito to Arnold Schwarzenegger in their 1988 film?

2 Which Bruce starred in "Die Hard"?

3 Which singer won an Oscar for "Moonstruck"?

4 Out of which continent were Meryl Streep and Robert Redford in 1985?

5 In which film did Dustin Hoffman dress up as a woman?

6 What was Richard Gere in the film with Debra Winger?

7 What does an inventor tell Honey he has Shrunk in the 1989 movie?

8 What does ET stand for in the 1982 film?

9 What sort of Attraction was there between Michael Douglas and Glenn Close?

10 Which bored housewife Shirley had an unforgettable Greek holiday?

11 Which disfigured Man did John Hurt portray in the 1980 film?

12 Which film told the story of two athletes in the 1924 Olympics?

13 What is Australian adventurer Mick Dundee's nickname?

14 Which adventurer Indiana was played by Harrison Ford?

15 Which Indian leader was played by Ben Kingsley?

16 What sort of Busters were Dan Aykroyd and Sigourney Weaver?

17 Which composer did Tom Hulse play in "Amadeus"?

18 Which film with Bob Hoskins is also the name of a painting?

19 Which former actor became president of the USA in 1980?

20 What was the Fish Called in the 1988 movie?

21 Which Naked film was the first in the series with Leslie Nielsen?

22 Who played James Bond in "For Your Eyes Only"?

23 What Strikes Back in the 1980 film?

24 Where was Eddie Murphy a Cop in the film series?

25 Where was Michael J. Fox Back to in 1985?

26 The Return of what was the sixth film in the "Star Wars" series?

27 Which US pop superstar starred in "Moonwalker"?

28 Which cartoon Rabbit was Framed in 1988?

29 Which famous ship did they try to Raise in the 1980 film?

30 How many Men looked after Baby in 1987?

31 Which Attenborough brother directed "Gandhi"?

32 What is the nationality of the hero of "Crocodile Dundee"?

33 Which Raging animal is in the title of the 1980 De Niro film?

34 The Return of what was the

third of the "Star Wars" trilogy?

35 Whose Choice won Meryl Streep an Oscar in 1982?

36 Which British film was about the 1924 Olympics?

37 The Adventures of which Baron proved to be one of the greatest cinematic flops in history?

38 Which Crusade featured in the title of the 1989 "Indiana Jones" movie?

39 In which city does "Beverly Hills Cop" take place?

40 What sort of People were the stars of the 1980 Donald Sutherland film?

41 Which Henry and Katharine won Oscars for "On Golden Pond"?

42 In which film did Bob Hoskins play opposite a cartoon character?

43 Who renewed his battle against the Joker in 1989?

44 How many Men starred with a baby in the 1987 movie?

45 In which 1982 film did Dustin Hoffman appear in drag?

46 In which US state was the Best Little Whorehouse in 1982?

47 Which organization is "Married to the Mob" about?

48 Which country did the DJ say Good Morning to in the 1987 film?

49 Which continent featured in the Robert Redford/Meryl Streep film about Karen Blixen?

50 Whom was the chauffeur Driving in the 1989 film?

1. Ian Fleming. 2. Leonardo da Vinci. 3. The Republicans. 4. The Spanish Steps. 5. Cricket. 6. Benazir Bhutto. 7. The Chinese Communist party. 8. The Middle Kingdom. 9. Queensland and Northern Territories Air Service. 10. Lake Victoria. 11. Sri Lanka. 12. Lion. 13. The Indian subcontinent. 14. Cambridge. 15. Multiple sclerosis. 16. Thomas Hardy. 17. The kidneys. 18. Bile. 19. The lawn mower. 20. The first monument of this kind was built at Halicarnassus to house the body of Mausolus. 21. Tsars and Tsarinas. 22. A surface-to-air-missile. 23. Japan. 24. Ezra Pound. 25. The Central Criminal Court. 26. Mark Chapman. 27. Lynette (Squeaky) Fromm. 28. Richard Nixon. 29. Someone who deputizes for a doctor or clergyman. 30. A dance. 31. Wallis Simpson. 32. Laos. 33. Republic of Ireland. 34. Scarlett O'Hara in Gone With the Wind. 35. Gaelic. 36. Joseph Heller. 37. 1967. 38. West. 39. The Godfather. 40. Eeyore. 41. A funeral rite or ceremony. 42. Ruth Ellis. 43. 1914. 44. Country and western. 45. Ernest Hemingway. 46. Breakfast at Tiffany's; Capote wrote the novel, Hepburn played the lead in the film. 47. Every four years. 48. Undertaker and mortician. 49. Cul is a vulgar word for buttocks. 50. Goolagong.

Quiz 99 Around Europe

MEDIUM - LEVEL TWO

1 Which country's capital is Tirana?

2 Where is a passion play staged every ten years?

3 Which state was Macedonia part of from 1945 to 1991?

4 Which island holds the George Cross?

5 Which country's highest mountain is the Grossglockner?

6 Which countries are on the Iberian Peninsula?

7 Where is The Netherlands' seat of government and administration?

8 What are the Dardanelles and where are they?

9 Which southern German city is famous for its October beer festival?

10 Which country is called Elleniki Dimokratia or Hellenic Republic?

11 Which country's chief river is the Po?

12 Which country, whose capital is Vaduz, has no armed forces?

13 Which sea lies to the north of Poland?

14 In which four countries are the Alps?

15 Which country covers 10% of the globe's land surface?

16 By what English name is Köln known?

17 Which country's landscape is made up of volcanoes and geysers?

18 Between which countries does the Skagerrak lie?

19 What are Bessarabia, Moldavia and a former part of the USSR now known as?

20 Which country has had a prime minister called Wim Kok?

21 Albert II became king of which country in 1993?

22 A region of eastern France has a girl's name with another girl's name as its capital. What are they?

23 Which country do Greenland and the Faeroe Islands belong to?

24 What is France's highest point?

25 Whose upper house of Parliament is called the Bundesrat?

26 Which country's currency is the lev?

27 What are the two official languages of Finland?

28 Which aid organization's emblem is the Swiss flag with its colours reversed?

29 Which Portuguese province borders Spain and the Atlantic Ocean?

30 Which is Europe's largest country after Russia?

31 In which city is the largest Christian church in the world?

32 What is the official home of the French President?

33 On which island is Ajaccio?

34 What is the French town of Limoges famous for?

35 Which part of Paris is famous as the artists' quarter?

36 Where is the European Court of Justice?

37 Ibiza and Majorca are part of which island group?

38 The Oise and the Marne are tributaries of which river?

39 Where is the Abbey Theatre?

40 What is Germany's highest mountain?

41 On which river does Florence stand?

42 Which Mediterranean island was the HQ of the Knights of St John?

43 Which country has most European neighbours?

44 The RER is part of which city's underground system?

45 The Azores belong to which European country?

46 How many Benelux countries are there?

47 Andorra is among which mountains?

48 Piraeus is the port of which city?

49 In which country is Lake Garda?

50 Where does the river Loire flow into the Atlantic?

Answers to Quiz 98, 80s Films

1. Twin. 2. Willis. 3. Cher. 4. Africa. 5. Tootsie. 6. An Officer and A Gentleman. 7. The Kids. 8. Extra Terrestrial. 9. Fatal. 10. Valentine. 11. Elephant Man. 12. Chariots of Fire. 13. Crocodile. 14. Jones. 15. Gandhi. 16. Ghost. 17. Mozart. 18. Mona Lisa. 19. Ronald Reagan. 20. Wanda. 21. Naked Gun. 22. Roger Moore. 23. The Empire. 24. Beverly Hills. 25. The Future. 26. The Jedi. 27. Michael Jackson. 28. Roger. 29. The Titanic. 30. Three. 31. Richard. 32. Australian. 33. Bull. 34. The Jedi. 35. Sophie's. 36. Chariots of Fire. 37. Munchhausen. 38. Last. 39. Los Angeles. 40. Ordinary. 41. Fonda, Hepburn. 42. Who Framed Roger Rabbit?. 43. Batman. 44. Three. 45. Tootsie. 46. Texas. 47. Mafia. 48. Vietnam. 49. Africa. 50. Miss Daisy.

Quiz 100 Pot Luck

UIZ 100

MEDIUM - LEVEL TWO

1. Which swimmer won seven gold medals at the 1972 Olympics?

2. What is the zodiac sign of the Archer?

3. Which Palace in London started a television service?

4. Who had a No 1 hit with the song "Imagine"?

5. Which brass musical instrument shares its name with an ice-cream?

6. What is another name for the plant woodbine?

7. Which university featured Hugh Laurie, Tony Slattery and Emma Thompson in its 1981 revue?

8. What type of pre-wedding party is for women only?

9. What is the cord high above the ground which acrobats perform on?

10. What are pipistrelles?

11. Which nickname did saxophonist Julian Adderley acquire?

12. Who wrote "Solo", "Butterflies" and "Luv"?

13. It's a tail lamp in the USA, what's this part of the car called in the UK?

14. Who wrote "Lord Jim"?

15. St Albans started and Bosworth finished which hostilities?

16. Which Concern is a charity about the needs of the elderly?

17. In which police drama was Stick a source of information on criminal activity?

18. Which group recorded "I'm The Urban Spaceman"?

19. In which part of Germany might you find a chocolate gâteau with cream and cherries?

20. What type of food is canneloni?

21. How many laps are completed in a speedway race?

22. What was the title of Pearl Jam's first album?

23. In which TV series did Marilyn have an Uncle Herman?

24. Where are the headquarters of the Rugby Union?

25. Which fictional pirate had a bosun named Smee?

26. What is the theme song in the cartoon "The Snowman"?

27. Which bird has the Latin name *Troglodytes troglodytes*?

28. Who gives his name to Radio 2's "News Huddlines"?

29. In which sport did Neal Adams win Olympic medals?

30. Who is Victoria Wood's comic partner?

31. "I Got Plenty of Nuthin'" comes from which Gershwin work?

32. Who answers the phone by saying, "the lady of the house speaking"?

33. What would you find in an arboretum?

34. Who recorded the album "12 Deadly Cyns ... And Then Some"?

35 Which record label turned down The Beatles?

36 In which country is the dong used as currency?

37 What line goes before the line, "In the windmills of you mind"?

38 What is the antirrhinum more commonly known as?

39 Who was Queen of England for nine days before she was beheaded?

40 Which country has had two kings called Carol on the throne this century?

41 On TV, what type of shop does Des Barnes work in?

42 Who created the series "Prime Suspect"?

43 What's the surname of cartoon hero Quick Draw?

44 What colour is muscovado sugar?

45 In which unusual way does Yorick first appear on stage in "Hamlet"?

46 How many sides has a cube?

47 What is the currency of Israel?

48 Who created the crazy Captain Kremmen?

49 Which major river flows through Bristol?

50 What is the surname of rugby players Tony and Rory?

A nswers to
Quiz 99, AROUND EUROPE

1. Albania. 2. Oberammergau. 3. Yugoslavia. 4. Malta. 5. Austria's. 6. Spain and Portugal. 7. The Hague. 8. Strait, Turkey. 9. Munich. 10. Greece. 11. Italy. 12. Liechstenstein. 13. Baltic. 14. France, Italy, Switzerland and Austria. 15. Russia. 16. Cologne. 17. Iceland. 18. Denmark and Norway. 19. Moldova. 20. The Netherlands. 21. Belgium. 22. Lorraine and Nancy. 23. Denmark. 24. Mont Blanc. 25. Germany's. 26. Bulgaria. 27. Finnish and Swedish. 28. Red Cross. 29. The Algarve. 30. Ukraine. 31. Rome. 32. Elysee Palace. 33. Corsica. 34. Porcelain. 35. Montmartre. 36. Luxembourg. 37. Balearics. 38. Seine. 39. Dublin. 40. Zugspitze. 41. Arno. 42 Malta. 43. Germany (Six). 44. Paris. 45. Portugal. 46. Three. 47. Pyrenees. 48. Athens. 49. Italy. 50. Nantes.

Q UIZ 101 | Space

1 Which planet appears brightest to the naked eye?

2 What creatures were Laska and Beny, who went into space in 1958?

3 Which space first was Vladimir Komarov in 1967?

4 Who first predicted correctly the intermittent return of a famous comet?

5 In which US state is the Keck Telescope?

6 Which planet's moons have names of Shakespearean characters?

7 How are Corona Australis and Corona Borealis also known?

8 How many Apollo missions resulted in successful moon landings?

9 When the Earth or the moon enters the other's shadow what is it called?

10 Which is the only sign of the zodiac named after two living things?

11 Jodrell Bank is the observatory of which university?

12 Which planet did Johann Galle discover in 1846?

13 What is the system of numbering asteroids?

14 Which "Star Trek" character is asteroid No. 2309 named after?

15 Whose spacecraft was called *Vostok VI*?

16 In moon exploration what was EVA?

17 Which planet lies between Venus and Mars?

18 How many orbits of the Earth did Gagarin make in *Vostok I*?

19 What are the Northern Lights also known as?

20 Ganymede and Io are moons of which planet?

21 How long does it take the moon to complete a revolution of Earth?

22 Which planet did Clyde Tombaugh discover in 1930?

23 Which planet's rings and moons were photographed by *Voyager I* in 1980?

24 Which theory states that the universe came into being as a result of an explosion?

25 What does the abbreviation 'ly' stand for?

26 Which planet has two moons called Phobos and Demos?

27 In relation to the sun in which direction does a comet's tail point?

28 Which planet in our solar system is slightly smaller than Earth?

29 What is the nearest star to our sun?

30 The sidereal period is the time it takes a planet to orbit what?

31 Which planet is closest to the sun?

32 Which Big theory explains the formation of the universe?

33 What is another name for the star constellation the Plough?

34 Which Helen became the first Briton in space?

35 What is the term for a giant group of stars held together by gravity?

36 In 1981, *Columbia I* was the first flight of which distinctive craft?

37 What can be a red dwarf or a white dwarf?

38 Which planet is the largest in our solar system?

39 Who or what was Hale-Bopp?

40 In 1986, what happened to *Challenger 52* after take-off?

41 Cape Canaveral took on board the name of which US President?

42 Where is the Sea of Tranquillity?

43 What is it that keeps planets moving round the sun?

44 Tiros, Echo and Sputnik were types of what?

45 What is the name for the study of the structure of the universe?

46 Which John was the first American to orbit Earth?

47 What was the name of the project that first put man on the moon?

48 Alphabetically, which is last in the list of planets in our solar system?

49 What is Yuri Gagarin's famous first?

50 How long does it take the Earth to travel round the sun?

A nswers to Quiz 100, POT LUCK

1. Mark Spitz. 2. Sagittarius. 3. Alexandra. 4. John Lennon. 5. Cornet. 6. Honeysuckle. 7. Cambridge. 8. Hen party. 9. Tightrope. 10. Small bat. 11. Cannonball. 12. Carla Laine. 13. Rear light. 14. Joseph Conrad. 15. War of the Roses. 16. Age Concern. 17. Spender. 18. The Bonzo Dog Doo-Dah Band. 19. Black Forest. 20. Pasta. 21. Four. 22. Ten. 23. The Munsters. 24. Twickenham. 25. Captain Hook. 26. Walking in the Air. 27. Wren. 28. Roy Hudd. 29. Judo. 30. Julie Walters. 31. Porgy and Bess. 32. Hyacinth Bouquet. 33. Trees. 34. Cyndi Lauper. 35. Decca. 36. Vietnam. 37. Like the circles that you find. 38. Snapdragon. 39. Lady Jane Grey. 40. Romania. 41. Betting shop. 42. Lynda La Plante. 43. McGraw. 44. Brown. 45. Appears as a skull picked up by Hamlet. 46. Six. 47. Shekel. 48. Kenny Everett. 49. Avon. 50. Underwood.

QUIZ 102 Pot Luck

MEDIUM – LEVEL TWO

1   What is the national flower of Austria?

2   Who played Remmington Steele?

3   Which John plays snooker in "Big Break"?

4   What was the earlier name of Cape Canaveral?

5   What does the "EastEnders" Deals On Wheels sell?

6   Which monarch is credited with writing "Greensleeves"?

7   Which Jill teamed up with Nick Ross to present "Crimewatch UK"?

8   Which spiky tree has the scientific name *Ilex aquifolium*?

9   How many old pence were there in £1?

10 Which TV sleuth has the car registration number ST1?

11 In which month is St Patrick's Day?

12 The song starting, "Starry, starry night" is about whom?

13 Which pre-decimal coin do you shove in a table game?

14 Which is the most famous restaurant in the fictitious town of Middleton?

15 What did German botanist Leonhard Fuchs give his name to?

16 Curtly Ambrose plays international cricket for which team?

17 Which name is shared by actress Elizabeth and snooker star Dennis?

18 What sort of quick writing did Pitman invent?

19 What are Marty Pellow, Graeme Clark, Tom Cunningham and Neil Mitchell better known as?

20 What's the link between the Boy Scouts and Uncle Scar?

21 What is dried in an oast house?

22 Who wrote "Hotel"?

23 Which great English batsmen had the initials M.C.C.?

24 What is a young kangaroo called?

25 Which major golf championship is decided by a four-hole playoff?

26 Which programme started with the words, "There is nothing wrong with your television set...."?

27 Historically, what is the name of Japan's warrior class?

28 Which sport is Chris Boardman famous for?

29 Which Australian had a hit with "I Should Be So Lucky"?

30 Which fantasy game has its name made up of places of imprisonment and legendary creatures?

31 What is a smolt?

32 Which song contains the words,"If you lose your teeth when you're out to dine borrow mine!"

33 Which country is a car from if it has the international registration

208

letters MEX?

34 Who came first as monarch, Queen Elizabeth I or Henry II?

35 The Charge of the Light Brigade took place during which battle?

36 In snooker, how many points are scored by potting the yellow ball?

37 Cu is the symbol of which chemical element?

38 Which soap pub sells Newton and Ridley?

39 What is the first month of the year to have exactly 31 days and follow a month of 31 days?

40 What are dried plums called?

41 In the past, which animal did doctors use to drain blood from the sick?

42 Who recorded the album "Post"?

43 What is the word for a group of porpoises?

44 What are the two main flavours in a banoffee pie?

45 What sort of bird was Edd, the 1992 British Olympic mascot?

46 What is the medical name for dizziness due to heights?

47 Which county shares its name with a make-up selling lady?

48 On a map, what are lines called that join places of equal height above sea level?

49 How many pints in three quarts?

50 What is the name of TV cook Floyd?

Answers to Quiz 101, SPACE

1. Venus. 2. Mice. 3. First human fatality. 4. Halley. 5. Hawaii. 6. Uranus. 7. Southern Crown and Northern Crown. 8. Six. 9. Eclipse. 10. Gemini. 11. Manchester. 12. Neptune. 13. Order of discovery. 14. Mr Spock. 15. Valentina Tereshkova. 16. Extra Vehicular Activity. 17. Earth. 18. One. 19. Aurora Borealis. 20. Jupiter. 21. 27.3 days. 22. Pluto. 23. Saturn. 24. Big Bang Theory. 25. Light year. 26. Mars. 27. Away from it. 28. Venus. 29. Proxima Centauri. 30. The Sun. 31. Mercury. 32. Big Bang. 33. Ursa Major (the Great Bear). 34. Sharman. 35. Galaxy. 36. Space Shuttle. 37. Star. 38. Jupiter. 39. Comet. 40. It exploded. 41. Kennedy. 42. The Moon. 43. Gravity. 44. Satellites. 45. Cosmology. 46. Glenn. 47. Apollo. 48. Uranus. 49. First man in space. 50. A year.

QUIZ 103 The 80s

1 Which Alfred, a master film maker, died in 1980?

2 What was Southern Rhodesia renamed?

3 Which crack force stormed the Iranian Embassy in London in 1980?

4 Lech Walesa led strikers in which country?

5 Which Beatle was shot dead in New York?

6 What name was given to murderer Peter Sutcliffe?

7 Which former Hollywood actor became US President?

8 Which MP Edwina became "Eggwina" after a salmonella scare?

9 Over 250 people died in an air crash at which Scottish town?

10 What was Lester Piggott sent to jail for avoiding?

11 What natural disaster hit Armenia in 1988?

12 What topped 3,000,000 in Britain for the first time since the 1930s?

13 Who became a princess by marrying Prince Charles?

14 In which city did the Barbican arts centre open?

15 Which Islands were the cause of a war between Britain and Argentina?

16 Whose London bedroom did Michael Fagin break into?

17 What was "The Mary Rose" which reappeared after 400 years?

18 Which Neil became leader of the Labour Party in 1983?

19 In 1988 Mitterrand was re-elected president of which country?

20 What name was given to young upwardly mobile persons?

21 Which Colonel Oliver starred in the US "Irongate" court hearing?

22 How many general elections did Thatcher win in the 1980s?

23 What was the "The Herald Of Free Enterprise" which met disaster in 1987?

24 Which stout company was implicated in a share scandal?

25 President "Baby Doc" fled from which country?

26 Which Mikhail became Soviet leader in 1985?

27 Bob Geldof organized Live Aid to provide food for which country?

28 What was Piper Alpha?

29 Which George was elected US president?

30 Which cabinet minister Cecil was forced to resign after his jilted mistress told her side of events to the press?

31 Which British jockey was jailed for tax evasion in 1987?

32 General Galtieri was ousted as president of which country?

33 In which month was the hurricane that swept Britain?

34 Which London race was held for the first time?

35 Who founded of Band Aid?

36 The Solidarity movement opposed communists in which country?

37 Which England cricket captain rowed with a Pakistani umpire?

38 Which Derby winning horse was kidnapped while in Ireland?

39 Which ex-movie actor became President of the US?

40 The IRA bombed a Tory Party conference at which seaside venue?

41 Which Fatima won Olympic gold for Britain in the javelin?

42 Which Michael became leader of the Labour Party?

43 Young upwardly mobile persons became known as what?

44 Where were Prince Charles and Lady Diana Spencer married?

45 Which David stood down as Liberal leader in 1988?

46 President Sadat of which country was assasinated?

47 Which John ended Borg's Wimbledon dominance?

48 Who was the special representative of the Archbishop of Canterbury taken hostage in Beirut?

49 What did the D stand for in the newly formed political party?

50 Which Michael took over as head of Channel Four?

1. Edelweiss. 2. Pierce Brosnan. 3. Virgo. 4. Cape Kennedy. 5. Cars. 6. Henry VIII. 7. Dando. 8. Holly. 9. 240. 10. The Saint. 11. March. 12. Vincent Van Gogh (By Don McLean). 13 .Ha'penny. 14. Pie In the Sky. 15. Fuchsia. 16. West Indies. 17. Taylor. 18. Shorthand. 19. Wet Wet Wet. 20. Be prepared. Motto of the Boy Scouts, song of Scar. 21. Hops. 22. Arthur Hailey. 23. Colin Cowdrey. 24. Joey. 25. British Open. 26. The Outer Limits. 27. Samurai. 28. Cycling. 29. Kylie Minogue. 30. Dungeons and Dragons. 31. A young salmon. 32. Friendship (From Anything Goes). 33. Mexico. 34. Henry II. 35. Balaclava. 36. Two. 37. Copper. 38. Rovers' Return. 39. August. 40. Prunes. 41. Leech. 42. Björk. 43. School. 44. Banana and toffee. 45. Duck. 46. Vertigo. 47. Avon. 48. Contour lines. 49. Six. 50. Keith.

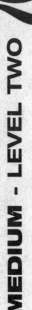QUIZ 104 | The 40s & 50s

MEDIUM - LEVEL TWO

1 Which Winston took over as prime minister in 1940?

2 Who was the German leader throughout World War II?

3 What name was given to the persistent air attack on London?

4 What does POW stand for?

5 Who was known as the Forces' Sweetheart?

6 What was the popular name for the Home Guard ?

7 Which country was Stalin leader of?

8 Which continent is El Alamein in?

9 In which country did the D Day landings take place?

10 V-E Day commemorated victory on which continent?

11 World War II ended in which year?

12 Whose engagement to Philip Mountbatten was announced in 1947?

13 Which Jewish state was founded in 1948?

14 Which competition did Miss Sweden win the first of in 1951?

15 Which type of denim trousers took Britain by storm in 1955?

16 Which future US president did Jacqueline Bouvier marry in 1953?

17 Which country launched the first satellite – Sputnik 1 – in space?

18 What was climbed by Edmund Hillary and Tensing in 1953?

19 Which craft which floats on an air cushion was invented in 1958?

20 What type of prize-winning Bonds were introduced?

21 Which large plastic hoop became a sports craze in the 1950s?

22 Which small car did Austin and Morris launch in 1959?

23 What was the name of the London to Birmingham motorway?

24 Which word for 13- to 19-year olds was first coined in the 1950s?

25 A frothy version of which non-alcoholic drink became popular in this era?

26 What did Billy Butlin found in the 1950s?

27 What type of parking payment machine was introduced in London?

28 Where did spies Burgess, Maclean and Philby defect to?

29 Which type of 1950s music used a washboard?

30 What did CND marchers on the way to Aldermaston want to ban?

31 In 1959, which party was elected for the third time in a row in Britain?

32 Which Donald set a world water speed record in the Lake District?

33 Which monarch died at

34 Sandringham in 1952?

34 "The Mousetrap" opened its London stage run, but who wrote it?

35 Colonel Nasser nationalized which canal?

36 The first of which contest was won by a woman from Sweden in 1951?

37 Which American evangelist Billy led a London crusade?

38 Which 77-year-old was returned as British Prime Minister?

39 Which Sir Gordon won the Derby for the first time?

40 Which Anthony became British Prime Minister in the 50s?

41 "Lord of the Flies" was written by which author William?

42 How did James Dean die?

43 Who died in the 50s and was played on film by Madonna in the 90s?

44 What was the peak of Edmund Hilary's achievements in 1953?

45 Which film classification was introduced to show films were unsuitable for the under 16s?

46 Which Rocky retired undefeated as a professional boxer?

47 Which character in comics was the "Pilot Of The Future"?

48 Robert Menzies was PM of which country throughout the 50s?

49 Fidel Castro seized power in which country?

50 What, according to Marilyn Monroe, were a girl's best friend?

Answers to Quiz 103, THE 80s

1. Hitchcock. 2. Zimbabwe. 3. SAS. 4. Poland. 5. John Lennon. 6. Yorkshire Ripper. 7. Ronald Reagan. 8. Edwina Currie. 9. Lockerbie. 10. Paying income tax. 11. Earthquake. 12. Unemployment. 13. Lady Diana Spencer. 14. London. 15. Falkland. 16. Queen Elizabeth II's. 17. A ship. 18. Kinnock. 19. France. 20. Yuppies. 21. North. 22. Two. 23. Car ferry. 24. Guinness. 25. Haiti. 26. Gorbachev. 27. Ethiopia. 28. Oil rig. 29. Bush. 30. Parkinson. 31. Lester Piggott. 32. Argentina. 33. October. 34. Marathon. 35. Bob Geldof. 36. Poland. 37. Mike Gatting. 38. Shergar. 39. Ronald Reagan. 40. Brighton. 41. Whitbread. 42. Foot. 43. Yuppies. 44. London. 45. Steel. 46. Egypt. 47. McEnroe. 48. Terry Waite. 49. Democrat. 50. Grade.

QUIZ 105 | Pot Luck

1 What kind of dancer was Mr Bojangles?

2 Which William featured as a team captain in "A Question of Sport"?

3 Where did William III defeat a French and Irish army in 1690?

4 Which famous novelist's middle name was Sydenstricker?

5 What was American inventor Thomas Edison's middle name?

6 What does hydrogen combine with to form water?

7 Where in the House of Lords do peers with no party loyalties sit?

8 What is the northernmost point of the British mainland?

9 Which cartoon cat is the creation of Jim Davis?

10 What is the process by which plants use light to make food?

11 Which branch of medical science is concerned with muscle?

12 Which actor's real name was Reginald Carey?

13 Prince George of Denmark was the husband of which English queen?

14 What was the true vocation of the detective in the stories by G. K. Chesterton?

15 In darts, who won the World Masters five times between 1977 and 1984?

16 Whom did Orpheus attempt to rescue from the underworld?

17 In the song, how many little girls were in the back seat a-kissin' and a-huggin' with Fred?

18 What does ENO stand for?

19 A plant produced by crossing different species is known as what?

20 What was the Birmingham Royal Ballet previously known as?

21 Which cartoon character has a tattoo of an anchor on his arm?

22 On what day in 1939 did Britain declare war on Germany?

23 Which French writer lived with the composer Chopin?

24 Which programme has Judith Harn and Carol Vorderman presented?

25 What is the most abundant gas in the atmosphere?

26 Who was the first woman elected to the British Parliament?

27 Where on the human body is the skin the thinnest?

28 What breed originated in the 1850s when a greyhound was mated with an Irish wolfhound?

29 Which advertiser says, "We care because you do"?

30 Which "ology" is concerned with the study and treatment of crime?

31 Whose famous theorem is concerned with the sums of the squares of the sides of right-angled triangles?

32 What was "Mastermind" winner Fred Housego's job?

33 Whom did Neil Kinnock succeed as leader of the Labour party?

34 What relation was Mary I to Elizabeth I?

35 In which suburb was "The Good Life" set?

36 Which ocean lies to the north of Russia?

37 In which mythology does Yggdrasil feature?

38 What did the "S" stand for in Harry S. Truman?

39 Which country is Afrika Bambaataa from?

40 What is *Cortaderia selloana* better known as?

41 Of which ballet is Prince Siegfried hero?

42 What was William Gladstone's middle name?

43 Who led the British forces during the Siege of Mafeking?

44 Who wrote "The Thorn Birds"?

45 In which decade did John Logie Baird invent television?

46 What gas is given off by pouring dilute sulphuric acid on to granulated zinc?

47 Who produces "the appliance of science"?

48 What colour is the "This Is Your Life" book

49 What is another name for the Russian wolfhound?

50 What is the boiling point of water on the Fahrenheit Scale?

1. Churchill. 2. Hitler. 3. The Blitz. 4. Prisoner of war. 5. Vera Lynn. 6. Dad's Army. 7. USSR. 8. Africa. 9. France. 10. Europe. 11. 1945. 12. Princess Elizabeth. 13. Israel. 14. Miss World. 15. Jeans. 16. John F. Kennedy. 17. Russia. 18. Everest. 19. Hovercraft. 20. Premium Bonds. 21. Hula hoop. 22. Mini. 23. M1. 24. Teenagers. 25. Coffee. 26. Holiday camps. 27. Meters. 28. USSR. 29. Skiffle. 30. The Bomb. 31. Conservative. 32. Campbell. 33. George VI. 34. Agatha Christie. 35. Suez. 36. Miss World. 37. Graham. 38. Winston Churchill. 39. Richards. 40. Eden. 41. Golding. 42. Car crash. 43. Eva Péron (Evita). 44. Reaching Everest's summit. 45. X certificate. 46. Marciano. 47. Dan Dare. 48. Australia. 49. Cuba. 40. Diamonds.

Game Shows

MEDIUM - LEVEL TWO

1 Which game show is based on snooker?

2 Where are prizes passed through on a conveyor belt?

3 Which show's biggest prizes are on the gold run?

4 Which word and numbers game show was the first programme on Channel 4?

5 Who preceded Les Dawson as host of "Blankety Blank"?

6 Which Cilla Black show has girls and guys choosing unseen partners?

7 Which show is based on a game of darts?

8 Which show has famous folk answering questions sitting in boxes?

9 Which board game inspired a TV whodunnit show?

10 What type of Maze was presented by Richard O'Brien?

11 Whose Fortunes are won in the show presented by Les Dennis?

12 Which Factor is a contest of physical and mental agility?

13 Who followed Bruce Forsyth as host of "You Bet!"?

14 Which DJ Nicky hosts "Wheel of Fortune"?

15 Who was ready for a Challenge and took part in a helicopter-oriented "Treasure Hunt"?

16 What must celebrities look through in the show with David Frost?

17 Which Addicts are quizzed by Noel Edmonds?

18 Which Michael presents "Strike It Lucky"?

19 Which show tests contestants on what things cost in the shops?

20 What must you Play Right in the show with Bruce Forsyth?

21 Which international show was also called "Jeux Sans Frontières"?

22 Which show was based on the parlour game charades?

23 Which Roy presents "Catchphrase"?

24 What must Every Second do in the show with Paul Daniels?

25 In which show might you compete with Amazon, Rhino, Jet and Wolf?

26 What might you Raise in the show with Bob Holness?

27 Which Phillip presents "Talking Telephone Numbers"?

28 Who presents "Masterchef"?

29 Which Des presented the revamped "Take Your Pick"?

30 Chris Evans told his audience, Don't Forget Your what?

31 Who presents "Fifteen To One"?

32 What was top prize on Anthea Turner's "Turner Round the World"?

33 Which Channel 4 show was devised and presented by Tim

Vine?

34 What is the name of Channel 5's gardening quiz?

35 Who was host for the first series of "The Other Half"?

36 How many contestants were there on each show of "Blankety Blank"?

37 Which show handed out a bendy Bully?

38 Who was the first female presenter of "Busman's Holiday"?

39 Who hosted "Call My Bluff" in the late 90s?

40 Who was the first presenter of "Celebrity Squares"?

41 Which show has been hosted by Richard Madeley and Chris Tarrant?

42 Which show did Armand Jammot create?

43 Who did Ed Tudor-Pole replace in "The Crystal Maze"?

44 What was the top prize in "Double Your Money"?

45 Which quiz show had a dummy keyboard?

46 Which late afternoon quiz is hosted by Martyn Lewis?

47 Who was the second hostess on "The Generation Game"?

48 Who succeeded Bob Monkhouse as presenter of "Family Fortunes"?

49 Who originally recorded the theme song to "Whatever You Want"?

50 What shape are the letter blocks in "Blockbusters"?

A nswers to Quiz 105, Pot Luck

1. A tap dancer. 2. Bill Beaumont. 3. At the Battle of the Boyne. 4. Pearl S. Buck. 5. Alva. 6. Oxygen. 7. On the cross benches. 8. Dunnet Head. 9. Garfield. 10. Photosynthesis. 11. Myology. 12. Rex Harrison. 13. Queen Anne. 14. He was a Catholic priest. 15. Eric Bristow. 16. Eurydice. 17. Seven. 18. English National Opera. 19. A hybrid. 20. Sadlers Wells Opera Ballet. 21.Popeye. 22. 3rd September. 23. George Sand. 24. Tomorrow's World. 25. Nitrogen. 26. Countess Markievicz. 27. On the eye. 28. Kangaroo hound. 29. Boots. 30. Criminology. 31. Pythagoras. 32. Taxi driver. 33. Michael Foot. 34. She was her half-sister. 35. Surbiton. 36. The Arctic Ocean. 37. Scandinavian. 38. Nothing at all. 39. USA. 40. Pampas grass. 41. Swan Lake. 42. Ewart. 43. Robert Baden-Powell. 44. Colleen McCullough. 45. The 1920s. 46. Hydrogen. 47. Zanussi. 48. Red. 49. Borzoi. 40. 212 degrees.

QUIZ 107 | Pot Luck

MEDIUM – LEVEL TWO

1 Who or what is Sweet William?
2 How did Princess Grace of Monaco die?
3 Which horror movie actor's real name is William Pratt?
4 Who "discovered" whom at Ujiji in 1871?
5 Which gas has the chemical symbol H?
6 Which character says, "He is the very pineapple of politeness"?
7 Which breed of setter is named after a British duke?
8 Who wrote "Paradise Postponed"?
9 In which fictional county do The Archers live?
10 Which George did the Prince Regent become?
11 What is Hyacinth Bucket's absentee son called?
12 Who claimed to be the Listening Bank?
13 Which "ologists" study bumps on the human head?
14 Who wrote the book "William the Detective"?
15 Which Russian city used to be called Leningrad?
16 How many faces did the Romans believe Janus to have?
17 kHz is an abbreviation for what?
18 What is Radio 4's morning news programme called?
19 *Hedera helix* is better known as what?
20 What kind of dances are Hamilton House and Petronella?
21 Which duo wrote and first recorded "Mud Mud, Glorious Mud"?
22 Which group of men who took part in the American War of Independence have given their name to an American rocket?
23 Who wrote the novel "The Bell"?
24 Which planet did Herschel discover in 1781?
25 How many atoms of oxygen are there in one molecule of water?
26 What is philosophy the study of?
27 Who is Emma Forbes's mother?
28 The USSR annexed three Baltic states in 1940. Latvia and Lithuania were two: what was the third?
29 Who was Helen of Troy's husband?
30 What does the "C" in TUC stand for?
31 Who wrote the music for the "The Threepenny Opera"?
32 Which botanist gave his name to fuchsias?
33 What nationality was ballet star Rudolf Nureyev?
34 Who is known as "The Big Yin"?
35 Which two countries fought for supremacy in the Punic Wars?
36 Who left an unfinished novel called "Sanditon"?
37 Which former newsreader has

advertised Vaseline hand cream?

38 Who was LB in "Dynasty"?

39 Who carried the spirits of dead warriors to Valhalla?

40 The Soviet secret police are known by their initials: what are they?

41 Who took over the ITV franchise from TVS in 1991?

42 Which ballet company is "resident" at London's Royal Opera House?

43 Which William was married to Mary II?

44 Who said, "To err is human but it feels divine"?

45 What does Magnus Magnusson say he will do if he's started?

46 Which fruit is dried to make prunes?

47 If an elderly couple are happily married who are they likened to?

48 Who's real name is Sofia Scicolone?

49 Which sport is played at Rosslyn Park?

50 What do we call a period of play in polo?

Answers to Quiz 106, GAME SHOWS

1. Big Break. 2. The Generation Game. 3. Blockbusters. 4 .Countdown. 5. Terry Wogan. 6. Blind Date. 7. Bullseye. 8. Celebrity Squares. 9. Cluedo. 10. Crystal. 11. Family. 12. Krypton. 13. Matthew Kelly. 14. Campbell. 15. Anneka Rice. 16. Keyhole. 17. Telly. 18. Barrymore. 19. The Price is Right. 20. Your Cards. 21. It's A Knockout. 22. Give Us A Clue. 23. Walker. 24. Count. 25. Gladiators. 26. Roof. 27. Schofield. 28. Loyd Grossman. 29. O'Connor. 30. Toothbrush. 31. William G. Stewart. 32. Two round-the-world air tickets. 33. "Fluke" 34. "The Great Garden Game". 35. Dale Winton. 36. Four. 37. "Bullseye". 38. Sarah Kennedy. 39. Bob Holness. 40. Bob Monkhouse. 41. "Cluedo". 42. "Countdown". 43. Richard O'Brien. 44. £1,000. 45. "Face the Music". 46. "Today's the Day". 47. Isla St Clair. 48. Max Bygraves. 49. Status Quo. 50. Hexagonal.

Q UIZ 108 | The 60s

MEDIUM - LEVEL TWO

1 Who defeated Richard Nixon to become US president in 1960?

2 James Hanratty was charged with a murder on which A road?

3 Which European city was divided into East and West by a Wall?

4 Which Adolf was executed in May 1962 for his part in the Holocaust?

5 Which screen sex symbol was found dead in a bungalow near Hollywood in August 1962?

6 Which Harold became leader of the Labour Party in 1963?

7 Which Doctor wielded his axe on the railway network?

8 Who made a speech proclaiming, "I have a dream"?

9 Which Conservative resigned as prime minister in 1963?

10 Which model Jean was known as "The Shrimp"?

11 What type of creature was Goldie who made the headlines by escaping from London Zoo?

12 Mrs Indira Gandhi was appointed prime minister of which country?

13 Which notorious Murders involved Hindley and Brady?

14 Which Ian declared independence for Rhodesia?

15 On which Isle was there a 1969 rock festival featuring Bob Dylan?

16 Leonid Brezhnev became leader of which country?

17 Which Charles led "The Family"

in the Sharon Tate murder?

18 Willi Brandt became chancellor of which country?

19 In 1969 which actress and singer Judy died at the age of 47?

20 Which Kennedy was involved in the car accident at Chappaquiddick?

21 Which member of the royal family was invested as Prince of Wales?

22 Neil Armstrong became the first man to set foot where?

23 Which gangland twins Ronald and Reginald were jailed?

24 Golda Meir became the first woman prime minister of which country?

25 LSE, the scene of student protest, was the London School of what?

26 What type of Power symbolized the 1967 peace and love festivals?

27 Which Donald was killed trying to break the world water speed record?

28 Which type of skirt was the main fashion of the 1960s?

29 Soviet tanks moved to crush the Dubcek reforms in which country?

30 Brian Epstein was the manager of which pop group?

31 Who made the "wind of change" speech?

32 George Cohen was a member of the world's winners at which

sport?

33 Which call-girl was involved in a government scandal?

34 Which future Princess of Wales was born in the 60s?

35 Edwin Aldrin became the second person to walk where?

36 Who played piano while Peter Cook sang?

37 Whom did Anthony Armstrong-Jones marry in 1960?

38 How did the English comic Tony Hancock die?

39 Whom did Richard Burton marry in Canada in 1964?

40 Where did Gaddafi seize power?

41 Which D.H. Lawrence book from the 20s featured in an Old Bailey obscenity trial?

42 Bob Dylan starred at a 1969 rock Festival on which British isle?

43 Which doctor's report led to the cutting of the railway network?

44 George Blake gained notoriety as what?

45 Which Francis sailed solo round the world?

46 Who became the youngest ever USA President?

47 Who was involved with John Lennon in a "bed-in" for peace?

48 Which President originally blocked Britain's entry into the EEC?

49 Which country banned a tour by England's cricketers?

50 Which country made the first manned space flight?

1. A plant. 2. Car crash. 3. Boris Karloff. 4. Henry Morton Stanley discovered David Livingstone. 5. Hydrogen. 6. Mrs Malaprop in Sheridan's The Rivals. 7. The Gordon setter (after the Duke of Richmond and Gordon). 8. John Mortimer. 9. Borsetshire. 10. George IV. 11. Sheridan. 12. Midland. 13. Phrenologists. 14. Richmal Compton. 15. St Petersburg. 16. Two. 17. Kilohertz. 18. Today. 19. Ivy. 20. Scottish country dancing. 21. Flanders and Swan. 22. The Minutemen. 23. Iris Murdoch. 24. Uranus. 25. One. 26. Being, knowledge and right conduct. 27. Nanette Newman. 28. Estonia. 29. Menelaus. 30. Congress. 31. Kurt Weill. 32. Leonhard Fuchs. 33. Russian. 34. Billy Connolly. 35. Rome and Carthage. 36. Jane Austen. 37. Pamela Armstrong. 38. Little Blake. 39. The Valkyries. 40. KGB. 41. Meridian. 42. The Royal Ballet. 43. William III. 44. Mae West. 45. Finish (I've started so I'll finish). 46. Plums. 47. Darby and Joan. 48. Sophia Loren. 49. Rugby Union. 50. Chukka.

QUIZ 109 Pot Luck

MEDIUM - LEVEL TWO

1 Which Verdi opera is set in Berkshire in England?

2 Who created a garden at Sissinghurst in Kent?

3 Who sang the James Bond theme "From Russia With Love"?

4 What is Prince William's second name?

5 What chicken dish is named after a battle of the Napoleonic Wars?

6 Who wrote the 1988 novel "Prime Time"?

7 During which war were concentration camps first introduced?

8 Which famous writer was married to archaeologist Sir Max Mallowan?

9 Who invented the Flying Shuttle in 1733?

10 What kind of gas was used in the trenches during World War I?

11 Who sang "Islands In The Stream"?

12 Which Sondheim musical tells the story of a murdering barber?

13 What breed of retriever takes its name from a North American bay?

14 What does a Geiger Counter measure?

15 In which "ology", founded in the early 1950s, is self awareness paramount?

16 When does Britain's lease on Hong Kong officially expire?

17 Who defeated Richard III at Bosworth in 1485?

18 Which Hollywood actress's real name was Lucille Le Sueur?

19 Beaumaris, Conway and Harlech are famous for what type of building?

20 Whom did the religious assassins known as Thugs worship?

21 If you were an LLD what would you do?

22 Which famous brothers made a movie called "A Night at the Opera"?

23 What is a tine?

24 Who was the first regular female presenter of "Points of View"?

25 Which William featured in the title of a Benjamin Britten opera?

26 Which country was invaded during Operation Barbarossa?

27 Which famous children's author and artist lived and worked in the Lake District for much of her life?

28 How many of Henry VIII's wives were called Anne?

29 What did miners use to find out if there was gas in a pit?

30 Of which party were Bill Rodgers and Roy Jenkins founder members?

31 Which English boxer had Muhammad Ali (Cassius Clay) on the floor?

32 Who bought Queen Elizabeth II

her first corgi?

33 Which highly insoluble substance is opaque to X-rays?

34 What is the study of human societies called?

35 "Lay your head upon my pillow" appears in which Perry Como song?

36 Which king and queen ruled Britain jointly from 1689 to 1694?

37 What nationality was detective writer Ngaio Marsh?

38 What branch of Christianity still flourishes in Russia?

39 Whom did Zeus seduce when he assumed the guise of a swan?

40 What does "SWALK" stand for?

41 On TV, who played George Smiley in "Smiley's People"?

42 What is the male reproductive organ of a plant called?

43 In the song, "I danced with a man, who danced with a girl who danced with..." whom?

44 Which William was concerned with abolishing slavery?

45 Who commanded the Prussian troops at the Battle of Waterloo?

46 Who took her pen name from Ibsen's "Rosmersholm"?

47 Whose real name is Bernard Schwarz?

48 Krypton, neon, radon, xenon and helium are what kind of gases?

49 Who was the last prime minister to be created an earl?

50 In the Bible, which book comes after Saint John?

Answers to Quiz 108, THE 60s

1. John F. Kennedy. 2. 6. 3. Berlin. 4. Eichmann. 5. Marilyn Monroe. 6. Wilson. 7. Beeching. 8. Martin Luther King. 9. Harold Macmillan. 10. Shrimpton. 11. Eagle. 12. India. 13. Moors. 14. Smith. 15. Wight. 16. Russia. 17. Manson. 18. West Germany. 19. Garland. 20. Edward. 21. Prince Charles. 22. The Moon. 23. Kray. 24. Israel. 25. Economics. 26. Flower. 27. Campbell. 28. Mini. 29. Czechoslovakia. 30. The Beatles. 31. Harold Macmillan. 32. Football. 33. Keeler. 34. Lady Diana Spencer. 35. On the moon. 36. Dudley Moore. 37. Princess Margaret. 38. Committed suicide. 39. Elizabeth Taylor. 40. Libya. 41. Lady Chatterley's Lover. 42. Isle of Wight. 43. Beeching. 44. A spy. 45. Chichester. 46. John Kennedy. 47. Yoko Ono. 48. De Gaulle. 49. South Africa. 50. USSR.

Quiz 110 | Crime

1   In which sensational case was wireless telegraphy first used to apprehend a murderer?

2   At what number in Rillington Place did John Christie live?

3   In the 60s who did James Earl Ray assassinate?

4   What treasure trove did Colonel Thomas Blood try to steal in the 17th century?

5   To two years, when was the last hanging in Britain?

6   In 1981, which leading figure was wounded by John Hinckley?

7   Which parts of the body went into a pillory?

8   Albert de Salvo was better known as what?

9   In which city did Burke and Hare operate?

10 In light opera who wanted "to let the punishment fit the crime"?

11 To ten years each way, when was Dick Turpin hanged?

12 In which month was President Kennedy assassinated?

13 Mary Ann Nicholas and Mary Kelly were victims of who?

14 In which Gloucester street was the West's House of Horrors?

15 The Old Bailey figure of justice holds a sword and what else?

16 What was the the profession of Mary Cotton, hanged in 1873?

17 Who was Britain's last chief hangman?

18 Alphonse Bertillon and Sir Francis Galton invented which aid to criminal detection?

19 George Cornell was shot in which East End pub?

20 In the 70s who was accused of stealing a fur coat and passport from Miss World?

21 In the 17th century which judge sat for the so-called Bloody Assizes?

22 Hawley Harvey were the first names of which murderer?

23 On August 6 1890, Auburn Prison, New York, had the first what?

24 In what decade was flogging finally abolished in Britain?

25 What weapon was used to murder the Bulgrian defector Georgi Markov in London in the 70s?

26 In the 90s which Kray brother was found guilty of drug trafficking?

27 Who shot the person believed to have shot President Kennedy?

28 Who was the first British PM murdered while in office?

29 In the 70s who became the first convict executed in the US for ten years?

30 Which doctor was at the centre of the Profumo affair?

31 Jack the Ripper operated in which city?

32 What nationality was the fictional sleuth Hercule Poirot?

33 Who was Burke's body-snatching partner?

34 Who wrote the comic opera *Trial By Jury*?

35 What is the name of a secret crime society based in Hong Kong?

36 Al Capone was imprisoned in the 30s for what offence?

37 Which notorious American island prison closed in March, 1963?

38 How were the US outlaws Parker and Barrow better known?

39 Which criminal was released by Pontius Pilate instead of Jesus?

40 Which Myra was involved in the Moors Murders?

41 Policemen got the nickname Peelers from whom?

42 How did Frederick West take his life?

43 When did the Knave of Hearts steal the tarts?

44 In which city was John Lennon murdered?

45 Which Kray twin died?

46 What is the Flying Squad in cockney rhyming slang?

47 What name is given to the crime of deliberately burning someone else's property?

48 Which Nick got nicked for the Barings Bank scam?

49 In which decade was the Great Train Robbery?

50 Whom did Dr Crippen murder?

Q UIZ 111 TV Gold

MEDIUM - LEVEL TWO

1 In which sitcom did Bootsie and Snudge first appear?

2 Who played Bertie Wooster in the 60s Wodehouse adaptation?

3 What was Terry's sister called in "The Likely Lads"?

4 Who played the blustering headmaster in "Whack-O!"?

5 Who was the third of "Take Three Girls" with Kate and Avril?

6 How was the "Tomorrow's World" presenter Robert Alexander Baron Symes-Schutzmann von Schutzmannstorf better known?

7 Who was Jim London in "Up the Elephant and Round the Castle"?

8 What relation was Hattie Jacques to Eric in their "Sykes and ..." series?

9 What did Harold Steptoe always call his father?

10 Who played Sid Stone in the UK sitcom "Taxi"?

11 What was the Richard O'Sullivan spin-off from "Man About the House"?

12 Who lived in the Suffolk village of Stackton Tressel?

13 Daphne Manners and Hari Kumar were characters in which series?

14 Jimmy Jewel and Hylda Baker were Eli and Nellie Pledge in which show.

15 Which TV family were headed by Herman and Lily?

16 Which veteran actress played the wife in "Meet the Wife"?

17 In which classic did you find Blanco, Lukewarm and Gay Gordon?

18 What was Bernard Hedges' nickname in "Please Sir"?

19 Who were the two stars of "Marriage Lines"?

20 What was the surname of George and Mildred?

21 What does M*A*S*H* stand for?

22 Which flatmates originally lived in Huskisson Road, Liverpool?

23 Who or what was Mr Ed?

24 Which classic drama centred on the Marchmain family?

25 What make of car did Nurse Emmanuel drive in "Open All Hours"?

26 In which show did Reg Varney play Stan Butler?

27 Who was the fourth Doctor?

28 What was the name of the young blonde witch in "Bewitched"?

29 In which series were Figgis, Glover and Norman hospital patients?

30 Which sitcom about Fenner Fashions starred Miriam Karlin?

31 In which series did the London copper say "Evening, all"?

32 Which veteran presented "Gardening Club" in the 50s and 60s?

33 Who had a sidekick called Tonto?

34 "All Gas and Gaiters" was one of the first sitcoms to poke fun at whom?

35 Who was the female half of Mork and Mindy?

36 Which blonde actress played Purdey in "The New Avengers"?

37 Which Pamela was a regular on "Not the Nine O'Clock News"?

38 What is the world's longest-running current-affairs programme?

39 Which sitcom featured Bernard Hedges of Fenn Street School?

40 In which century was "Poldark" set?

41 Which king was played by Keith Michell in 1970?

42 Was it Starsky or Hutch who started a trend for chunky cardigans?

43 Which series featured the Cartwrights of the Ponderosa?

44 Which 60s sitcom was about the oil rich Clampett family?

45 In "A Family at War" where did the Ashtons live?

46 Which show recreated the era of music hall?

47 Which Saga was the last the BBC produced in black and white?

48 What were the real-life surnames of Terry and June?

49 Which 50s/60s medical drama was set in Oxbridge General Hospital?

50 What breed of dog was Rin-Tin-Tin?

Answers to Quiz 110, CRIME

1. Dr Crippen. 2. 10. 3. Martin Luther King. 4. The Crown Jewels. 5. 1964. 6. President Reagan. 7. Neck and wrists. 8. The Boston Strangler. 9. Edinburgh. 10. The Mikado. 11. 1739. 12. November. 13. Jack the Ripper. 14. Cromwell Street. 15. Scales. 16. Nurse. 17. Harry Allen. 18. Fingerprints. 19. The Blind Beggar. 20. George Best. 21. Judge Jeffreys. 22. Dr Crippen. 23. Death by electrocution. 24. 1940s. 25. An umbrella (injected him with poison). 26. Charlie. 27. Jack Ruby. 28. Spencer Percival. 29. Gary Gilmore. 30. Stephen Ward. 31. London. 32. Belgian. 33. Hare. 34. Gilbert and Sullivan. 35. Triad. 36. Tax evasion. 37. Alcatraz. 38. Bonnie and Clyde. 39. Barabbas. 40. Hindley. 41. Sir Robert Peel. 42. Hanged himself. 43. On a summer's day. 44. New York. 45. Ronnie. 46. Sweeney Todd. 47. Arson. 48. Leeson. 49. 1960s. 50. His wife.

QUIZ 112 | The 70s

MEDIUM - LEVEL TWO

1 Which Edward became prime minister in 1970?

2 What type of currency was introduced to Britain in 1971?

3 Idi Amin seized power in which country?

4 Henry Cooper retired from which sport?

5 What type of short pants became the fashion craze for women?

6 Bangladesh was formed from the eastern part of which country?

7 Which Sir Anthony was declared to be a Russian spy?

8 Which Mother won a Nobel Peace Prize?

9 Which Conservative leader became prime minister in 1979?

10 The Shah of which country was forced into exile?

11 The strike-bound months of 1978 and 1979 became known as the Winter of what?

12 Which Liberal leader resigned after allegations about his private life?

13 Which princess sought a divorce from the Earl of Snowdon?

14 In which sea off the British coastline was oil discovered?

15 What was produced from a test tube for the first time in July 1978?

16 Whose shroud went on display at St John's Cathedral in Turin?

17 Steve Biko died in a cell in which country?

18 What sport did Kerry Packer try to take over with his cash offers?

19 Which king of rock died in Tennessee in 1977?

20 Freddie Laker brought cut-price travel in what type of transport?

21 Which Jubilee did Queen Elizabeth II celebrate in 1977?

22 The Sex Pistols were the leaders of the movement known as what kind of rock?

23 Which leader of Communist China died in 1976?

24 Which 'Lucky' Lord vanished after the murder of his child's nanny?

25 Which scandal forced Richard Nixon to resign as US President?

26 Which countries fought in the 1973 Yom Kippur War?

27 What did the Amoco Cadiz spill off the Brittany coastline?

28 How many days were in a working week during the 1974 power shortage?

29 Which earl was murdered by the IRA in 1979?

30 Which Labour MP James became prime minister?

31 Which Spaniard won a British Open at golf?

32 Whom did Ted Heath replace as British PM?

33 The tennis superstar Bjorn Borg

came from which country?

34 In the UK, the age of majority was lowered from 21 to what?

35 The song "Bright Eyes" was about what type of animal?

36 Haile Selassie was deposed in which country?

37 Which rock legend died at his mansion Graceland?

38 D-Day in 1971 introduced what to Britain?

39 Which athlete Sebastian broke three world records in six weeks?

40 Which art historian Sir Anthony was revealed to be a spy?

41 Idi Amin became President of which country?

42 Who vanished after the murder of Lady Lucan's nanny?

43 The Ayatollah Khomeini drove the Shah from which country?

44 Which Princess was named Sportswoman of the Year?

45 Which legendary artist Pablo died in 1973?

46 Which organization bombed pubs in Guildford and Birmingham?

47 In 1971, 200,000 people demonstrated in the US against which war?

48 Bobby Fischer became a world champion in which game?

49 Olga Korbut delighted the world in what?

50 Whose Silver Jubilee celebrations led to a week of festivities in 1977?

Answers to Quiz 111, TV GOLD

1. "The Army Game". 2. Ian Carmichael. 3. Audrey. 4. Jimmy Edwards. 5. Victoria. 6. Bob Symes. 7. Jim Davidson. 8. Sister. 9. "You dirty old man". 10. Sid James. 11. "Robin's Nest". 12. Hinge and Bracket. 13. "The Jewel in the Crown". 14. "Nearest and Dearest". 15. The Munsters. 16. Thora Hird. 17. "Porridge". 18. Privet. 19. Richard Briers, Prunella Scales. 20. Roper. 21. Mobile Army Surgical Hospital. 22. "The Liver Birds". 23. A talking horse. 24. "Brideshead Revisited". 25. Morris Minor. 26. "On the Buses". 27. Tom Baker. 28. Samantha. 29. "Only When I Laugh". 30. "The Rag Trade". 31. "Dixon of Dock Green". 32. Percy Thrower. 33. The Lone Ranger. 34. The clergy. 35. Mindy. 36. Joanna Lumley. 37. Stephenson. 38. "Panorama". 39. "Please Sir". 40. 18th. 41. Henry VIII. 42. Starsky. 43. "Bonanza". 44. "The Beverly Hillbillies". 45. Liverpool. 46. "The Good Old Days". 47. "The Forsyte Saga". 48. Scott, Whitfield. 49. "Emergency Ward 10". 50. Alsatian.

Quiz 113 Pot Luck

MEDIUM - LEVEL TWO

1. What have these in common: Job, Judges and Habakkuk?

2. Which device is used on a guitar fretboard to raise the pitch of the strings?

3. Which king was reigning in Britain at the start of the First World War?

4. In imperial measurement, how many yards are in a chain?

5. What kind of tree is an osier?

6. On TV, "who was feared by the bad, loved by the good"?

7. With what do you play a vibraphone?

8. On a ship what are the scuppers?

9. With which sport is Peter Alliss associated?

10. Who became ruler of Spain after the Spanish Civil War?

11. In literature, how many Arabian Nights were there?

12. Which singer said, "You're not drunk if you can lie on the floor without holding on"?

13. Black, Italian and Lombardy are all types of which tree?

14. In which war was the Battle of Jutland?

15. What is the square root of 169?

16. Which actress's real name is Camille Javal?

17. What is the name given to the lowest layer of the atmosphere?

18. What was added to rum to make the drink grog?

19. In London where is Poet's Corner?

20. In ads, who is "your flexible friend"?

21. For which of these games would you use dice: ludo, whist, hopscotch, snakes-and-ladders?

22. What instrument would you use to measure the diameter of a cylinder?

23. In which month is Michaelmas Day?

24. In which English county would you find the coastal resort of California?

25. In which game does the term "cannon" occur?

26. For what is Elizabeth Fry chiefly remembered?

27. What fruit do we get from a rose?

28. What was Cleo Laine's job before she was a singer?

29. Which ocean is crossed to sail from San Francisco to Sydney?

30. Who was the British member of The Monkees?

31. From which wood were longbows made?

32. In which country is the Corinth Canal?

33. Which month is "fill-dike"?

34. Of which European country are Madeira and the Azores a part?

35. Which club did Gary Lineker play for immediately before going to

Barcelona?

36 In a poem by Edward Lear, what was peculiar about the "Pobble"?

37 Pascal, Cobol and Basic are all types of what?

38 In yards, how long was a rod, pole, or perch?

39 What was the first No 1 single of the 80s?

40 What is or was a tin lizzie?

41 Which comedian's catch phrase was, "Now there's a funny thing"?

42 What name is given to the unit of electrical power?

43 According to the proverb what do drowning men clutch?

44 What is a copper's nark?

45 What is the modern equivalent for the word behest?

46 Back, blanket and buttonhole are all types of what?

47 In which Shakespeare play is Shylock introduced?

48 Which folk singer wrote the song "The Times They are A-Changin'"?

49 In pop, who was King of the wild frontier?

50 How does a grasshopper produce its distinctive sound?

1. Heath. 2. Decimal. 3. Uganda. 4. Boxing. 5. Hot. 6. Pakistan. 7. Blunt 8. Teresa. 9. Margaret Thatcher. 10. Iran. 11. Discontent. 12. Jeremy Thorpe. 13. Margaret. 14. North Sea. 15. A baby. 16. Jesus Christ. 17. South Africa. 18. Cricket. 19. Elvis Presley. 20. Aircraft. 21. Silver. 22. Punk. 23. Mao Tse-tung. 24. Lucan. 25. Watergate. 26. Egypt, Syria and Israel. 27. Oil. 28. Three. 29. Mountbatten. 30. Callaghan. 31. Severiano Ballesteros. 32. Harold Wilson. 33. Sweden. 34. 18. 35. Rabbit. 36. Ethiopia. 37. Elvis Presley. 38. Decimal coins. 39. Coe. 40. Blunt. 41. Uganda. 42. Lord Lucan. 43. Iran. 44. Anne. 45. Picasso. 46. IRA. 47. Vietnam. 48. Chess. 49. Gymnastics. 50. Queen Elizabeth II.

QUIZ 114 The Media .

MEDIUM - LEVEL TWO

1 What does BAFTA stand for?

2 Jeremy Isaacs was the first chief executive of which channel?

3 Which title is given to the chief executive of the BBC?

4 Which London-based Sunday paper was founded in 1990?

5 In which town is Red Rose radio based?

6 What is the more common name for a teleprompt?

7 Who sets the rate for the television licence?

8 *Izvestia* was a Soviet newspaper. What does Izvestia mean?

9 Which channel has the slogan "Make the voyage"?

10 In a TV studio what is a dolly?

11 What is a studio's chief electrician called?

12 Which was the first British newspaper to issue a colour supplement?

13 In comics what was Black Bob?

14 What is the American Express magazine called?

15 Which daily publication is Britain's oldest?

16 Where is the "Western Mail" based?

17 In which country is "Yomiuri Shimbun" a daily newspaper?

18 How many Sky channels were there originally in 1989?

19 Which TV technician is responsible for hardware such as props, cranes etc.?

20 Which newspaper did the "Sun" replace in 1964?

21 Which newspaper group is David Sullivan associated with?

22 Which UK broadsheet has issues published in Frankfurt and New York?

23 Which publication, founded in 1868, consists wholly of adverts?

24 What is Liverpool's own regional daily paper called?

25 In 1997 Michael Barry stepped down in his post at which independent radio station?

26 What does ILR stand for in the media?

27 What has been published anually since 1697?

28 Which telext system was replaced on ITV by Teletext UK?

29 What was HTV originally called?

30 What did the ITC replace in 1991?

31 What does CNN stand for?

32 Who was the first director general of the BBC?

33 What must not be shown during religious broadcasts?

34 What is a squarial?

35 Which organisation's magazine is called "En Route"?

36 What is Manchester's own regional daily paper called?

37 BSkyB was an amalgam of which two companies?

38 Who was chief executive of Channel 4 from 1989 to 1997?

39 What was played at the end of daily transmission before the arrival of 24-hour TV?

40 In which decade was the "Beano" first issued?

41 What is the RSPB's own magazine called?

42 Which girls' magazine did "Mandy and Judy" amalgamate with in 1997?

43 Where is the "Eastern Daily Press" based?

44 Which subscription-bought periodical was founded in 1922 in the US?

45 Which channel had the slogan "From viewing to doing"?

46 What caused a change in licence fee funding in 1967?

47 What replaces Channel 4 in Wales?

48 What does CBS stand for?

49 How was the London Television Consortium better known?

50 Which women's weekly owned by H. Bauer was in the bestsellers list during the 90s?

Answers to Quiz 113, Pot Luck

1. Books of the Old Testament. 2. Capo. 3. George V. 4. 22. 5. Willow. 6. Robin Hood. 7. With small hammers. 8. Holes to allow water to run off the deck. 9. Golf. 10. General Franco. 11. 1001. 12. Dean Martin. 13. Poplar. 14. First World War. 15. 13. 16. Brigitte Bardot. 17. The troposphere. 18. Water. 19. Westminster Abbey. 20. Access card. 21. Ludo and snakes-and-ladders. 22. Callipers. 23. September (29th). 24. Norfolk. 25. Billiards (accept Russian Pool). 26. Prison reform. 27. Hips. 28. Hairdresser. 29. Pacific. 30. Davy Jones. 31. Yew. 32. Greece. 33. February. 34. Portugal. 35. Everton. 36. It had no toes. 37. Computer languages. 38. Five and a half. 39. Brass In Pocket. 40. Model T Ford. 41. Max Wall. 42. Watt. 43. Straws. 44. A spy or informer. 45. Order or command. 46. Stitches. 47. The Merchant of Venice. 48. Bob Dylan. 49. Adam Ant. 50. By rubbing it legs against its wings or together.

QUIZ 115 Pot Luck

FOR ANSWERS SEE QUIZ NO 116

MEDIUM - LEVEL TWO

1   What size was Tim in "A Christmas Carol"?

2   What is the zodiac sign of the Goat?

3   What is held in a creel?

4   Who had a No 1 hit with the song "Lady In Red"?

5   What did Al Capone have on his face that gave him his nickname?

6   What two colours are on the flag waved at the end of a motor race?

7   In nursery rhyme, where did Mary's little lamb follow her to?

8   In which way did the village of Los Barcos become famous?

9   Which half of Robson and Jerome played the part of Paddy Garvey?

10   What were Liberius, Sissinius and Constantine?

11   In the political sector, what does MEP stand for?

12   Who backed B. Bumble?

13   The ancient city of Troy is in which modern country?

14   Who founded the Methodist movement?

15   What do sprinters start from in a track race?

16   Who ordered the execution of Mary Queen of Scots?

17   What do volleyball players hit the ball with?

18   According to the proverb, what does the devil make work for?

19   Which rugby nation was readmitted to international competition in 1993?

20   What type of food is a pomelo?

21   What is another name for a cavy?

22   Who said, "You cannot be serious!"?

23   What was the eighth month of the Roman calendar?

24   Which Olympic water sport includes twists, tucks and pikes?

25   Who recorded the original track "Stairway To Heaven"?

26   Which race meeting is as famous for its hats as for its horses?

27   What letter features on a snooker table?

28   What type of food is gazpacho?

29   How is Western actor Marion Morrison better known?

30   Who is Griff Rhys-Jones' comic partner?

31   "Up Where We Belong" was the theme from which film?

32   What is the currency of Italy?

33   What is another name for the wildebeeste?

34   What word goes before glove, hound and trot?

35   What is Ryan O'Neal's actress daughter called?

36   Which English queen never married?

37   In rhyming slang what is a north and south?

38 How is Terry Nelhams better known?

39 What was the name of the Elephant Man?

40 To ten years either way, when was the Automobile Association formed?

41 In the plant world, what do the letters RHS stand for ?

42 Between which two African countries are the Victoria Falls?

43 Which country is golfer Ian Woosnam from?

44 Gemma Jones became the Duchess of where?

45 What does the word hirsute mean?

46 What word relates to Enya, The Wombles and Venezuela?

47 In feet how wide is a hockey goal?

48 Who wrote "Little Men"?

49 Which major river flows through New Orleans?

50 Whose last words were, "Thank God I have done my duty"?

A nswers to Quiz 114, THE MEDIA

1. British Academy of Film and Television Arts. 2. Channel 4. 3. Director General. 4. Independent on Sunday. 5. Preston. 6. Autocue. 7. Parliament. 8. News. 9. The Discovery Channel. 10. A mounting for a camera. 11. Gaffer. 12. Sunday Times. 13. Sheepdog. 14. Expression! 15. Lloyd's List. 16. Cardiff. 17. Japan. 18. Four. 19. Grip. 20. Daily Herald. 21. Sport Newspapers. 22. Financial Times. 23. Exchange and Mart. 24. Liverpool Echo. 25. Classic FM. 26. Independent Local Radio. 27. Old Moore's Almanac. 28. Oracle. 29. Harlech Television. 30. IBA. 31. Cable News Network. 32. Lord Reith. 33. Adverts. 34. Small satellite dish. 35. The Caravan Club. 36. Manchester Evening News. 37. Sky Television and BSB. 38. Michael Grade. 39. The National Anthem. 40. 1930s. 41. Birds. 42. Bunty. 43. Norwich. 44. Reader's Digest. 45. Discovery Channel. 46. Arrival of colour TV. 47. S4C. 48. Columbia Broadcasting System. 49. London Weekend Television. 50. Take A Break.

QUIZ 116 | Pop Music

MEDIUM - LEVEL TWO

1 Which duo were Solid?

2 Which track on Kate Bush's "The Kick Inside" was a No. I single?

3 What was Rod Stewart's first No. I album?

4 "The Weight" by the Band was on which album?

5 "Dead Ringer" was the first No. I album for who?

6 Who released a series of Singalonga songs?

7 Which composer gave Nigel Kennedy the chance to chart through the four seasons?

8 Who recorded "Graffiti Bridge"?

9 Mike Oldfield's "Tubular Bells" came out on which label?

10 What was the Spice Girls first album called?

11 In the 70s which singer/songwriter recorded "Back To Front"?

12 Which 60s group came back in the 90s producing a "Carnival Of Hits"?

13 Whose album was "Made In Heaven"?

14 Who were the voices behind Derek and Clive?

15 Who was on Neck and Neck with Mark Knopfler?

16 On "Sergeant Pepper", how many holes were in Blackburn, Lancashire?

17 Which group's best-of album was called "Carry On Up The Charts"?

18 Which group had Jerry Hall as a siren on the rocks on an album cover?

19 What are the first names of the chart-topping Three Tenors?

20 Which David spent most weeks in the charts in 1973,1974 and 1983?

21 Who recorded "Captain Fantastic & The Brown Dirt Cowboy"?

22 Which group had eight No. I albums in a row from 1969 to 1979?

23 Which album did Paul Young record with an almost French title?

24 Who in 1987 became the first solo female to spend most weeks in the charts?

25 Which group produced their "Greatest Hits" before their "Arriva"!?

26 Who had a mid-80s No. I with "Invisible Touch"?

27 Which heavy rock group recorded "Fireball" and "Machine Head"?

28 Which Phil spent most weeks in the charts in 1990?

29 "Money For Nothing" first appeared on which Dire Straits album?

30 Which Beatles album featured a zebra crossing on the cover?

31 Who recorded "Rubber Soul"?

32 What goes after "What's The Story" in the title of Oasis's album?

33 Which Phil recorded "No Jacket Required"?

34 Who recorded "Dark Side of the Moon"?

35 Which Rod had six consecutive No. I albums in the 70s?

36 Who recorded "Purple Rain"?

37 Which group had a Night at the Opera and a Day at the Races?

38 Who recorded "Blue Hawaii"?

39 Paul McCartney was in which group for "Band On the Run"?

40 Who called their greatest hits album "End Of Part One"?

41 Which legendary guitarist recorded "From The Cradle"?

42 Who recorded "Off The Wall"?

43 Mike Oldfield presented what type of Bells?

44 Who recorded "The Colour Of My Love"?

45 Which Cat spent most weeks in the album charts in 1972?

46 Who recorded "Breakfast In America"?

47 Which Abba album had a French title?

48 Neil Diamond's film soundtrack album was about what type of singer?

49 Which easy-listening bandleader James has made over 50 albums?

50 Who recorded "Brothers In Arms"?

A nswers to
Quiz 115, POT LUCK

1. Tiny. 2. Capricorn. 3. Fish. 4. Chris de Burgh. 5. Scar. 6. Black and white. 7. School. 8. It was the setting for BBC's El Dorado. 9. Jerome. 10. Popes. 11. Member of the European Parliament. 12. The Stingers. 13. Turkey. 14. John Wesley. 15. Blocks. 16. Elizabeth I. 17. Hands. 18. Idle hands. 19. South Africa. 20. Fruit. 21. Guinea pig. 22. John McEnroe. 23. October. 24. Diving. 25. Led Zeppelin. 26. Ascot. 27. D. 28. Soup. 29. John Wayne. 30. Mel Smith. 31. An Officer And A Gentleman. 32. Lira. 33. Gnu. 34. Fox. 35. Tatum. 36. Elizabeth I. 37. Mouth. 38. Adam Faith. 39. John Merrick. 40. 1905. 41. Royal Horticultural Society. 42. Zimbabwe and Zambia. 43. Wales. 44. Duke Street. 45. Hairy. 46. Orinoco. 47. 12. 48. Louisa M. Alcott. 49. Mississippi. 50. Horatio Nelson.

Quiz 117 Pot Luck

MEDIUM – LEVEL TWO

1 In which secret agent spoof did Agent 99 appear?

2 In which TV programme do Sharon, Tracey and Dorien appear?

3 Which John became deputy Labour leader under Tony Blair?

4 What kind of animal features in the book "Watership Down"?

5 What flower is the emblem of the Labour Party?

6 Which instruments were featured in the hit single that came from the film "Deliverance"?

7 Who used a children's computer to 'phone home'?

8 Who did Dr Hook speak to when trying to get through to Sylvia?

9 What number does the Roman numeral IV stand for?

10 What is measured by a manometer?

11 In which month is St David's Day?

12 What type of animal is a natterjack?

13 Which Roman goddess of flowers is the name of a brand of margarine?

14 What are the initials of writer Tolkien?

15 What superhero can Peter Parker turn into?

16 Which sport does Murray Walker comment on?

17 Which city do Aston Villa come from?

18 In which film do Abbott and Costello land on Venus?

19 What are Sting, Stewart Copeland and Andy Summers better known as?

20 On what part of your body would you wear a stole?

21 What is the world's largest species of penguin called?

22 In a pack of cards how many jacks' eyes can be seen?

23 London's Denmark Street acquired which nickname?

24 In "Fifteen To One" how many contestants take part in the final round?

25 Where is the 19th hole on an 18 hole golf course?

26 Who or what was Laika?

27 Who was the man with the golden trumpet?

28 Which spacecraft was commanded by Steve Zodiac?

29 In which stadium did England win the 1966 World Cup Final?

30 What do the initials HGV stand for?

31 What name is given to the art of clipping hedges into shapes?

32 How many days in two non-leap years?

33 Which country is a car from if it has the international registration

238

letter P?

34 Who came first as Prime Minister, Macmillan or Chamberlain?

35 Which fruit is used to make the drink kirsch?

36 In darts, what is the highest score from three different trebles?

37 U is the symbol of which chemical element?

38 In "EastEnders" what did Michelle Fowler call her little girl?

39 What kind of creature is a flying fox?

40 How many miles are there in eight kilometres?

41 What type of canoe is spelt the same backwards and forwards?

42 Who recorded the album "So Far So Good"?

43 What is the word for a group of squirrels?

44 Which pop star began legal preceedings against Sony in 1993?

45 Which woodland area of Hampshire is noted for its ponies?

46 What is the name of the BBC's Birmingham studios?

47 Which German philosopher Karl wrote "Das Kapital"?

48 Who was Hare's grave-robbing partner in the 19th century?

49 How many sides in 15 triangles?

50 What is the name of TV cook Berry?

Answers to Quiz 116, Pop Music

1. Ashton and Simpson. 2. "Wuthering Heights". 3. Every Picture Tells A Story. 4. Music From Big Pink. 5. Meat Loaf. 6. Max Bygraves. 7. Vivaldi. 8. Prince. 9. Virgin. 10. Spice. 11. Gilbert O Sullivan. 12. The Seekers. 13. Queen. 14. Peter Cook and Dudley Moore. 15. Chet Atkins. 16. 4,000. 17. Beautiful South. 18. Roxy Music. 19. Jose, Luciano, Placido. 20. Bowie. 21. Elton John. 22. Led Zeppelin. 23. No Parlez. 24. Madonna. 25. Abba. 26. Genesis. 27. Deep Purple. 28. Collins. 29. Brothers In Arms. 30. Abbey Road. 31. The Beatles. 32. "Morning Glory". 33. Collins. 34. Pink Floyd. 35. Stewart. 36. Prince. 37. Queen. 38. Elvis Presley. 39. Wings. 40. Wet Wet Wet. 41. Eric Clapton. 42. Michael Jackson. 43. Tubular. 44. Celine Dion. 45. Stevens. 46. Supertramp. 47. Voulez-Vouz. 48. A jazz singer. 49. Last. 50. Dire Straits.

Quiz 118 | Science

MEDIUM – LEVEL TWO

1   Which drug is Alexander Fleming famous for discovering?

2   Which rays for examining the inside of the body did Röntgen discover?

3   What nationality was Aristotle?

4   What was Robert Bunsen famous for?

5   Which Pierre and Marie discovered radium?

6   What was the first name of German scientist Einstein?

7   Fahrenheit is associated with the measurement of what?

8   Which astronomer gave his name to the comet seen every 76 years?

9   What is the first name of physicist Hawking?

10   Which Sir Isaac discovered the law of gravity?

11   What was the nationality of astronomer Galileo?

12   What was Ernest Rutherford the first man to split?

13   Which juice did Jean Nicot extract from tobacco?

14   Which biologist Charles studied the evolution of the species?

15   Which instrument to magnify small objects was invented by Jansen?

16   Which Ernest discovered alpha, beta and gamma rays?

17   What does the scale named after Anders Celsius measure?

18   Which Italian painter drew early ideas for a helicopter?

19   Which American Thomas developed the light bulb?

20   Flymo developed a machine based on the hovercraft for cutting what?

21   Which naturalist Sir David has a film director brother Richard?

22   What did John Dalton define as the smallest particle of substance?

23   What did Lister discover which stopped wounds becoming septic?

24   Which zoologist Desmond broadcast discoveries about man in "The Naked Ape"?

25   What did Harvey discover is pumped round the body?

26   What was Kay's Flying Shuttle used for in 1733?

27   What is a common vegetable and flower used by Mendel in his theories on genetics?

28   On which continent have the Leakey family made discoveries about man's evolution?

29   What type of engines did George Stephenson develop?

30   What Spinning invention was named after its creator's daughter?

31   What name is given to a small, portable computer?

32   COBOL is common business-

orientated what?

33 A molecule of water contains how many atoms of oxygen?

34 The study of fluids moving in pipes is known as what?

35 What is the process by which plants make food using light?

36 In a three-pronged plug what is the colour of the live wire?

37 Which small portable tape players were introduced by Sony?

38 Frank Whittle first produced what type of engine?

39 What is the chemical symbol for lead?

40 What do the initials LCD stand for?

41 Gouache is a type of what ?

42 In the 30s the Biro brothers produced the first low-cost what?

43 What device produces the air/petrol mix used in internal combustion engines?

44 Which Alfred invented dynamite and gelignite?

45 Sellafield is in which county in England?

46 What name is given to a screen picture that represents a standard computer function?

47 Which vehicle did J.C. Bamford give his name to?

48 What fuel is used by a Bunsen burner?

49 Which Michael invented the dynamo and the transformer?

50 What sort of pressure does a barometer measure?

Answers to Quiz 117, Pot Luck

1. Get Smart. 2. Birds Of A Feather. 3. Prescott. 4. Rabbits. 5. Rose. 6. Banjos. 7. ET. 8. Sylvia's Mother. 9. Four. 10. Pressure of gases. 11. March. 12. Toad. 13. Flora. 14. J.R.R. 15. Spiderman. 16. Motor racing. 17. Birmingham. 18. Abbot and Costello Go To Mars. 19. Police. 20. Shoulders. 21. Emperor. 22. 12. 23. Tin Pan Alley. 24. Three. 25. The clubhouse. 26. The first dog in space. 27. Eddie Calvert. 28. Fireball XL5. 29. Wembley. 30. Heavy Goods Vehicle. 31. Topiary. 32. 730. 33. Portugal. 34. Chamberlain. 35. The cherry. 36. 171. 37. Uranium. 38. Vicki. 39. A bat. 40. Five. 41. Kayak. 42. Bryan Adams. 43. Dray. 44. George Michael. 45. New Forest. 46. Pebble Mill. 47. Marx. 48. Burke. 49. 45. 50. Mary.

Q UIZ 119 | The 90s

MEDIUM - LEVEL TWO

1 Which party won a fourth consecutive term of office in the UK in 1992?

2 Which Middle Eastern country was defeated in the Gulf War?

3 Which country was reunified in 1990?

4 Who became Deputy Prime Minister of the UK in 1995?

5 Which Manchester jail was the scene of rioting in 1990?

6 Which envoy was released from the Lebanon?

7 Which three times winner of the Grand National died?

8 Which rock legend's daughter did Michael Jackson marry?

9 Who succeeded Barbara Bush as the USA's First Lady?

10 Which Dimbleby interviewed the Prince of Wales on TV?

11 Who was the first female to present "National Lottery Live"?

12 Which member of the royal family divorced and remarried?

13 Which Labour leader resigned after the 1992 General Election?

14 Assassinated Prime Minister Rabin was from which country?

15 Which tax was abandoned in favour of the Council Tax?

16 Which country won Eurovision in consecutive years in the first half of the decade?

17 Who described 1992 as an annus horribilis?

18 Which heavyweight boxing champion went to prison?

19 Which media magnate drowned in mysterious circumstances?

20 George Carey succeeded Robert Runcie in which post?

21 Jill Morrell conducted a campaign to free which Beirut hostage?

22 Who became president of South Africa in 1994?

23 Which US singer celebrated his 80th birthday in December 1995?

24 Benazir Bhutto returned as prime minister of which Asian country?

25 Which Boris became president of the Russian Federation in 1991?

26 Which meat was at the heart of a scare about BSE?

27 Which link between England and France was opened?

28 Which American football star was acquitted of his wife's murder?

29 The imprisonment of Nick Leeson followed the collapse of which bank?

30 What replaced TV am as ITV's weekly breakfast programme?

31 Who described 1992 as an "annus horribilis"?

32 Which widely taken test had a theory element added in 1996?

33 Who became the first Prime Minister to be made a baroness?

34 Dying of cancer at 22, Mel Appleby had been part of which

242

pop duo?

35 In which tunnel was there a major fire in autumn 1996?

36 Which former Beirut hostage wrote a book with Jill Morrell?

37 Who lost when Bill Clinton first became US President?

38 Which Richard became the first to 400 Test wickets?

39 Before he was elected an MP in 1997, who was Martin Bell's employer?

40 Which Pakistan cricketer was named in the Botham/Lamb libel case?

41 Which Scottish city was the Cultural Capital of Europe in 1990-1?

42 Who voted themselves a 26-percent pay rise in 1996?

43 Who managed England's soccer team in Italia 90?

44 Hale-Bopp hit the headlines in the 90s, but who or what was it?

45 Which former "Minister of Fun" resigned over a scandal with an actress?

46 Who was John Major's Deputy Prime Minister?

47 Which country dominated Eurovision in the 90s?

48 Which Olympics were blighted by the Centennial Park bomb?

49 Which golfer became the first British woman in history to earn a million from her sport?

50 Which Party did Sir James Goldsmith found before the 1997 election?

A nswers to Quiz 118, SCIENCE

1. Penicillin. 2. X-rays. 3. Greek. 4. Bunsen burner. 5. Curie. 6. Albert. 7. Temperature. 8. Halley. 9. Stephen. 10. Newton. 11. Italian. 12. The atom. 13. Nicotine. 14. Darwin. 15. Microscope. 16. Rutherford. 17. Temperature. 18. Leonardo Da Vinci. 19. Edison. 20. Grass. 21. Attenborough. 22. Atom. 23. Antiseptic. 24. Morris. 25. Blood. 26. Weaving. 27. Pea. 28. Africa. 29. Steam. 30. Spinning Jenny. 31. Laptop. 32. Language. 33. One. 34. Hydraulics. 35. Photosynthesis. 36. Brown. 37. Walkmans. 38. Jet. 39. Pb. 40. Liquid crystal display. 41. Paint. 42. Biro (ball-point pen). 43. Carburettor. 44. Nobel. 45. Cumbria. 46. Icon. 47. JCB. 48. Gas. 49. Faraday. 50. Atmospheric.

Q₁₂₀UIZ 90s Films

MEDIUM - LEVEL TWO

1 Which male star shot to fame in "Four Weddings and a Funeral"?

2 In which film shot in Ireland did Australian Mel Gibson play a Scot?

3 Who had to 'Carry On' 500 years after the discovery of America?

4 In which film did Robin Williams dress up as a Scottish nanny?

5 What was the name of the Dustin Hoffman film about Peter Pan?

6 In which film did Whoopi Golberg first get into the habit?

7 Who joined Walter Matthau in the film "Grumpy Old Men"?

8 What did Schindler draw up in the Spielberg film?

9 What is Beethoven in the 1992 film?

10 What is Casper?

11 Who won an Oscar for "Forrest Gump" and "Philadelphia"?

12 Who starred with Demi Moore in "Ghost"?

13 Who was Whitney Houston's Bodyguard?

14 In which film did Anthony Hopkins play the role of Hannibal Lecter?

15 How was Macaulay Culkin left at Home in 1990?

16 What did the cub Simba become in the 1994 Disney film?

17 What kind of Proposal did Robert Redford make concerning Demi Moore?

18 What was Wrong in the Wallace and Gromit Oscar-winning film?

19 Who was the Pretty Woman in the 1990 film?

20 Who did Harry meet in the film with Billy Crystal?

21 Which Park was the Spielberg film about dinosaurs?

22 Where was someone Sleepless in the film with Meg Ryan?

23 Which Disney movie contained an American Indian heroine?

24 In which series of films would you find Robin and The Joker?

25 Daniel Day-Lewis starred in the Last of what 1992?

26 In which film was Robin Williams the voice of the genie?

27 Who was Nicole Kidman's co star in "Far and Away" whom she later married?

28 Which Judge does Stallone play in the comic cult movie?

29 On which street was there A Miracle in the Xmas movie with Richard Attenborough?

30 What colour is the Eye in the 007 film?

31 In which film did Hannibal Lecter feature?

32 Which Steven Spielberg film was described as "65 million years in the making"?

33 Which film gave Macaulay Culkin

244

his first huge success?

34 Which English film swept the Oscar board in 1997?

35 In which film did Robin Williams dress as a Scottish housekeeper?

36 Which actor was the ghost in the film of the same name?

37 Who did Kevin Costner protect in "The Bodyguard"?

38 Which musical instrument was the title of a 1993 Oscar winner?

39 Which comedy was described as "Five good reasons to stay single"?

40 In which film was Robin Williams the voice of the genie?

41 Which hero was Prince of Thieves in 1991?

42 Which creatures had the prefix Teenage Mutant Ninja?

43 In which film is Peter Pan a father and a lawyer?

44 In which Disney film was Captain Smith saved?

45 In which movie did Nigel Hawthorne play an English monarch?

46 Which 1990 Western had Kevin Costner as actor and director?

47 Which Disney film included "The Circle of Life"?

48 Who played Eva Duarte in a 1996 musical?

49 In which film did Susan Sarandon play a nun who visits a prisoner on Death Row?

50 Which Disney Story was the first to be computer-generated?

Answers to Quiz 119, The 90s

1. Conservatives. 2. Iraq. 3. Germany. 4. Michael Heseltine. 5. Strangeways. 6. Terry Waite. 7. Red Rum. 8. Elvis. 9. Hillary Clinton. 10. Jonathan. 11. Anthea Turner. 12. Princess Royal. 13. Neil Kinnock. 14. Israel. 15. Poll tax. 16. Ireland. 17. The Queen. 18. Mike Tyson. 19. Robert Maxwell. 20. Archbishop of Canterbury. 21. John McCarthy. 22. Nelson Mandela. 23. Frank Sinatra. 24. Pakistan. 25. Yeltsin. 26. Beef. 27. Channel Tunnel. 28. OJ Simpson. 29. Barings. 30. GMTV. 31. The Queen. 32. Driving test. 33. Margaret Thatcher. 34. Mel and Kim. 35. Channel tunnel. 36. John McCarthy. 37. George Bush. 38. Hadlee. 39. The BBC. 40. Imran Khan. 41. Glasgow. 42. MPs. 43. Bobby Robson. 44. Comet. 45. David Mellor. 46. Michael Heseltine. 47. Ireland. 48. Atlanta in 1996. 49. Laura Davies. 50. The Referendum Party.

Q UIZ 121 Hollywood

1 Which singer starred in "The Bodyguard"?

2 Which actress Keaton starred in "Father of the Bride II"?

3 Which actor Tom won Oscars in 1993 and again in 1994?

4 Which Holly won an Oscar for a silent role in "The Piano"?

5 Which silent movie star was played by Robert Downey Jr in 1992?

6 Which Welsh actor starred with Jodie Foster in "The Silence of the Lambs"?

7 Which Bob starred in "Mona Lisa" before finding it 'good to talk'?

8 Which Steven directed "Schindler's List"?

9 Which actor Sylvester has the nickname Sly?

10 Who is Donald Sutherland's actor son?

11 What is the first name of "Pulp Fiction" director Tarantino?

12 Which actress Melanie married Don Johnson – twice?

13 Which Nick co starred with Barbra Streisand in "The Prince of Tides"?

14 What is the first name of actress Sarandon ?

15 Which Johnny starred as Edward Scissorhands?

16 Which Scottish actor Sean has an actor son Jason?

17 Which Emilio starred in "Young Guns" I and II?

18 Which Macaulay became one of the highest-paid child stars ever?

19 Which actress Glenn had a "Fatal Attraction"?

20 Which Al starred in "The Godfather" and "Scent of a Woman"?

21 Which actor Mel was born in the US but brought up in Australia?

22 What is the surname of father and daughter Peter and Bridget?

23 Which Robin became Mrs Doubtfire?

24 Which blond Daryl had adventures with the Invisible Man?

25 Who was Alec Baldwin's real and screen wife in "The Getaway"?

26 What is the first name of Joanne Whalley-Kilmer's husband?

27 Liza Minnelli and Lorna Luft are daughters of which Hollywood great?

28 Which actor succeeded Timothy Dalton as James Bond?

29 Which film director's real name is Allen Stewart Konigsberg?

30 Which actor won an Oscar as director of "Dances with Wolves"?

31 Which actress married André Agassi in 1997?

32 Which Jenny played Roberta in "The Railway Children"?

33 In which country was Arnold Schwarzenegger born?

34 Which Sharon played opposite Michael Douglas in "Basic Instinct"

35 What did Susan Weaver change her first name to?

36 Which Leslie stars in "The Naked Gun" series of films?

37 Which Superman actor was seriously injured in a riding accident?

38 In which country was Gerard Dépardieu born?

39 Who is Donald Sutherland's actor son?

40 Which Ms Turner was the speaking voice of Jessica Rabbit?

41 Who directed "Psycho" and "The Birds"?

42 What is the first name of Michael Douglas's father?

43 What is the first name of Ms Arquette, star of "Desperately Seeking Susan"?

44 Which Drew was in "E.T." and "Batman Forever"?

45 Which chart-topper was in "Silkwood" and "Moonstruck"?

46 In which film did Val Kilmer play the rock star Jim Morrison?

47 Which star of "Evita" was the first wife of the actor Sean Penn?

48 Which Joanne is Mrs Paul Newman?

49 How is Mary Elizabeth Spacek better known?

50 Which Tony is the father of Jamie Lee?

Answers to Quiz 120, 90s Films

1. Hugh Grant. 2. Braveheart. 3. Columbus. 4. Mrs Doubtfire. 5. Hook. 6. Sister Act. 7. Jack Lemmon. 8. List. 9. A dog. 10. A ghost. 11. Tom Hanks. 12. Patrick Swayze. 13. Kevin Costner. 14. The Silence Of The Lambs. 15. Alone. 16. The Lion King. 17. Indecent. 18. Trousers. 19. Julia Roberts. 20. Sally. 21. Jurassic. 22. Seattle. 23. Pocahontas. 24. Batman. 25. Mohicans. 26. Aladdin. 27. Tom Cruise. 28. Dredd. 29. 34th. 30. Golden. 31. The Silence of the Lambs. 32. Jurassic Park. 33. Home Alone. 34. The English Patient. 35. Mrs Doubtfire. 36. Patrick Swayze. 37. Whitney Houston. 38. The Piano. 39. Four Weddings and a Funeral. 40. Aladdin. 41. Robin Hood. 42. Turtles. 43. Hook. 44. Pocahontas. 45. The Madness of King George. 46. Dances With Wolves. 47. The Lion King. 48. Madonna. 49. Dead Man Walking. 50. Toy Story.

Geography

MEDIUM - LEVEL TWO

1 The Bay of Biscay lies to the north of which country?

2 Which Gulf lies between Iran and Saudi Arabia?

3 Brittany is part of which country?

4 Which US city is known by its initials LA?

5 Which South American country shares its name with a nut?

6 Near which large city is the Wirral?

7 Which is Britain's most southerly point on the mainland?

8 In which country is Shanghai?

9 In which county is Lake Windermere?

10 To which country does the island of Bermuda belong?

11 The state of the Vatican is in which city?

12 Is San Francisco on the east or west coast of the USA?

13 Which Union was Ukraine once part of?

14 In which country is Zurich?

15 In which country is the holiday destination of Bali?

16 Which island lies to the south of India?

17 In which country would you hear the language Afrikaans?

18 Which group of islands does Gran Canaria belong to?

19 Where would you be if you had climbed Mount Olympus?

20 In which US state is Orlando?

21 Which Ocean is to the west of Portugal?

22 In which country is The Hague?

23 Monte Carlo is in which principality?

24 Which US state has the Arctic Circle running through it?

25 Which Land in Denmark is made up of bricks?

26 Which Falls are on the Canadian/US border?

27 Which country's women might wear a kimono?

28 Which Ocean's name means peaceful?

29 Which country originally produced Peugeot cars?

30 What is the English for what the French call an autoroute?

31 What did Iran used to be called?

32 In which World are underdeveloped countries said to be?

33 Normandy is part of which country?

34 In which Sea is the island of Majorca?

35 Which country does the island of Rhodes belong to?

36 In which US state is Disney World?

37 Which county is abbreviated to Oxon?

38 In which country is the Costa del Sol?

39 Which is further south Yarmouth

or Brighton?

40 Is Torremolinos on the coast or inland?

41 Which sea lies between Italy and the former Yugoslavia?

42 On which coast of France are Cannes and St Tropez?

43 If you took a holiday in Gstaad what sport would you practise?

44 In which country is Buenos Aires?

45 In which continent is the holiday destination of Ibiza?

46 Where would you speak English and Maltese?

47 Which island lies at the eastern end of the Mediterranean?

48 Which group of islands does Tenerife belong to?

49 What is the Matterhorn?

50 What is the continent around the South Pole called?

A nswers to
Quiz 121, HOLLYWOOD

1. Whitney Houston. 2. Diane. 3. Hanks. 4. Hunter. 5. Charlie Chaplin. 6. Anthony Hopkins. 7. Hoskins. 8. Spielberg. 9. Stallone. 10. Kiefer. 11. Quentin. 12. Griffith. 13. Nolte. 14. Susan. 15. Depp. 16. Connery. 17. Estevez. 18. Culkin. 19. Close. 20. Pacino. 21. Gibson. 22. Fonda. 23. Williams. 24. Hannah. 25. Kim Basinger. 26. Val. 27. Judy Garland. 28. Pierce Brosnan. 29. Woody Allen. 30. Kevin Costner. 31. Brooke Shields. 32. Agutter. 33. Austria. 34. Stone. 35. Sigourney. 36. Nielsen. 37. Christopher Reeve. 38. France. 9. Kiefer. 40. Kathleen. 41. Alfred Hitchcock. 42. Kirk. 43. Rosanna. 44. Barrymore. 45. Cher. 46. The Doors. 47. Madonna. 48. Woodward. 49. Sissy. 50. Curtis.

QUIZ 123 | Pot Luck

MEDIUM - LEVEL TWO

1 St Winifred's School Choir sang about which relative?

2 Which colour describes Victorian photographs?

3 In which decade of the 20th century was Joan Baez born?

4 What word can go after "egg" and before "board"?

5 How is Rocco Marchegiano better known?

6 In the 90s, which London club had the "Famous Five" strike force?

7 Who wrote the novel "The Water Babies"?

8 What colour is a female blackbird?

9 What does VE stand for in VE Day?

10 What type of pastry is used to make profiteroles?

11 In the group's name, what comes after Bonzo Dog?

12 Which Nicholas starred in "Goodnight Sweetheart"?

13 In which country is the city of Antwerp?

14 How many degrees in a semicircle?

15 In the 80s, who had a No. 1 with "One Moment In Time"?

16 Which BBC TV gardener died suddenly of a heart attack in 1996?

17 If Boxing Day is a Friday what day is December 1?

18 Which Al won an Oscar for Best Actor in "Scent Of A Woman"?

19 What is the female equivalent of the rank of Earl?

20 What word can follow "light", "green" and "slaughter"?

21 Dennis Amis is associated with which sport?

22 What is a scout rally called?

23 Puccini died in which century?

24 Whose catchphrase was "Stop messing about"?

25 Au is the chemical symbol for which element?

26 What, according to proverb, breeds contempt?

27 Which French phrase used in English means a false step or mistake?

28 In which TV series did the characters Steed and Emma Peel appear?

29 What is the square root of 9?

30 What does the C stand for in the business organization the CBI?

31 If it's Friday and it's five o'clock, what else is it in children's TV terms?

32 Which two colours are most frequently confused in colour blindness?

33 In which decade of the 20th century was Roger Bannister born?

34 What word can go after

250

"neighbour" and before "wink"?

35 In the 90s, who had a No. I with "Always On My Mind"?

36 Moving anticlockwise on a dartboard, what number is next to 4?

37 Who wrote the novel "Lady Chatterley's Lover"?

38 Dennis Andries is associated with which sport?

39 In which country is the city of Bulawayo?

40 In which TV series did Sharon, Tracey and Dorian appear?

41 How many pints in a gallon?

42 What was the name of Dick Turpin's horse?

43 In which decade did Radio I start?

44 Wilkins Micawber appears in which Charles Dickens novel?

45 How is Allen Konigsberg better known?

46 Who was the only Robbie in England's Euro 96 squad?

47 Which group of workers does ABTA represent?

48 The character Pete Beal appeared in which TV soap?

49 What can be cardinal or ordinal?

50 In "Cinderella", what was the pumpkin turned in to?

A nswers to Quiz 122, GEOGRAPHY

1. Spain. 2. Persian Gulf. 3. France. 4. Los Angeles. 5. Brazil. 6. Liverpool. 7. Lizard. 8. China. 9. Cumbria. 10. Britain. 11. Rome. 12. West. 13. Soviet. 14. Switzerland. 15. Indonesia. 16. Sri Lanka. 17. South Africa. 18. Canary Islands. 19. Greece. 20. Florida. 21. Atlantic. 22. Holland. 23. Monaco. 24. Alaska. 25. Legoland. 26. Niagara. 27. Japan. 28. Pacific. 29. France. 30. Motorway. 31. Persia. 32. Third World. 33. France. 34. Mediterranean. 35. Greece. 36. Florida. 37. Oxfordshire. 38. Spain. 39. Brighton. 40. On the coast. 41. Adriatic. 42. South. 43. Skiing. 44. Argentina. 45. Europe. 46. Malta. 47. Cyprus. 48. Canary Islands. 49. Mountain. 50. Antarctica.

The Arts

QUIZ 124

MEDIUM - LEVEL TWO

1 Which is London's oldest theatre?

2 The Royal Opera House in London is home to which branch of the arts other than opera?

3 How is Mozart's "Die Zauberflöte" known in English?

4 Who wrote "Tosca'?

5 Including intervals, approximately how long does Wagner's "Götterdämmerung" last?

6 Where is the Ballet Rambert based?

7 In which city is Europe's largest opera house?

8 Which theatre was the National's temporary home from 1963?

9 Who wrote the ballet "The Nutcracker"?

10 Which cornetist/pianist was considered to be the first great white jazz musician?

11 Which Duke's first names were Edward Kennedy?

12 Which London theatre was gutted by fire in 1990?

13 Which US clarinettist's real name was Arthur Jacob Arshawsky?

14 In 1984 The Society of West End Theatre Awards were renamed in honour of whom?

15 In which town is the largest stage in the UK?

16 How is "The Marriage of Figaro" known in Italian?

17 What is Shakespeare's longest play?

18 Which former prime minister's wife shares her name with a Bellini opera?

19 What nationality are two of the Three Tenors?

20 Which US director was the impetus behind the new Globe Theatre in London?

21 How is the Ballets Russes of Sergei Diaghelev now known?

22 What was "The Madness of King George" called as a play?

23 Which British playwright wrote the trilogy "The Norman Conquests"?

24 Which Czech-born playwright wrote "Jumpers and Arcadia"?

25 Who laid the foundation stone for the National Theatre on the South Bank?

26 Which newspaper presents awards for excellence in the London theatre?

27 Which of the three theatres within the National was named after the theatre's first Lord?

28 Who first produced "Les Miserables" in London?

29 In which street is London's Savoy Theatre?

30 In which city is the world's largest opera house?

31 Diaghilev was associated with which branch of the arts?

32 In which London lane is the

Theatre Royal?

33 Guiseppe Verdi is most famous for which type of musical work?

34 In which city is the Bolshoi Theatre?

35 Who wrote "HMS Pinafore"?

36 What was the nationality of the pianist and composer Claude Debussy?

37 How many symphonies did Beethoven write after the ninth?

38 Which series of concerts is held in late summer at the Albert Hall?

39 Which dance band leader disappeared during World War II?

40 In which branch of the arts did Joan Sutherland achieve fame?

41 In which Italian city is La Scala?

42 Which musical instrument does Stephane Grappelli play?

43 What type of entertainment did the Americans call vaudeville?

44 If you receive a Tony you performed in which country?

45 What kind of entertainment did Barnum call "the Greatest Show on Earth"?

46 What do you wish a performer when you say "break a leg"?

47 What is the name of the music centre that is the capital of Tennessee?

48 Which playwright married the TV doctor, Miriam?

49 How many sisters were in the title of the play by Chekhov?

50 What were the first names of Nureyev and Fonteyn?

A nswers to Quiz 123, POT LUCK

1. Grandma. 2. Sepia. 3. 40s. 4. "Cup". 5. Rocky Marciano. 6. Spurs. 7. Charles Kingsley. 8. Brown. 9. Victory In Europe. 10. Choux. 11. Doo-Dah Band. 12. Lyndhurst. 13. Belgium. 14. 180. 15. Whitney Houston. 16. Geoff Hamilton. 17. Monday. 18. Pacino. 19. Countess. 20. "House". 21. Cricket. 22. Jamboree. 23. 20th. 24. Kenneth Williams. 25. Gold. 26. Familiarity. 27. Faux pas. 28. "The Avengers". 29. 3. 30. Confederation. 31. "Crackerjack". 32. Red and green. 33. 20s. 34. "Hood". 35. Pet Shop Boys. 36. 18. 37. D.H. Lawrence. 38. Boxing. 39. Zimbabwe. 40. "Birds Of A Feather". 41. Eight. 42. Black Bess. 43. 1960s. 44. David Copperfield. 45. Woody Allen. 46. Fowler. 47. Travel agents. 48. "EastEnders". 49. Numbers. 50. A coach.

QUIZ 125 Communications

MEDIUM - LEVEL TWO

1 How would you orally address an Archbishop?

2 Which seaside resort has Squires Gate airport?

3 Which charity can you phone on 0345 90 90 90 from anywhere in the country?

4 Which is a Freephone prefix other than 0800?

5 What is the emergency phone number in the US?

6 In Braille which letter consists of a single dot?

7 What does CompuServe provide access to?

8 What is a TAM ?

9 In telecommunications what is polling?

10 Which number can be used as an alternative to 999?

11 How often is *Reader's Digest* published?

12 What number do you dial for BT UK Directory Enquiries?

13 What do you dial if you do not want the person you are calling to know your phone number?

14 What would an Italian call a motorway?

15 What colour are telephone boxes in France?

16 What is the maximum weight you can send letters at the basic rate?

17 Which three cities are termini for the Eurostar service?

18 What is a local rate number other than 0345?

19 What colour is a 1p postage stamp?

20 What colour is an airmail sticker?

21 Which two cities are the termini for the Anglia rail region?

22 Which underground line goes to Heathrow Terminals?

23 In which US city is O'Hare airport?

24 Between which hours are BT's evening and night time phone rates?

25 What is the UK's oldest Sunday newspaper?

26 What do you dial for International Directory Enquiries?

27 Which newspaper cartoon strip is translated into Latin with characters Snupius and Carolius Niger?

28 Before 1991 which periodical had the highest circulation?

29 What colour is the logo for Virgin trains?

30 What is the most expensive denomination of UK postage stamp?

31 What does 'e' stand for in e-mail?

32 What was the world's first stamp called?

33 Which country has most first-language speakers of English?

34 What does the abbreviation BT stand for?

35 If A is for Alpha and B is for Bravo, what is C for ?

36 What did Samuel Morse design for communications?

37 When a number of computers are connected what are they called?

38 Which punctuation mark and letters indicate a UK Internet user?

39 How much do you pay for phone calls which begin with 0800?

40 In speech how should you - officially, at least - address a pope?

41 The Braille alphabet is made up of raised what?

42 Oftel is an independent watchdog relating to which service?

43 What does Hon. mean in the form of address Right Hon.?

44 A physician is addressed as Doctor; how is a male surgeon addressed?

45 The Greek letter beta corresponds with which letter of our alphabet?

46 Sputnik I was the first artificial what?

47 Which country has Le Monde as a major national newspaper?

48 What is Reuters?

49 In communication terms what is the Washington Post?

50 In which city is the headquarters of the Scotsman newspaper?

A nswers to Quiz 124, THE ARTS

1. Theatre Royal Drury Lane. 2. Ballet. 3. The Magic Flute. 4. Puccini. 5. Six hours. 6. UK. 7. Paris. 8. The Old Vic. 9. Tchaikovsky. 10. Bix Beiderbecke. 11. Ellington. 12. The Savoy. 13. Artie Shaw. 14. Olivier. 15. Blackpool. 16 Le Nozze di Figaro. 17. Hamlet. 18. Norma (Major). 19. Spanish. 20. Sam Wanamaker. 21. Kirov Ballet. 22. The Madness of George III. 23. Alan Ayckbourn. 24. Tom Stoppard. 25. The Queen Mother when Queen consort. 26. Evening Standard. 27. Olivier. 28. Cameron Mackintosh. 29. The Strand. 30. New York. 31. Ballet. 32. Drury Lane. 33. Opera. 34. Moscow. 35. Gilbert and Sullivan. 36. French. 37. None. 38. The Proms. 39. Glenn Miller. 40. Opera. 41. Milan. 42. Violin. 43. Music Hall. 44. USA. 45. Circus. 46. Good luck. 47. Nashville. 48. Tom Stoppard. 49. Three. 50. Rudolph, Margot.

QUIZ 126 Hobbies

MEDIUM - LEVEL TWO

1 What is the national game of Japan?

2 Which card game is based on dealing on the stock market?

3 Who is the only known unmarried person in Cluedo?

4 What is painted on to fabric in batik?

5 Carillon is a popular branch of what?

6 At which stately home would you see trees laid out in the form of troops at a famous battle?

7 In which month would you go to a Burns Night celebration?

8 Where is the National Museum of Geography?

9 The YOC is the junior branch of which society?

10 In bungee-jumping, what is a bungee?

11 Which type of wax is most commonly used in candle-making?

12 What is the traditional women's outfit in Scottish country dancing?

13 In which county would you visit St Michael's Mount?

14 What would you be making if you were following the bobbin or pillow method?

15 What order are trumps normally played at a whist drive?

16 How many counters does each player have at the start of a game of backgammon?

17 Which two Cluedo weapons are traditional weapons?

18 What are the two main activities in macrame?

19 Which manufacturer produces Sonic the Hedgehog computer games?

20 Which French theme park is named after a cartoon character?

21 Metroland is near which town?

22 In which city would you be if you went to the Ashmolean Museum?

23 In which resort is the golfing area of Birkdale?

24 How is the former Museum of Ornamental Art in London now known?

25 Which cathedral has ceiling decorations designed by "Blue Peter" viewers?

26 Which shopping centre in north-west London is near the foot of the M1?

27 Which world heritage site is near Amesbury in southern England?

28 Which is England's largest castle?

29 Which Safari Park is near Liverpool?

30 What is Edinburgh's main shopping street?

31 How many court cards are there in a standard pack?

32 In which game would you have a pitcher's mound and an outfield?

256

33 How many cards are needed for a game of canasta?

34 Which card game is also called vingt-et-un?

35 What is the name of the hedgehog in Sega's computer game?

36 Which London Palace has a famous maze?

37 Where are the Crown Jewels housed?

38 What colour flag is awarded by the EC to beaches of a certain standard?

39 What would you collect if you collected Clarice Cliff?

40 Near which city is Cadbury World?

41 What is the junior version of Lego called?

42 Where in Scotland is an Old Blacksmith's shop a tourist attraction?

43 What type of wildlife attraction is Longleat famous for?

44 Which Rosemary is famous for her keep-fit books and videos?

45 Which Norfolk seaside resort has a famous Pleasure Beach?

46 In knitting, which yarn is thicker, double-knitting or four-ply?

47 In chess, which piece can be called two different things?

48 How many cards do you deal to each player in rummy?

49 In Scrabble what colour are the triple-word score squares?

50 Which is the oldest swimming stroke?

Answers to
Quiz 125, COMMUNICATIONS

1. Your Grace. 2. Blackpool. 3. The Samaritans. 4. 0500. 5. 911. 6. A. 7. The Internet. 8. Telephone Answering Machine. 9. The ability to receive information from another fax machine. 10. 112. 11. Monthly. 12. 192. 13. 141. 14. Autostrada. 15. Yellow. 16. 60g. 17. London, Paris, Brussels. 18. 0645. 19. Dark red. 20. Blue. 21. London, Norwich. 22. Piccadilly. 23. Chicago. 24. 6 p.m. to 8 a.m.. 25. The Observer. 26. 153. 27. Peanuts. 28. Radio Times. 29. Red-and-grey. 30. £10. 31. Electronic. 32. Penny Black. 33. USA. 34. British Telecom. 35. Charlie. 36. Morse code. 37. Network. 38. .uk. 39. Nothing. 40. Your Holiness. 41. Dots. 42. Telecommunications. 43. Honourable. 44. Mr. 45. B. 46. Satellite. 47. France. 48. A news agency. 49. Newspaper. 50. Edinburgh.

Q^{UIZ}_{127} Pot Luck

MEDIUM - LEVEL TWO

1 Who founded the Royal Hospital in Chelsea?

2 What popular drink was known in China as early as 2737 BC?

3 What is the other name for the star Polaris?

4 On how many stone tablets were the Ten Commandments engraved?

5 Who wrote "The Three Sisters"?

6 What was the nickname of Edward Prince of Wales, son of Edward III?

7 Which insects communicate with one another by dancing?

8 Which disease was deliberately introduced in rabbits in the UK?

9 Where are the semicircular canals in the body?

10 What part of a cola tree is used to flavour drinks?

11 Which is the largest Greek island?

12 Whose last two TV series' were aired posthumously on both BBC 1 and Channel 4?

13 Who married Joséphine de Beauharnais and Princess Marie Louise?

14 Lack of iron in the diet may cause which disease?

15 On children's TV, if it's Friday and it's five o'clock what show was on ?

16 Riyadh is the capital of which country?

17 In which Far Eastern country was the Unification Church (Moonies) founded in 1954?

18 Which minister of health inaugurated the National Health Service?

19 Which strait links San Francisco Bay with the Pacific?

20 Which famous gardener helped landscape Blenheim and Stowe?

21 Which insect sometimes eats its male mate during copulation?

22 What was the first national park established in the United States in 1872?

23 What is the scientific name for the windpipe?

24 Which bean is the richest natural vegetable food?

25 In which city would you find the Blue Mosque?

26 What is the currency of Algeria?

27 In which port did Sir Francis Drake "singe the King of Spain's beard"?

28 Where was Mohammed born?

29 What is the commonest element in the Earth's crust?

30 Which George Orwell novel showed the dangers of excessive state control?

31 What became Glenn Miller's signature tune?

32 Picardy is in the northeast of which country?

33 NUPE was the National Union of

what?

34 Which cathedral has the highest spire in Britain?

35 Who sang "Hey, babe, take a walk on the wild side"?

36 The Brenner Pass links which two countries?

37 Which two fruits are anagrams of each other?

38 What is the chief member of a lifeboat crew called?

39 In geography, which term means the joining of two rivers?

40 Which musical note follows fah?

41 How many phases of the moon are there in a lunar month?

42 Which river flows through Cambridge?

43 In geometry what type of line bisects a circle?

44 Which university is based at Milton Keynes?

45 What on your body would a trichologist be concerned with?

46 Which instrument did Jack Benny play?

47 What was Gilbert White's field of work?

48 In the board game Cluedo what is the name of the Reverend?

49 Brussels, Honiton and Nottingham are all renowned for which product?

50 Which radio serial is "an everyday story of country folk"?

A nswers to Quiz 126, HOBBIES

1. Go. 2. Pit. 3. Miss Scarlet. 4. Wax. 5. Bell ringing. 6. Blenheim. 7. January. 8. Bradford. 9. RSPB. 10. A rope. 11. Paraffin wax. 12. Dress with a tartan sash. 13. Cornwall. 14. Lace. 15. Hearts, clubs, diamonds, spades. 16. 15. 17. Dagger, revolver. 18. Knotting, plaiting. 19. Sega. 20. Parc Asterix. 21. Gateshead. 22. Oxford. 23. Southport. 24. Victoria and Albert Museum. 25. York Minster. 26. Brent Cross. 27. Stonehenge. 28. Windsor. 29. Knowsley. 30. Princes Street. 31. 12. 32. Baseball. 33. 108. 34. Pontoon. 35. Sonic. 36. Hampton Court. 37. Tower of London. 38. Blue. 39. Pottery. 40. Birmingham. 41. Duplo. 42. Gretna Green. 43. Safari Park. 44. Conley. 45. Great Yarmouth. 46. Double-knitting. 47. Rook/castle. 48. Seven. 49. Red. 50. Breast stroke.

Quiz 128 | Sport

MEDIUM - LEVEL TWO

1 Which country does Ian Baker-Finch come from?

2 How many reds are there at the start of a snooker game?

3 What does BDA stand for?

4 What sport do the Buffalo Bills play?

5 In which sport is the Giro D'Italia - the Tour of Italy?

6 Which sport combines cross-country skiing and rifle shooting?

7 What is the nickname of the heavyweight James Douglas?

8 Which rugby league team are the Bears?

9 How often is golf's US Masters held?

10 Whittaker captained which side to the County Championship?

11 How many people are there in a hurling team?

12 Shannon Miler is famous for which sport?

13 In golf, what is the term for one under par for a hole?

14 In boxing, what is the lowest weight category?

15 Hale Irwin is famous for which sport?

16 Which England captain helped set up Kerry Packer's cricket "circus"?

17 The Mackeson Gold Cup is run at which course?

18 Dave Whitcombe plays darts for which country?

19 In the 90s, who lost the two major English finals and were relegated?

20 In 1996, which country was expelled from rugby's Five Nations?

21 AXA Equity & Law League cricket games are played on which day?

22 Wentworth golf course is in which county?

23 Which newspaper supported a darts tournament from 1948 to 1990?

24 Which ball in snooker is worth seven points?

25 A cricket umpire raises both arms above his head to signal what?

26 On what day of the week is the Prix De L'Arc de Triomphe race held?

27 Aikido is the ancient Japanese art of what?

28 Which county cricket club has its home at Grace Road?

29 Was Bertie Blunt the name of the rider or the horse that won the 1996 Badminton Horse Trials?

30 In what decade did David Gower first play cricket for England?

31 The green jacket is presented to the winner of which event?

32 Which country did the cricketer Graham Roope play for?

33 In boxing, what weight division is directly below heavyweight?

34 In horse racing, in which month is the Melbourne Cup held?

35 The 1994 Olympics took place in which country?

36 Who won the Wimbledon women's singles most times in the 80s?

37 Which two USA cities stage major marathons?

38 Phil Hubble is associated with which sport?

39 How often is cycling's Tour of Spain held?

40 The golfer Nick Price comes from which country?

41 A cricket umpire extends both arms horizontally to signal what?

42 The boxers Ray Leonard and Ray Robinson were both known as what?

43 In which sport did Michelle Smith find fame?

44 In golf, what is the term for two under par for a hole?

45 What sport do the Pittsburgh Steelers play?

46 The Harry Vardon Trophy is presented in which sport?

47 Which country won the 1996 cricket World Cup Final?

48 Which county cricket club has its home at Old Trafford?

49 What is the nickname of rugby union's William Henry Hare?

50 In horse racing, which of the five Classics is held at Doncaster?

A nswers to Quiz 127, Pot Luck

1. Charles II. 2. Tea. 3. Pole or North Star. 4. Two. 5. Anton Chekhov. 6. Black Prince. 7. Bees. 8. Myxomatosis. 9. The inner ear. 10. Nuts. 11. Crete. 12. Dennis Potter. 13. Napoleon Bonaparte. 14. Anaemia. 15. Crackerjack. 16. Saudi Arabia. 17. South Korea. 18. Aneurin Bevan. 19. Golden Gate. 20. Capability Brown. 21. Praying Mantis. 22. Yellowstone, Wyoming. 23. Trachea. 24. Soya. 25. Istanbul. 26. Dinar. 27. Cadiz. 28. Mecca. 29. Oxygen. 30. 1984. 31. Moonlight Serenade. 32. France. 33. Public Employees. 34. Salisbury. 35. Lou Reed. 36. Austria and Italy. 37. Lemon and melon. 38. Coxswain. 39. Confluence. 40. Soh. 41. Four. 42. The Cam. 43. Diameter. 44. Open University. 45. Hair. 46. Violin. 47. Naturalist. 48. Green. 49. Lace. 50. The Archers.

Quiz 129 | Pastimes

MEDIUM - LEVEL TWO

1 How many different coloured squares are there on a chessboard?

2 What would you buy from a Gibbons' catalogue?

3 Whose three-dimensional cube became a 70s and 80s craze?

4 If 3 is on the top side of a dice, what number is on the hidden side?

5 What does a snorkel help you do?

6 What is the art of knotting cord or string in patterns?

7 In Scrabble what is the value of the blank tile?

8 What does the musical term largo mean?

9 What fairground attraction did George Ferris construct in the 1890s?

10 Jokers apart, how many red cards are there in a standard pack?

11 What does a twitcher look for?

12 Which game features Miss Scarlet and the Reverend Green?

13 What do we call the art of paper-folding, which originated in Japan?

14 How many discs does each player have to start with in draughts?

15 What type of dancing was originally only performed by men, usually dressed in white, with bells and garlands?

16 If you practise calligraphy what do you do?

17 If you're involved in firing, throwing and glazing what do you do?

18 Which game has a board, cards and wedges?

19 In which leisure pursuit might you do a Bunny Hug?

20 How many people can you normally fit in a go-kart?

21 What is a John Innes No. 1?

22 If you combine k and p to make cables what is your hobby?

23 What was developed to experience the excitement of surfing on land?

24 Which exercises are designed to increase oxygen consumption and speed blood circulation?

25 What is a whist competition or tournament called?

26 A Royal Flush is the best hand you can get in which card game?

27 Which British game is known as checkers in the USA?

28 Which card game has a pegboard used for scoring?

29 Where on your body would you wear flippers?

30 Which playing card is the Black Lady?

31 If you practised callisthenics what type of activity would you be doing?

32 If you were watching someone

on a PGA tour what would you be watching?

33 Which board game has a Genus Edition?

34 Which toy was Hornby most famous for?

35 What do you hit with a racket in badminton?

36 What was the traditional colour for Aran wool?

37 What sort of toy was a Cabbage Patch?

38 In which board game do you draw the meaning of a word?

39 Which game is also the name of a gourdlike vegetable?

40 How many balls are used in a game of billiards?

41 How many members make up a water polo team?

42 What type of food would you get at Harry Ramsden's?

43 Which game has lawn and crown green varieties?

44 In which sport would you wear blades or quads?

45 In DIY, which is shinier - emulsion or gloss?

46 Which is normally larger, a pool table or a billiards table?

47 In Scrabble what colour are the double-word-score squares?

48 In which county is Alton Towers?

49 Which London museum is named after a queen and her cousin?

50 In which sport would you use a sabre, foil or épée?

1. Australia. 2. 15. 3. British Darts Association. 4. American Football. 5. Cycling. 6. Biathlon. 7. Buster. 8. Oldham. 9. Annually. 10. Leicestershire. 11. 15. 12. Gymnastics. 13. Birdie. 14. Straw-weight. 15. Golf. 16. Tony Greig. 17. Cheltenham. 18. England. 19. Middlesbrough. 20. England. 21. Sunday. 22. Surrey. 23. News Of the World. 24. Black. 25. Boundary for six runs. 26. Sunday. 27. Self-defence. 28. Leicestershire. 29. Horse. 30. 1970s. 31. US Masters. 32. England. 33. Cruiserweight. 34. November. 35. Norway. 36. Martina Navratilova. 37. Boston and New York. 38. Swimming. 39. Annually. 40. Zimbabwe. 41 A wide. 42. Sugar Ray. 43. Swimming. 44. Eagle. 45. American Football. 46. Golf. 47. Sri Lanka. 48. Lancashire. 49. Dusty. 50. St Leger.

QUIZ 130 | TV Times

MEDIUM - LEVEL TWO

1 Which Clive chaired "Whose Line is it Anyway"?

2 Which 80s drama centred on Liverpudlian Yosser Hughes?

3 In which US city did the action of "Cheers" take place?

4 Which Doctor abandoned his Casebook in the 90s revival of the series?

5 Who played Jeeves to Hugh Laurie's Bertie Wooster?

6 In "Neighbours" Erinsborough is a suburb of which city?

7 On which night does "Noel's House Party" take place?

8 What were Rita Garnett's parents called?

9 In which series did Richard de Vere buy Grantleigh Manor?

10 Which animals did Barbara Woodhouse usually appear with?

11 Which soap was a spin-off from "Dallas"?

12 What is "Jimmy's"?

13 Who plays the Chef at the Le Château Anglais in Oxfordshire?

14 Which British actress played Alexis Carrington in "Dynasty"?

15 Which two Michaels have hosted "Give Us A Clue"?

16 What was James's wife called in "All Creatures Great and Small"?

17 Which Kate is famous for her news reports from Tiananmen Square ?

18 What is Charlie Fairhead's job at Holby City Hospital?

19 In "Dallas" which character returned from the dead in the shower?

20 Which Doctor has had assistants called Vicki, Jo, Melanie and Ace?

21 Which 90s series featured Guy Lofthouse and Guy MacFadyean?

22 Where was "Harry's Game" set?

23 What is the House in TV's "House of Cards"?

24 Which drama features Claude Jeremiah Greengrass?

25 Which comedy show is TV's answer to radio's "News Quiz"?

26 Who is the male presenter of BBC TV's "Children in Need"?

27 Which two comedians were famous for their 'head-to-head' scenes?

28 Which TV war reporter became an MP in 1997?

29 Which all-round entertainer's catchphrase is "Awight!"?

30 Which soap was trailed as "sex, sun and sangria"?

31 Who was the first permanent female presenter of "Points of View"?

32 Which Team heroically helped those in trouble in the 80s?

33 Who replaced Leslie Crowther on "The Price is Right"?

34 In which country is "Prisoner Cell Block H" set?

35 Which quiz features a picture

board and "what happens next"?

36 Which political programme is based on radio's "Any Questions"?

37 Which series focused on the King's Fusiliers Infantry Regiment?

38 What were the "Spitting Image" puppets made from?

39 Which racing driver was BBC Sports Personality of the Year twice in the 90s?

40 Which decade was the setting for "Tenko"?

41 Who was the main female presenter of "That's Life"?

42 Which "EastEnders" character died on his allotment?

43 Which country is Rab C. Nesbitt from?

44 Which former "Opportunity Knocks" presenter died in 1997?

45 Who is resident cook on "Food and Drink"?

46 Who always embarked on a long monologue in "The Two Ronnies"?

47 What did Denis Neville and Oz say to those they left behind in the North-East in the 80s?

48 In which series does Assumpta Fitzgerald appear?

49 In which decade did the action of "M*A*S*H" take place?

50 Which sort of containers are Yogi Bear's favourite?

Answers to Quiz 129, PASTIMES

1. Two. 2. Stamps. 3. Rubik's. 4. 4. 5. Breathe under water. 6. Macramé. 7. Nil. 8. Slowly. 9. Ferris Wheel. 10. 26. 11. Birds. 12. Cluedo. 13. Origami. 14. 12. 15. Morris. 16. Handwriting. 17. Pottery. 18. Trivial Pursuit. 19. Ballroom dancing. 20. One. 21. Garden compost. 22. Knitting. 23. Skateboard. 24. Aerobics. 25. Whist drive. 26. Poker. 27. Draughts. 28. Cribbage. 29. Feet. 30. Queen of Spades. 31. Keep fit. 32. Golf. 33. Trivial Pursuit. 34. Train sets. 35. Shuttlecock. 36. Cream. 37. Doll. 38. Pictionary. 39. Squash. 40. Three. 41. Seven. 42. Fish and chips. 43. Bowls. 44. Roller skating. 45. Gloss. 46. Billiards table. 47. Pink. 48. Staffordshire. 49. Victoria and Albert. 50. Fencing.

Pot Luck

MEDIUM - LEVEL TWO

1 On which label did the Beatles have their first hit record?

2 What was the television pioneer John Baird's middle name?

3 In which decade of the 20th century was Paddy Ashdown born?

4 What word can go after "nut" and before "jack"?

5 How is Derek Jules Gaspard Ulrich Van Den Bogaerde better known?

6 Which soccer team does Nigel Kennedy support?

7 Who wrote the novel The Murder Of Roger Ackroyd?

8 Peter Allis is associated with which sport?

9 Who is the US state of Virginia name after?

10 Which Elvis song has the words "you ain't never caught a rabbit"?

11 Which stimulant is found in tea and coffee?

12 Who has a dog called Gnasher?

13 Which Leonard starred in "The Rise And fall Of Reginald Perrin"?

14 What word can go before "down", "jumping" and "off"?

15 Which make-up item is the French word for red?

16 Who wrote "Send In The Clowns"?

17 Which French phrase used in English means already seen?

18 What number is represented by the Roman numeral M?

19 The airline Labrador Airways is from which country?

20 In which TV series did the character René Artois appear?

21 Which day of the week is Shrove once a year?

22 Which Tom won an Oscar for Best Actor in "Forrest Gump"?

23 What two colours of squirrel are found in Britain?

24 The "War Cry" is the magazine of which organization?

25 Whose catchphrase is "Yabba-dabba-doo!"?

26 In Cockney rhyming slang what are mince pies?

27 Who had a 70s No. I with "Message In a Bottle"?

28 In which country is the city of Alexandria?

29 Ash Wednesday is the first day of which period of fasting?

30 On a Monopoly board, what colour is Mayfair?

31 In which month is Epiphany?

32 Who went with Christopher Robin to Buckingham Palace?

33 In which TV series did Mrs Slocombe and Mr Humphries first appear?

34 What word can go after "sand" and before "account"?

35 In which country is the city of Amritsar?

36 Which Amateur Association has

266

the abbreviation AAA?

37 Who wrote the novel *Rebecca*?

38 The characters Jason and Sable appeared in which TV soap?

39 Moving clockwise on a dartboard what number is next to 1?

40 In which decade of the 20th century was Richard Attenborough born?

41 What is the name of Del Trotter's local?

42 How many yards in a chain?

43 The zodiac sign Pisces covers which two calendar months?

44 Steve Backley is associated with which branch of athletics?

45 How is Charles Holley better known?

46 Who was the first German to be "Football Writers" Player of the Year?

47 In the Bible, which Book immediately follows Genesis?

48 What is 80 per cent of 400?

49 Frigophobia is the fear of what?

50 In the 80s, who had a No. 1 with "Eternal Flame"?

A nswers to Quiz 130, TV TIMES

1. Anderson. 2. "Boys From the Blackstuff". 3. Boston. 4. Finlay. 5. Stephen Fry. 6. Melbourne. 7. Saturday. 8. Alf and Else. 9. "To the Manor Born". 10. Dogs. 11. "Knots Landing". 12. A hospital. 13. Lenny Henry. 14. Joan Collins. 15. Aspel, Parkinson. 16. Helen. 17. Adie. 18. Nurse. 19. Bobby Ewing. 20. Who. 21. "The Good Guys". 22. Northern Ireland. 23. House of Commons. 24. "Heartbeat". 25. "Have I Got News For You". 26. Terry Wogan. 27. Smith and Jones. 28. Martin Bell. 29. Michael Barrymore. 30. "Eldorado" 31. Anne Robinson. 32. The A-Team. 33. Bruce Forsyth. 34. Australia. 35. "A Question of Sport". 36. "Question Time". 37. "Soldier Soldier". 38. Rubber. 39. Damon Hill. 40. 1940s. 41. Esther Rantzen. 42. Arthur Fowler. 43. Scotland. 44. Hughie Green. 45. Michael Barry. 46. Corbett. 47. Auf Wiedersehen Pet. 48. "Ballykissangel". 49. 1950s. 50. Picnic baskets.

QUIZ 132 Painting

1 Who painted "The Blue Boy" and "Mr and Mrs Andrews"?

2 Which Pierre-Auguste painted "Umbrellas" and "The Bathers"?

3 What is Leonardo da Vinci's "La Gioconda" also known as?

4 Which English cricketer is a keen amateur watercolour artist?

5 Whose Progress did William Hogarth paint?

6 What is arguably the most famous painting by Dutchman Frans Hals?

7 Which Egyptian sculpture is more than 73 metres long?

8 Which 1960s art vogue was based on optical illusion?

9 What is paint applied to in a fresco?

10 Which sculpture did Auguste Bartholdi give to the United States?

11 What is notable about the woman in Ingres' "Valpinçon Bather"?

12 What type of work is Albrecht Dürer famous for?

13 Where in the United States would you find Washington's head 18 metres high?

14 What art form is a Japanese netsuke?

15 Who painted "Bubbles", which has been used in a soap ad?

16 Which English sculptor produced rounded forms such as "Reclining Figure"?

17 Which Spaniard is known for his hallucinatory paintings?

18 Which Dutch painter is well known for his self-portraits?

19 Who painted Campbell soup tins and Marilyn Monroe?

20 What type of paintings is Joshua Reynolds famous for?

21 A statue in Afghanistan of which religious teacher is 53 metres high?

22 Whose "Irises" and "Sunflowers" were two of the world's most expensive paintings at auction?

23 What is the binding medium in gouache technique?

24 Which Spaniard founded the Cubist movement?

25 Of which school of painting was Claude Monet a leading exponent?

26 For which art style is David Hockney famous?

27 Which performers were a favourite subject for painter/sculptor Degas?

28 In which country was the French painter Marc Chagall born?

29 In which county is "Constable country", named after its famous son?

30 What was the first name of sculptor Epstein?

31 Which John painted "The Haywain"?

32 What was the surname of outrageous artist Salvador?

33 Which city, famous for its canals, did Canaletto paint?

34 What was the first name of Impressionist painter Cézanne?

35 Which Leonardo painted Mona Lisa?

36 Which parts of the Venus de Milo are missing?

37 Which animals is George Stubbs famous for painting?

38 Which Paul was famous for paintings of the South Seas?

39 Which Vincent lost an ear?

40 What was the first name of pop artist Warhol?

41 How is Francisco de Goya y Lucientes more simply known?

42 Which Greek artist's name means 'The Greek'?

43 Which Spanish painter Pablo was the founder of Cubism?

44 Who was famous for his posters of French dance halls and cabarets?

45 What was the nationality of Rembrandt?

46 Edouard and Claude were Manet and Monet. Which was which?

47 Which items useful on a rainy day did Renoir paint?

48 Which branch of the arts was Barbara Hepworth famous for?

49 What was the nationality of Albrecht Dürer?

50 Which art gallery is in Trafalgar Square?

A nswers to Quiz 131, POT LUCK

1. Parlophone. 2. Logie. 3. 40s. 4. "Cracker". 5. Dirk Bogarde. 6. Aston Villa. 7. Agatha Christie. 8. Golf. 9. Queen Elizabeth I. 10. "Hound Dog". 11. Caffeine. 12. Dennis the Menace. 13. Rossiter. 14. "Show". 15. Rouge. 16. Stephen Sondheim. 17. Déjà vu. 18. 1,000. 19. Canada. 20. "'Allo 'Allo". 21. Tuesday. 22. Hanks. 23. Grey and red. 24. Salvation Army. 25. Fred Flintstone. 26. Eyes. 2.7 Police. 28. Egypt. 29. Lent. 30. Dark blue. 31. January. 32. Alice. 33. "Are You Being Served".34. "Bank". 35. India. 36. Athletics. 37. Daphne du Maurier. 38. "The Colbys". 39. 18. 40. 20s. 41. The Nag's Head. 42. 22. 43. February, March. 44. Javelin. 45. Buddy Holly. 46. Jurgen Klinsmann. 47. Exodus. 48. 320. 49. Being cold. 50. The Bangles.

Quiz 133 | Movies

MEDIUM - LEVEL TWO

1 Who starred in "The Towering Inferno" and "Naked Gun 2$^1/_2$ "?

2 Who played Cruella de Vil in the "real" version of "101 Dalmatians"?

3 Which movie star played Shylock in London's West End in 1989?

4 Who played the aunts in "James and the Giant Peach"?

5 Who directed "Born on the Fourth of July" and "Natural Born Killers"?

6 Who played the latest Saint?

7 Who played Heathcliff in the 90s "Wuthering Heights"?

8 Who was the British star of "Fierce Creatures"?

9 Who played the Elephant Man?

10 Who married Mickey Rooney and Frank Sinatra?

11 Who insured whose legs for a million dollars with Lloyd's of London?

12 Who was the heroine in the 30s version of "King Kong"?

13 Who played the mother in "Mermaids"?

14 Who did Alan Rickman play in "Robin Hood, Prince of Thieves"?

15 Who was known in Los Angeles as BK 4454813 OG 2795?

16 Whose film production company is called Jagged Films?

17 Who played Batman in the 1997 "Batman and Robin?"

18 Which blonde screen legend made only 11 films, three for Hitchcock?

19 Which rock star did Angela Bassett play in a 1993 biopic?

20 Who was Jack in "Somersby"?

21 Who wrote the screenplay of "The Crucible"?

22 How are Felix Ungar and Oscar Madison better known?

23 Who played Robin Williams's estranged wife in "Mrs Doubtfire"?

24 Who directed "Pulp Fiction" and "Reservoir Dogs"?

25 Who played Vince Vega in "Pulp Fiction"?

26 Which ex-007 appeared for two minutes at the end of "Robin Hood: Prince of Thieves"?

27 Who was never seen in his most successful pre-'93 performance?

28 Which actress directed "Prince of Tides" and "Yentl"?

29 Which role did Dooley Wilson play in "Casablanca"?

30 Who produced the Hugh Grant movie "Extreme Measures"?

31 Who played Garrett Breedlove in "Terms of Endearment"?

32 Who was the male co-star with Sigourney Weaver and Melanie Griffith in "Working Girl"?

33 How is Margaret Mary Emily Anne Hyra better known?

34 Which superstar was mayor of Carmel, California?

270

35 Who was contestant No. 24 in the 1950 Mr Universe contest?

36 Whose line was "Frankly, my dear, I don't give a damn"?

37 Who used Eleanor Roosevelt as her inspiration for her role in "The African Queen"?

38 Clark Gable, Marlon Brando and Mel Gibson have all played which sailor on film?

39 Who did Mae West ask to "come up some time an' see me"?

40 What was Tom Hanks's profession in "Philadelphia"?

41 Who starred with Paul Newman in "The Color of Money"?

42 Who had the line "Greed is good" in "Wall Street" in 1987?

43 Who sang "Makin' Whoopee" on Jeff Bridges' piano in "The Fabulous Baker Boys"?

44 Who won an Oscar as Charlie Allnut in "The African Queen"?

45 For which film did Al Pacino win his first Oscar?

46 Who received an Oscar nomination for his last film "Guess Who's Coming to Dinner"?

47 What is Bob Hope's signature tune?

48 Who were first paired on screen in "Flying Down to Rio"?

49 Which actress was the subject of the film "Mommie Dearest"?

50 Who married the journalist Maria Shriver, a niece of President Kennedy?

QUIZ 134 History

HARD - LEVEL THREE

1 In which year were England and Scotland united?

2 Who was president between 1877 and 1881?

3 Which prison was stormed at the start of the French Revolution?

4 Which king did the Romans drive out in 510BC?

5 To what does the adjective Carolingian refer?

6 Who beat the Roman army at the Battle of Cannae?

7 What was remarkable about the way Rome was ruled in AD68–9?

8 Did the Chinese only use gun powder for fireworks?

9 Where were the Normans from?

10 What famous Australian landmark was opened in 1932?

11 When was the survey for the Mason-Dixon line concluded?

12 Which city was the original home of Abraham?

13 Which family ruled Milan from 1277 to 1447?

14 Who were the Valois family?

15 Which notable building was started by the Emperor Vespasian?

16 To which Native American tribe did Geronimo belong?

17 Which civilization did Pizzaro destroy when he invaded Peru?

18 By what name did the 'louisette' become infamous?

19 Who led Czechoslovakia before the 1968 Soviet invasion?

20 How was the French legal system reformed in 1804?

21 What horror stalked the streets of London in 1888?

22 Name the French Jewish soldier falsely accused of selling secrets to the Germans in 1894.

23 Which revolutionary was killed in Mexico in 1940?

24 What happened at Kill Devil Hill?

25 Which Spanish knight seized Valencia from the Moors in 1094?

26 What name connects a biscuit and an Italian general?

27 Which British general and his French opponent were both killed at Quebec in 1759?

28 Who were: Divorced, Beheaded, Died, Divorced, Beheaded, Survived?

29 Which royal dynasty was named after its gentian flower emblem?

30 What was Alexander the Great's horse. What did it mean?

31 Name Mary Queen of Scots' preferred musician, who was murdered in Holyrood Palace.

32 Which event first took place in New Orleans in 1827?

33 Which French premier was known as 'The Tiger'?

34 What was remarkable about the Rochdale Society of Equitable Pioneers founded in 1844?

35 The island of Tortuga played host to people of a notorious

272

profession. What were they?

36 Which Christian priest and king was supposed to have ruled an empire in Africa or Asia?

37 Which British general was killed at the siege of Khartoum?

38 A stream near Washington DC gave its name to two American Civil War battles. Name it.

39 In which town did Samuel Langhorne Clemens grow up?

40 Who said: 'The only thing we have to fear is fear itself'?

41 Who said: "A man who is good enough to shed his blood for his country is good enough to be given a square deal afterwards"?

42 Name the stone upon which all British monarchs are crowned.

43 Who said: "I beseech you, in the bowels of Christ, think it possible you may be mistaken"?

44 What did Generals George Crook, Henry Ware Lawton, and Nelson Miles have in common?

45 Who led the US marines who captured John Brown?

46 Name the German theologian and leader of the Reformation.

47 The phrase 'hocus pocus' is a corruption of what Latin phrase?

48 Which South American hero was made president of Greater Colombia and helped liberate Peru and Bolivia?

49 What was Tokyo formerly called?

50 Which African lake was first sighted by John Speke and Sir Richard Burton in 1858?

Answers to Quiz 197, MOTOWN

1. Reach Out, I'll Be There. 2. Berry Gordy. 3. Dave. 4. Aretha Franklin. 5. Holland. 6. Otis Redding. 7. The Broken Hearted. 8. Jackie Wilson. 9. The Isley Brothers. 10. James Brown. 11. The Supremes. 12. After the song Tammy by Debbie Reynolds. 13. You Keep me Hangin' On. 14. Wilson Pickett. 15. The Vandellas. 16. Arthur Conley. 17. I'm Still Waiting. 18. Lionel Richie. 19. Gladys Knight. 20. Bobby Brown. 21. Stevie Wonder. 22. The Temptations. 23. Jimmy Mack. 24. William. 25. Midnight. 26. Reflections. 27. Marvin Gaye. 28. Atlantic. 29. Edwin Starr. 30. Junior Walker. 31. Supremes. 32. James Brown. 33. Whitney Houston. 34. 1980s. 35. Georgia. 36. Billie Holliday. 37. Aretha Franklin. 38. Berry Gordy. 39. Organ. 40. Shot (by his father). 41. Aretha Franklin. 42. Gladys Knight. 43. "I Want You Back". 44. Michael Bolton. 45. Stevie Wonder. 46. Jimmy Ruffin. 47. The Wicked Pickett. 48. Four Tops. 49. 1966. 50. The Commodores.

QUIZ 135 Money

HARD - LEVEL THREE

1 What is the site of the US Gold Bullion Depository?

2 What is the process of imprinting a blank coin with a design?

3 Where were the earliest known coins made?

4 What is the Polish currency?

5 In 1979, a dollar coin was with drawn due to lack of popularity. Who did the coin portray?

6 Which country uses the lek as its unit of currency?

7 Before Wilhem I became Emperor of Germany in 1871, which was the main unit of currency?

8 In which year did the full decimalization of the British currency take place?

9 Which is the basic unit of currency in Morocco?

10 Which three places in the UK use different coins from the rest of the country?

11 What is the name of the famous gambling center situated on the Mediterranean coast?

12 Where was an obol used and what was it made from?

13 In German currency, how much is one mark worth?

14 What is the name given to the study or collection of money?

15 What was a sovereign made from?

16 Where did the ecu coin originate?

17 Which was the first coin to be issued in the USA?

18 How many old pennies was the English shilling worth?

19 What types of leaf were used as money in Virginia and Maryland in the 17th and 18th centuries?

20 Which country issued the first printed paper money in Europe?

21 Which is the basic unit of currency in Hungary?

22 Into which smaller currency unit is the French franc divided?

23 What type of printing plate is used for printing banknotes?

24 Which nation first started to handle money in the form of printed paper documents?

25 After the Gold Rush, in which form was gold first used as a method of payment?

26 What is the Indian currency?

27 What was the name of the paper money issued during the French Revolution?

28 Which English gold coin issued between 1663 and 1813 was worth one pound and one shilling?

29 What do the currencies of Mexico, Cuba, and the Philippines have in common?

30 What is the South African currency?

31 Who issued pieces of eight?

32 What has been the main feature on French coins since the revolution?

33 Which is Swedish currency called?

34 Name the coin used in Great

Britain that was worth a fourth of an old penny?

35 In which country is the yen the basic unit of currency?

36 Which Scandinavian country has a different coinage system from the others?

37 Who first developed a round coin with a design on both sides?

38 In which countries was the doubloon formerly used?

39 Which were the biggest coins ever made?

40 Which European city issued ducats and sequins in the 13th century?

41 During the Roman Empire, what was on most coins?

42 What was the first Roman money made from?

43 Where did the practice of banking first begin?

44 Nowadays, which language appears on Belgian coins?

45 In which three countries is the ore in use?

46 What is the Turkish currency?

47 During the 1970s there was a shortage of small-denomination coins in Italy. What types of coin did shopkeepers give out instead?

48 Which smaller unit is the Dutch gulden divided into?

49 What is the trade where one type of goods is swapped for another type without money transactions?

50 What is the name for the South African bullion coins?

Answers to Quiz 134, HISTORY

1. 1707. 2. Rutherford B. Hayes. 3. The Bastille. 4. Tarquin VII. 5. Anything pertaining to Charlemagne. 6. Hannibal. 7. There were four emperors. 8. Not at all. The military potential was realized very quickly. 9. They were descended from Vikings. 10. Sydney Harbor Bridge. 11. 1767. 12. Ur of the Chaldees. 13. Visconti. 14. A dynasty of French kings. 15. The Colosseum. 16. The (Chiricahua) Apaches. 17. The Incas. 18. The guillotine. 19. Alexander Dubcek. 20. By the introduction of the Code Napoleon. 21. Jack the Ripper. 22. Alfred Dreyfus. 23. Leon Trotsky. 24. The Wright brothers make the first sustained, manned flights in a controled, gasoline-powered aircraft. 25. El Cid (Ruy Diaz de Bivar). 26. Garibaldi. 27. Wolfe and Montcalm. 28. The wives of Henry VIII. 29. The Plantagenets. 30. Bucephalus (ox head). 31. David Rizzio. 32. Mardi Gras. 33. Georges Clemenceau. 34. It was the first modern cooperative society. 35. Pirates. 36. Prester John. 37. General Charles Gordon. 38. Bull Run. 39. Hannibal, Missouri. 40. Franklin D. Roosevelt. 41. Teddy Roosevelt (1903). 42. The Stone of Scone. 43. Oliver Cromwell. 44. They all held Geronimo prisoner at one time or another. 45. Robert E. Lee. 46. Martin Luther. 47. Hoc est corpus (meum). 48. Simon Bolivar. 49. Edo. 50. Lake Tanganyika.

QUIZ 136 Transport

HARD - LEVEL THREE

1 What record did the American Voyager aircraft break in 1986 in its nine-day flight around the world?

2 What is the name of the French high-speed train service?

3 Where was the world's first underground railway line built?

4 In which year did Concorde go into service?

5 Which popular car was stopped being made in Germany in 1977?

6 What did the French Montgolfier brothers fly in 1783?

7 What was the name of Charles Lindbergh's plane?

8 Which incident put an end to the use of passenger airships in 1937?

9 What were the Big Boys?

10 Who designed the first successful American helicopter?

11 What was the name of the world's first jet airliner, and when did it enter service?

12 What new type of water transport did Christopher Cockerell design?

13 Which new device did Gottfried Daimler produce in 1885 that started the development of the automobile industry?

14 Which was the first-mass produced car in the USA?

15 What is the major advantage of the stealth bomber?

16 What is the name of a bicycle which two people can ride together?

17 On an aircraft, what is the purpose of a spoiler?

18 Which was the first steam-powered sailing ship to cross the Atlantic?

19 What is the main difference between hovercraft and the hydrofoil?

20 Which part of a ship is the hull?

21 What type of aircraft did Otto Lilienthal design?

22 What are most large ships powered by?

23 Which is the main difference between a rocket and a jet engine?

24 What type of vessel is a galleon?

25 What is the difference between the ignition of a petrol engine and that of a diesel engine?

26 What was New York's first public transit facility?

27 Which famous navigator and explorer sailed on the Endeavour?

28 Who built the first pedal-ridden bicycle?

29 What was the name of the ship Christopher Columbus sailed on to America?

30 What do you call a glider with a small engine driving a propeller?

31 What are the majority of heavy-goods vehicles powered by?

32 Which was the first ship to com

plete a voyage around the world?

33 What type of vessel is a cog?

34 What is the name of the horse-drawn carriage which appeared for hire in London in the early 17th century?

35 Why do aeroplanes land into the wind?

36 Which was the main feature of a 'penny farthing' bicycle?

37 Which is the longest rail tunnel in the world?

38 Who built the first motorcycle?

39 What was the main disadvantage of steam-powered vehicles?

40 Which country operated the first public railway?

41 Which major new feature did the Draisienne bicycle boast?

42 In motorcycles, how is the gear box linked to the wheels?

43 Which major advance did Richard Trevithick introduce to rail travel?

44 Between which two cities did the Orient Express run?

45 Who was the first aviator to cross the English Channel?

46 What type of vehicle did Francis and Freelan Stanley develop?

47 What does the carburettor do?

48 Which was the first railroad tunnel going through the Alps?

49 Which was the predecessor of the American Greyhound bus?

50 Which was the first underwater ship used in war?

A nswers to Quiz 135, Money

1. Fort Knox in Kentucky. 2. Minting. 3. In the kingdom of Lydia, which is now known as Turkey. 4. The zloty. 5. Susan B. Anthony, a feminist leader. 6. Albania. 7. The thaler. 8. 1971. 9. The dirham. 10. The Isle of Man, and the Channel Islands of Guernsey and Jersey. 11. Monte Carlo. 12. It was a silver coin used in Ancient Greece. 13. 100 pfennig. 14. Numismatics. 15. Gold. 16. France. 17. The copper cent. 18. Twelve. 19. Tobacco leaves. 20. Sweden. 21. The forint. 22. The centime. 23. Intaglio plates. 24. China. 25. As dust. 26. The rupee. 27. Assignats. 28. The guinea. 29. They all use the peso. 30. The rand. 31. The Spanish conquerors of the Americas. 32. A female head representing the republic. It is popularly known as 'Marianne'. 33. The krona. 34. A farthing. 35. Japan. 36. Finland, which has a system that was introduced by the Russians. 37. The Ancient Greeks. 38. In Spain and Spanish America. 39. Copper plate money, from Sweden. 40. Venice. 41. A portrait of the emperor. 42. Copper, in the form of lumps. 43. In northern Italy. 44. There are two types of coin issued, one with French writing and one with Flemish writing. 45. Denmark, Sweden, and Norway. 46. The lira. 47. Telephone coins. 48. Cent. 49. Barter. 50. Krugerrands.

Q_{UIZ} 137 | Customs

1 With which festival is the practice of first footing associated?

2 What do American children traditionally do at Hallowe'en?

3 Which dance is associated with May Day?

4 What was wassailing?

5 Who is a cantor?

6 Which is the least important from a liturgical point of view: Easter, Christmas or Pentecost?

7 Who presided at traditional Christmas revelry in England during the 15th and 16th centuries?

8 Which festival, other than Haloween, is held on the eve of May Day and has supernatural associations?

9 Which people are commonly believed to kiss by rubbing noses?

10 Which people engage in a war dance called a haka?

11 In Germany, which festival is traditonally celebrated with fireworks?

12 What is watch night?

13 What is Seder?

14 Among which Native American people are pubescent girls anointed with pollen as part of their rite of passage?

15 What is the most venerated object of Islam?

16 What is a bat mitzvah?

17 How did the thugs dedictate their victims to Kali?

18 What creature is traditionally sent into the wilderness on the Day of Atonement?

19 What was a whipping boy?

20 Who would you expect to find at a pow-wow?

21 Which peoples might you expect to find at a ceilidh?

22 Who would attend a corroboree?

23 What name is given to an extended trip through the bush taken by an Aboriginal?

24 What do Aboriginals call the time of the creation of the world?

25 What custom is associated with the town of Pamplona?

26 Who were, by custom, buried in unconsecrated ground?

27 In Japanese ritual suicide, how did the victim usually die?

28 What did Native Americans do to seal important agreements?

29 What did the Egyptians do to ensure entry to the after life?

30 How, according to certain Native American tribes, does a person know he is to die?

31 What is the dance known as the tarantella supposed to achieve?

32 Which secret society would send someone a dead fish as a sign that he was to be murdered?

33 What is supposed to happen to a man who crosses the equator for the first time?

34 What, according to tradition, will

prevent a vampire from rising from the dead?

35 What is suttee?

36 In which festival do Muslims refuse food and drink during the hours of daylight?

37 In which festival do Hindus spray each other with colored water?

38 What food is traditionally associated with Shrove Tuesday?

39 When do devout Christians smear ash on their forehead?

40 On Burns Night, what dish is traditionally brought into the banqueting hall to the accompaniment of bagpipes?

41 In the British Parliament, who summons the members of the House of Commons to hear the Queen's Speech?

42 How is Black Rod received when he approaches the Commons?

43 Of whom do the British burn an effigy each year?

44 What popular American celebration occurs in November?

45 What was beating the bounds?

46 What, according to Winston Churchill, comprised the traditions of the Royal Navy?

47 What is a Kneip bath?

48 What custom is repudiated by Baptists?

49 Which way is the port passed at dinner?

50 What are people who follow the teachings of Zoroaster called?

1. First to fly around the world without refueling. 2. TGV – Trains à Grande Vitesse. 3. London. 4. 1976. 5. Volkswagen 'Beetle'. 6. A hot-air balloon. 7. Spirit of St. Louis. 8. The Hindenburg Disaster. 9. Steam locomotives used to haul freight trains across the Rocky Mountains. 10. Igor Sikorsky. 11. The de Havilland Comet 1, in 1952. 12. The hovercraft. 13. The internal combustion engine. 14. The Ford Model T. 15. It is invisible to radar. 16. A tandem. 17. To increase drag and reduce lift. 18. The Savannah. 19. Hovercraft is lifted by a cushion of air, hydrofoil by wings. 20. Its framework, excluding the engine and masts. 21. Gliders. 22. Steam turbines. 23. The jet engine obtains oxygen needed from the atmosphere whilst the rocket carries its own. 24. A sailing ship with a square rig and three masts. 25. In a petrol engine the fuel-air mixture is ignited by a spark, but in a diesel engine by compression of the air in the cylinders. 26. 12-seater horse-drawn bus. 27. Captain Cook. 28. Kirkpatrick Macmillan. 29. Santa Maria. 30. Microlight. 31. Diesel engines. 32. Magellan's Vittoria. 33. A single-masted sailing ship. 34. Hackney. 35. To maintain a safe air speed. 36. It had a large front wheel and a small rear wheel. 37. The Seikan tunnel. 38. Gottlieb Daimler. 39. Could not move off instantly as water had to boil to produce steam. 40. England. 41. A steerable front wheel. 42. By a drive chain. 43. He built the first steam-powered locomotive. 44. Paris and Istanbul. 45. Louis Bleriot. 46. A steam-powered automobile, the Stanley Steamer. 47. Produces an explosive fuel-air mixture. 48. The St. Gothard Tunnel. 49. The Pioneer Yelloway bus. 50. The Turtle.

Quiz 138 The Arts

HARD - LEVEL THREE

1 Who wrote, directed, and starred in "The Navigator" and "The General"?

2 Who starred in "The Kid", "The Goldrush", and "The Great Dictator"?

3 Who directed the 1957 film "A Farewell to Arms"?

4 Which opera did Borodin leave unfinished at his death?

5 What was Gizmo?

6 In Britain it was a music hall, but what was the American name?

7 Who played the beleaguered sheriff in High Noon?

8 In which 1975 film did a group of Australian schoolgirls vanish?

9 Who wrote "The Cask of Amontillado"?

10 Who wrote "Beyond the Wall of Sleep"?

11 Who starred in "The Blue Angel"?

12 Who starred as Sir Thomas More in both the stage and film versions of "A Man For All Seasons"?

13 For what did Eugene O'Neill get his 1957 Pulitzer Prize?

14 Who wrote "A Streetcar Named Desire"?

15 Which famous playwright was married to Marilyn Monroe?

16 Who wrote "On the Road"?

17 Who wrote "Leaves of Grass"?

18 For what work is Geoffrey Chaucer chiefly remembered?

19 Which jazz musician was known to his fans as 'Satchmo'?

20 Which girl singer gained fame with "Ruby Tuesday"?

21 Who won three Oscars for Wallace and Gromit?

22 Who won an Oscar for her adaptation of Jane Austen's "Sense and Sensibility"?

23 Who played Ophelia to Mel Gibson's Hamlet?

24 Which film star was suffocated by his best friend in "One Flew Over the Cuckoo's Nest"?

25 Two people combined to make one formidable villain in "Mad Max – Beyond Thunder Dome". What name did they go by?

26 Which actor was Down and Out in Beverly Hills?

27 Which country is invaded in Spielberg's "Empire of the Sun"?

28 Which glittering role did Gert Frobe land in a Bond movie?

29 From which film did the song "Everybody's Talkin' At Me" come?

30 Who traded places in a film version of a Mark Twain story?

31 Where did we see the Log Lady?

32 In which TV series do we meet Eugene Tooms?

33 In which round did Tyson defeat Bruno in the 1996 World Heavyweight Championship?

34 James Mason played Brutus, John Gielgud played Cassius, but who played Mark Antony in this film of

Julius Caesar?

35 In which film did Tom Cruise and Demi Moore play naval lawyers?

36 Who played Rooster Cogburn in "True Grit"?

37 What was the subtitle of "Superman IV"?

38 Which actor was swindled by Paul Newman and Robert Redford in "The Sting"?

39 Under what other name does the crime novelist Ruth Rendell write?

40 Who mounted the stage to criticize Michael Jackson's performance at the 1996 Brit Awards?

41 Which American author of "The Bell Jar" committed suicide?

42 Which American pop artist was noted for his large-scale depictions of comic book panels?

43 What is the link between the Guggenheim Museum and Simon & Garfunkel?

44 Who wrote "American Pie"?

45 In which Neil Simon play did two men share an apartment to their mutual discomfort?

46 Which tale, set in Paris and featuring a monstrous musician, became a hit musical?

47 In which Australian film were two children, lost in the outback, rescued by a young aborigine?

48 What is Bill Cosby's profession in "The Cosby Show"?

49 Which TV family is Morticia in?

50 Which collie dog starred in numerous films and on TV?

A nswers to Quiz 137, CUSTOMS

1. Hogmanay. 2. Trick or treat. 3. The maypole dance. 4. A festivity associated with much drinking. 5. The Jewish official who leads the musical part of a service. 6. Christmas. 7. The Lord of Misrule. 8. Walpurgis Night (also called the Eve of Beltane). 9. Inuit. 10. Maoris. 11. New Year's Eve? 12. A religious service held on New Year's Eve. 13. The feast commemorating the exodus of the Jews from Egypt. 14. The Apaches. 15. The Kaaba 16. A rite of passage for Jewish girls. 17. They strangled them. 18. A scapegoat. 19. A boy formerly raised with a prince or other young nobleman and whipped for the latter's misdeeds. 20. Native Americans. 21. Irish or Scots. 22. Australian Aboriginals. 23. Walkabout. 24. Dreamtime. 25. The bull run. 26. People who had committed suicide. 27. After disemboweling himself, he was decapitated by a friend. 28. Smoke a pipe. 29. Mummify the dead. 30. He hears an owl say his name. 31. It supposedly cures the poisonous bite from a spider. 32. The Mafia. 33. His friends shave him with an axe. 34. A stake being driven through the heart (garlic in the mouth is optional). 35. The Indian custom, now outlawed, of burning a widow on the pyre of her husband. 36. Ramadan. 37. Holi. 38. Pancakes. 39. Ash Wednesday. 40. A haggis. 41. Black Rod. 42. The door is slammed in his face. 43. Guy Fawkes. 44. Thanskgiving. 45. The borders of a parish were established by beating the hedges which formed them. 46. Rum, sodomy, and the lash. 47. A pit with the bottom covered in pebbles and full of melted snow from the mountains. Walking barefoot in the icy water is supposed to be refreshing. 48. Infant baptism. 49. To the left. 50. Parsses.

QUIZ 139 Current Affairs

HARD - LEVEL THREE

1 By which political group was Rajiv Ghandi assassinated?

2 Who was the world's first ever woman prime minister?

3 Which Greek head of state abolished the monarchy in 1973?

4 Who was the Argentinian president in the Falklands War?

5 Why did the Arab League move their HQ to Tunis in 1989?

6 Who was the first freely elected Marxist leader of the Americas?

7 What was the name of the guerrilla army in Namibia before the country's independence?

8 Which two members of the National Security Council were predominantly involved in the Iran-Contra Affair?

9 Who did the Gaza Strip belong to before Israel invaded?

10 The Schuman Plan lead to the formation of which organization?

11 When was the Iran-Iraq War?

12 What was the name of the Swedish prime minister assassinated in 1986?

13 Which Polish head of state banned Solidarity in 1982?

14 Where was Rudolf Hess held until his death in 1987?

15 Who signed the INF Treaty?

16 What was the aim of the hunger strikers in the Maze Prison?

17 Who succeeded Harold Wilson as British prime minister in 1976?

18 Who was the last viceroy of India before it became an independent nation?

19 In which country did Hafez al-Assad seize power in 1970?

20 Who is the leader of the first Spanish Socialist government since the Civil War?

21 Why did Willy Brandt resign as German chancellor in 1974?

22 Who was vice president under George Bush?

23 Name the Panamanian general who was captured in 1989 and convicted of drug-trafficking?

24 Who turned Albania into a republic in 1946?

25 Which three countries joined the EEC in 1973?

26 Name the spacecraft that Neil Armstrong used for his flight to the moon in 1969?

27 When did the Cultural Revolution in China take place?

28 Who was UN general secretary during the Gulf War?

29 Who was Tunisia's first president after independence?

30 What was François Duvalier, of Haiti, commonly known as?

31 Which German Nazi official was hanged by Israel in 1960?

32 When was Amnesty founded?

33 Who became Chinese premier after the formation of the People's

Republic in 1949?

34 Who preceded Nasser as Egyptian head of state?

35 Name the world's first man-made Earth satellite?

36 Which country became a US state in 1958?

37 Who did Mitterrand appoint as French premier in 1986?

38 Who was Armenia at war with after the collapse of the USSR?

39 Who became the first prime minister of Bangladesh?

40 Who succeeded Juan Perón as leader of Argentina?

41 What was Winnie Mandela convicted of in 1991?

42 In which year did the IRA bomb Harrod's in London?

43 Which three former Soviet states formed the Commonwealth of Independent States?

44 Which position did Jimmy Carter hold before becoming president?

45 Who became prime minister of Fiji in 1992, having previously led two military coups?

46 Name the first black prime minister elected in Southern Rhodesia in 1979?

47 Which party did the Irish prime minister Charles Haughey lead?

48 When was the first direct election to the European Parliament?

49 Who was Norway's first woman prime minister?

50 The followers of which religious cult committed mass suicide in the Guyana jungle in 1978?

Answers to Quiz 138, THE ARTS

1. Buster Keaton. 2. Charlie Chaplin. 3. Charles Vidor. 4. Prince Igor. 5. A gremlin. 6. Vaudeville. 7. Gary Cooper. 8. Picnic at Hanging Rock. 9. Edgar Allan Poe. 10. H.P. Lovecraft. 11. Marlene Dietrich. 12. Paul Scofield. 13. Long Day's Journey into Night. 14. Tennessee Williams. 15. Arthur Miller. 16. Jack Kerouac. 17. Walt Whitman. 18. The Canterbury Tales. 19. Louis Armstrong. 20. Melanie Safka. 21. Nick Park. 22. Emma Thompson. 23. Helena Bonham-Carter. 24. Jack Nicholson. 25. Master Blaster. 26. Nick Nolte. 27. China is invaded by Japan. 28. Goldfinger. 29. Midnight Cowboy. 30. Eddie Murphy and Dan Ackroyd in Trading Places. 31. 'Twin Peaks'. 32. 'The X Files'. 33. The third. 34. Marlon Brando. 35. A Few Good Men. 36. John Wayne. 37. The Quest for Peace. 38. Robert Shaw. 39. Barbara Vine. 40. Jarvis Cocker. 41. Sylvia Plath. 42. Roy Lichtenstein. 43. Simon & Garfunkel wrote the song 'So Long Frank Lloyd Wright', who designed the Guggenheim. 44. Don McLean. 45. The Odd Couple. 46. Phantom of the Opera. 47. Walkabout. 48. He is an obstetrician. 49. 'The Addams Family'. 50. Lassie.

QUIZ 140 Pot Luck

HARD - LEVEL THREE

1 Who was the last person to hold both water and land speed records?

2 Which general of ancient Carthage is associated with proboscidean mammals?

3 Who wrote the novel "The Seventh Scroll"?

4 In which park is the Serpentine?

5 Of which country is Baffin Island a part?

6 Who wrote the novel "Lord of the Flies"?

7 In South America, what is a gaucho?

8 What colour are the flowers of the hawthorn?

9 Which US writer created Tarzan?

10 Ipswich is the administrative headquarters of which English county?

11 What job is done by a concierge?

12 Which astronaut was the second man to set foot on the moon?

13 With what industry is the inventor Richard Arkwright associated?

14 What is the common name for calcium carbonate?

15 What do we call what the Germans call "Strumpfhose"?

16 In chess, how many squares can the king move at a time?

17 With which industry is the Royal Smithfield Show concerned?

18 On what type of surface is the sport of curling played?

19 What are the main two political parties in the United States?

20 Where in England was the first commercial nuclear power station built?

21 Who were the first landlords of the Rovers' Return?

22 Which French king was husband to Marie Antoinette?

23 What are bespoke clothes?

24 What can cats do with their claws that dogs cannot do?

25 According to the proverb, what shouldn't call the kettle black?

26 What sort of a holiday is it if you do the same thing as in your job?

27 Which actor's real name is Walter Matasschansayasky?

28 What is a peruke?

29 Whose catchphrase was "Hello, playmates"?

30 In the world of computing what is a bug?

31 What is the collective noun for whales?

32 To an Australian what is a woolgrower?

33 By what name is Formosa now known?

34 What have Thistle, Brent and Ninian in common?

35 Who became queen of The Netherlands in 1980?

36 Who wrote the poem that begins, "Shall I compare thee to a

summer's day"?

37 What name goes after Bobby to name a footballer and before Heston to name an actor?
38 What is Al Pacino's full first name?
39 Provence and Brittany are both parts of which country?
40 Who played the scarecrow, Worzel Gummidge, on television?
41 Nowadays, who might wear a wimple?
42 Which country lies immediately south of Estonia?
43 In geography, what is a cataract?
44 Which English soccer team plays at home at Molyneux?
45 In America what is Airforce One?
46 With which sport do you associate Karen Pickering?
47 Who was the lead singer of the group, The Who?
48 What does the reference book, Crockfords, list?
49 For which county does Dominic Cork play cricket?
50 Where in the body is the humerus?

Answers to Quiz 139, CURRENT AFFAIRS

1. Tamil separatists. 2. Sirimavo Bandaranaike of Sri Lanka. 3. George Papadopoulos. 4. Leopoldo Galtieri. 5. Egypt's membership was suspended because of its peace agreement with Israel. 6. Salvador Allende of Chile. 7. SWAPO. 8. Admiral John Poindexter and Lieutenant Colonel Oliver North. 9. Egypt. 10. The European Coal and Steel Community. 11. 1980–88. 12. Olof Palme. 13. General Wojciech Jaruzelzki. 14. Spandau Prison in Berlin. 15. Ronald Reagan and Mikhail Gorbachev. 16. They tried to achieve status as political prisoners. 17. James Callaghan. 18. Louis Mountbatten. 19. Syria. 20. Felipe Gonzalez Marquez. 21. An East German spy was discovered in his administration. 22. Dan Quayle. 23. Manuel Noriega. 24. Enver Hcxha. 25. Great Britain, Ireland, and Denmark. 26. Apollo 11. 27. 1966-9. 28. Javier Pérez de Cuellar. 29. Habib Bourguiba. 30. Papa Doc. 31. Adolf Eichmann. 32. 1961. 33. Chou En-Lai. 34. King Farouk. 35. Sputnik I. 36. Alaska. 37. Jacques Chirac. 38. Azerbaijan. 39. Sheik Mujibar Rahmann. 40. His third wife, Maria Estela (Isabel) Martínez de Perón. 41. The kidnapping and beating of four young men, one of whom died. 42. 1983. 43. Russia, Belorussia, and the Ukraine. 44. Governor of Georgia. 45. Sitiveni Rabuka. 46. Abel Muzorewa. 47. Fianna Fáil. 48. 1979. 49. Gro Harlem Brundtland. 50. The People's Temple.

QUIZ 141 | Rivers

HARD - LEVEL THREE

1 By what other name is the Delaware River known?

2 Of what major river is the Jefferson River a headwater?

3 Which disconcertingly named waterway joins the Wabash River?

4 On which river is London situated?

5 St. Louis, Missouri, is situated near the confluence of two great rivers. Which are they?

6 Which is the world's longest river?

7 Which is the longest river in China?

8 The delta of which river was the scene of bitter battles during the Vietnam War?

9 Jericho was a stronghold commanding the valley of which river?

10 The Mississippi is navigable by ocean-going vessels as far as which town?

11 Which is the chief river of central and south-east Europe?

12 Through which countries does the Elbe flow?

13 Near which town does the Seine reach the English Channel?

14 The Danube flows into which sea?

15 On which river is Düsseldorf situated?

16 Which Bavarian city is situated on the Isar River?

17 Which American river connects Tanana with Holy Cross and passes by the Kaiyuh Mountains?

18 Buenos Aires and Montevideo are to be found on which river?

19 Which river flows through the city of Moscow?

20 Which famous Russian river flows into the Caspian Sea?

21 What is the sacred river of India?

22 Which river flows through America's Grand Canyon?

23 On which river does New York stand?

24 Beside which river would you find the Bois de Boulogne?

25 The Tiergarten in Berlin is next to which river?

26 Which river in Thailand starred in a famous film?

27 Which city does the Chao Phraya flow through?

28 Which river connects the Sea of Galilee and the Dead Sea?

29 Which river flows through Kinshasa on its way to the Atlantic?

30 The river that separates Texas from Chihuaha has two names (depending on which bank you are standing on). What are they?

31 Which river connects Lake Ontario with the sea?

32 Which is the most important river in Brazil?

33 Which river flows through Colombia and Venezuela?

34 Liverpool is famous for its river. What is its name?

35 Name the two great rivers that flow through Portugal.

36 By what name do the citizens of Vienna know the Danube?

37 Which Indian city is situated on the Hugli River?

38 Which river of Pakistan flows through Hyderabad and into the Arabian Sea?

39 Near which river would you find Sheffield, Florence, and Athens?

40 Cincinnatti stands on the banks of which river?

41 Name the river that connects the Great Slave Lake with the Beaufort Sea?

42 On which river does Mobile, Alabama, stand?

43 On which river would you find Athens, Nanticoke, Berwick, and Columbia?

44 Which river, with the name of a fruit, forms the border between South Africa and Namibia?

45 Which river valley forms a north-south split in California?

46 Which river flows through North and South Dakota?

47 The upper course of which river is called the Isis?

48 What is the name of the main river that flows through New South Wales?

49 Which river forms the border between Thailand and Laos?

50 On which river does Cambridge, Massachusetts, lie?

1. Donald Campbell. 2. Hannibal. 3. Wilbur Smith. 4. Hyde Park. 5. Canada. 6. William Golding. 7. Cowboy. 8. White or red. 9. Edgar Rice Burroughs. 10. Suffolk. 11. Caretaker. 12. Buzz Aldrin. 13. Spinning. 14. Chalk. 15. Tights. 16. One. 17. Farming, agriculture. 18. Ice. 19. Democrat and Republican. 20. Calder Hill, Cumbria. 21. Jack and Annie Walker. 22. Louis XVI. 23. Made to measure. 24. Retract them. 25. The pot. 26. Busman's holiday. 27. Walter Matthau. 28. A wig. 29. Arthur Askey. 30. An error in a program. 31. A school. 32 .Sheep farmer. 33. Taiwan. 34. All are (North Sea) oil-fields. 35. Beatrix. 36. Shakespeare. 37. Charlton. 38. Alfredo. 39. France. 40. Jon Pertwee. 41. A nun. 42. Latvia. 43. Waterfall. 44. Wolverhampton Wanderers. 45. The president's plane. 46. Swimming. 47. Roger Daltry. 48. The clergy of the Church of England. 49. Derbyshire. 50. Upper arm.

Current Affairs

HARD - LEVEL THREE

1 What was the Palestinian uprising which started in 1988 called?

2 Nelson Mandela is the leader of which party?

3 Who succeeded Jimmy Carter as president?

4 What was the name of the Egyptian president who was assassinated by Islamic fundamentalists in 1981?

5 Which German chancellor was awarded the Nobel Peace Price?

6 From which country did Biafra try to secede?

7 Who came to power in Chile following a military coup in 1973?

8 Which African country became independent from France in 1962, after over seven years of war?

9 Which incident resulted in the Suez crisis?

10 Who was president of Zambia from 1964 to 1991?

11 What happened on June 17 1953 in East Berlin?

12 What were the South Vietnamese guerillas called?

13 Who was India's first prime minister after independence?

14 What was the name of the peace treaty signed in 1979 by Begin, Sadat, and Carter?

15 Where was Martin Luther King assassinated?

16 Where was Idi Amin dictator?

17 What was the name of the US space shuttle which exploded soon after take-off in 1986?

18 Which incident provoked the USA to bomb Libya in 1986?

19 Where was the EU Treaty signed?

20 When was the Berlin Wall dismantled?

21 For which city was the Pan Am Boeing bound that exploded over Lockerbie in 1989?

22 Which were the founder states of the EEC?

23 Which Communist leader was overthrown in 1989 and executed, together with his wife?

24 Who lost the 1960 presidential election to John F. Kennedy?

25 Where was the toxic gas leak at an insecticide plant that killed over 6,000 people in 1984?

26 Who was the longest-serving British prime minister of the 20th century?

27 What does OPEC stand for?

28 Who was the Soviet secretary of state during the Cuban missile crisis?

29 During which war did Israel capture the Golan Heights?

30 Which were the first two states of the former Yugoslavia to declare independence?

31 When was NATO established?

32 Which Soviet was awarded the Nobel Peace Prize in 1990?

33 To which movement did the

288

Cambodian leader Pol Pot belong?

34 When did Margaret Thatcher become prime minister?

35 What was the location of the unsuccessful CIA-sponsored invasion of Cuba?

36 Which surgeon completed the first human heart transplant?

37 Which Mediterranean island was invaded by Turkish troops in 1974?

38 What was the aim of the SALT treaties?

39 Who declared Iran an Islamic Republic in 1979?

40 What was Perestroika?

41 Which international organization was founded in 1945?

42 During the Korean War which outside forces joined the North Korean army?

43 Who headed the Polish trade union Solidarity?

44 Who became Zimbabwe's first prime minister?

45 Which African emperor was deposed in 1974?

46 Who was the longest-serving French president in history?

47 In which year was the oil crisis that resulted from an embargo by Arab Nations?

48 What was the Communist equivalent to NATO during the Cold War?

49 What was the Spring of 1968 in Czechoslovakia called?

50 Who became first president of Cyprus in 1960?

A nswers to Quiz 141, RIVERS

1. South River. 2. The Missouri. 3. The Embarrass River. 4. The Thames. 5. The Missouri and Mississippi. 6. The Nile. 7. The Yellow River. 8. The Mekong. 9. The Jordan. 10. Baton Rouge, Louisiana. 11. The Danube. 12. Czechoslovakia and Germany. 13. Le Havre. 14. The Black Sea. 15. The Rhein. 16. Munich. 17. The Yukon. 18. The River Plate. 19. The Moskva. 20. The Volga. 21. The Ganges. 22. The Colorado. 23. The Hudson. 24. The Seine. 25. The Spree. 26. The River Kwai. 27. Bangkok. 28. The River Jordan. 29. The Congo. 30. Rio Grande and Rio Brave del Norte. 31. The St Lawrence. 32. The Amazon. 33. The Orinoco. 34. The Mersey. 35. The Douro and the Tagus. 36. The Donau. 37. Calcutta. 38. The Indus. 39. The Tennessee. 40. The Ohio. 41. The Mackenzie. 42. The Alabama. 43. The Susquehanna. 44. The Orange. 45. The San Joaquin. 46. The Missouri. 47. The Thames. 48. The Darling. 49. The Mekong. 50. The Charles.

Quiz 143 Nature

FOR ANSWERS SEE QUIZ NO 144

HARD - LEVEL THREE

1 What is the male honey bee known as?

2 Hermit and spider are types of what?

3 What is another name for an insect's feelers?

4 What name is given to the body a parasite feeds on?

5 How many eyes does a bee have?

6 Which beetle was sacred to the Egyptians?

7 What is the process of casting skin, hair or feathers called?

8 What is a gurnard?

9 Which bird is associated with Lundy Island?

10 What is a conch?

11 What sort of animal is a papillon?

12 What is the olfactory sense?

13 What does the term metamorphosis mean?

14 What is a hummingbird's hum caused by?

15 Which is the largest member of the crow family?

16 What and where is Minsmere?

17 What is another name for thunderflies or thunderbugs?

18 How many parts are there to an insect's body?

19 What do lugworms live in?

20 What is a dunnock?

21 Which system controls touch, sight and hearing?

22 From which language does the word budgerigar come?

23 What do the Americans call what the British call a ladybird?

24 How many wings does a flea have?

25 For whom is the Glorious Twelfth not glorious?

26 What is another name for cartilage?

27 How does a stoat's appearance change in the winter?

28 What is a mavis?

29 What is the smallest living unit called?

30 What do polled cattle not have?

31 Which tree can be Dutch, English or wych?

32 What type of creature is a stingray?

33 How does a boa kill?

34 Which bird can be bald, golden or harpy?

35 How many humps does a Bactrian camel have?

36 What sort of animal is a Dandie Dinmont?

37 What is a mamba?

38 Would a tuber grow above or below the ground?

39 What is a chameleon famous for being capable of changing?

40 What is a monkey puzzle?

41 To which hemisphere do penguins belong?

42 Which creature constructs dams and lodges?

43 What is a female fox called?

44 What does a rattlesnake rattle when it is disturbed?

45 What is the larva of a butterfly or moth called?

46 Which country were Newfoundland dogs originally from?

47 The moose or elk are species of which creature?

48 What sort of plant is a common puffball?

49 On which continent is the opossum found in its natural habitat?

50 Which American creature is renowned for its foul-smelling defence mechanism?

A nswers to
Quiz 142, CURRENT AFFAIRS

1. Intifada. 2. The African National Congress. 3. Ronald Reagan. 4. Anwar Sadat. 5. Willy Brandt. 6. Nigeria. 7. Pinochet. 8. Algeria. 9. The nationalization of the Suez Canal. 10. Kenneth Kaunda. 11. Workers protested against the Soviet presence and the Russians moved into the capital with tanks. 12. The Viet Cong. 13. Jawaharlal Nehru. 14. Camp David Accords. 15. Memphis, Tennessee. 16. Uganda. 17. Challenger. 18. A terrorist bombing in a Berlin nightclub. 19. Maastricht. 20. In November 1989. 21. New York. 22. France, Germany, Italy, Belgium, The Netherlands, and Luxembourg. 23. Nicolae Ceaucescu. 24. Richard Nixon. 25. Bhopal in Central India. 26. Margaret Thatcher. 27. Organization of Petroleum Exporting Countries. 28. Nikita Khrushchev. 29. The Six Day War. 30. Slovenia and Croatia. 31. 1949. 32. Mikhail Gorbachev. 33. The Khmer Rouge. 34. 1979. 35. The Bay of Pigs. 36. Christiaan Barnard. 37. Cyprus. 38. To limit antiballistic missiles and nuclear missile systems in the USA and USSR. 39. Ayatollah Khomeini. 40. The restructuring of the Soviet economy and bureaucracy during the 1980s. 41. The United Nations. 42. Chinese Communist forces. 43. Lech Walesa. 44. Robert Mugabe. 45. Haile Selassie of Ethiopia. 46. François Mitterrand. 47. 1973. 48. The Warsaw Pact. 49. The Prague Spring. 50. Archbishop Makarios III.

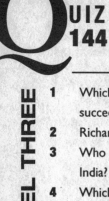

QUIZ 144 History

HARD - LEVEL THREE

1 Which British monarch succeeded Queen Victoria?

2 Richard III died at which battle?

3 Who was the last viceroy of India?

4 Which English monarch married Eleanor of Aquitaine?

5 Who was the last wife of Henry VIII?

6 Which country did Britain fight in the War of Jenkins' Ear?

7 Which King George did the Prince Regent become?

8 At the Siege of Mafeking who led the British forces?

9 The House of Lancaster kings were all called what?

10 Under what name is Gregor Efimovich better known?

11 Apart from Mad George which kinder nickname did George III have?

12 Which English queen married Prince George of Denmark?

13 Blucher commanded which country's troops at the Battle of Waterloo?

14 Who had a horse called Bucephalus?

15 Queen Elizabeth II's grandfather was which monarch?

16 Who was the Wisest Fool In Christendom?

17 Who was the first Prince of Wales?

18 Whose last words are reputed to be, "My neck is very slender"?

19 Which Spanish king sent his unsuccessful Armada?

20 Which monarch was murdered in Berkeley Castle?

21 In what year did Edward VIII abdicate?

22 In Britain, who first held the office that today is known as Prime Minister?

23 In the 15th century which Duke was drowned in Malmsey wine?

24 Who ruled England between Henry I and Henry II?

25 How did Lord Kitchener die?

26 Who with royal connections had the middle name Warfield?

27 In 1066 how many monarchs ruled England in the year?

28 Which ruler referred the English to a nation of shopkeepers?

29 Which monarch ordered the execution of Sir Walter Raleigh?

30 Which wife gave Henry VIII the male heir that he wanted?

31 Who was British monarch throughout the Second World War?

32 Which US President was assassinated at the theatre?

33 Which ruler was stabbed to death in Rome in March 44 BC?

34 Who was Queen Elizabeth I's husband?

35 Who led the British forces at the Battle of Waterloo?

36 Who was Queen of England for nine days?

37 Which monarch was forced to sign the Magna Carta?

38 Which teenage girl led the French army against the English in the 15th century?

39 Who was Henry VIII's first wife?

40 Who was the famous General killed at Khartoum?

41 Which King Henry ordered the murder of Thomas Becket?

42 Which unpleasant-sounding Ivan was crowned first Tsar of Russia?

43 What was the name of the first King of England and Scotland?

44 Who was the Younger PM who introduced income tax?

45 From 1714 to 1830 all British monarchs were called what?

46 Who had his tomb in the Valley of Kings discovered in the 1920s?

47 Who was the famous captain of the ship the *Golden Hind*?

48 Inigo Jones followed which profession?

49 Who were massacred by the Campbells at Glencoe?

50 Of British monarchs, have more been called William or Edward?

1. Drone. 2. Crab. 3. Antennae. 4. Host. 5. Five. 6. Scarab. 7. Moulting. 8. Fish. 9. Puffin. 10. Shell or shellfish. 11. Dog. 12. Smell. 13. Change of shape. 14. Beating its wings. 15. Raven. 16. Bird sanctuary in Suffolk. 17. Thrips. 18. Three. 19. Sand or mud. 20. Bird (hedge sparrow). 21. Nervous system. 22. Aboriginal Australian. 23. Ladybug. 24. None. 25. Grouse - it is the start of the grouse shooting season. 26. Gristle. 27. Its coat turns white. 28. Song thrush. 29. Cell. 30. Horns. 31. Elm. 32. Fish. 33. Constriction. 34. Eagle. 35. Two. 36. Breed of terrier. 37. Snake. 38. Below. 39. Its colour. 40. Tree. 41. Southern. 42. Beaver. 43. Vixen. 44. Its tail. 45. Caterpillar. 46. Canada. 47. Deer. 48.Fungus. 49. America. 50. Skunk.

Q UIZ 145 Words

1 Satrap means: (a) Eastern prince, (b) stirrup, (c) cloth.

2 Fuliginous means: (a) defamatory, (b) poetic, (c) sooty.

3 Calumny means: (a) war club, (b) defamation, (c) bridle.

4 Calabash means: (a) musical instrument, (b) flower, (c) gourd.

5 Gravid means: (a) pregnant, (b) heavy, (c) serious.

6 Apse means: (a) snake, (b) part of a church, (c) drop.

7 Malady means: (a) lies, (b) villain, (c) sickness.

8 Libretto means: (a) opera text, (b) debaucher, (c) singer.

9 Ululation means: (a) apotheosis, (b) howling, (c) rectification.

10 Pistil means: (a) firearm, (b) bat, (c) flower ovary.

11 Fedora means: (a) workman, (b) hat, (c) gypsy.

12 Recondite means: (a) explosive, (b) hidden, (c) pregnant.

13 Gibbous means: (a) half-witted, (b) quaint, (c) humped.

14 Fulgurate means: (a) explode, (b) flash, (c) detonate.

15 Moratorium means: (a) undertaker, (b) temporary ban, (c) piece of music.

16 Nictate means: (a) blink, (b) argue, (c) smoke.

17 Prosthesis means: (a) gratitude, (b) artificial body part, (c) poem.

18 Locum means: (a) place, (b) deputy, (c) doctor.

19 Morass means: (a) treacle, (b) marsh, (c) stew.

20 Meiosis means: (a) a disease of rabbits, (b) a literary device, (c) cell division.

21 Grandiloquent means (a) effulgent, (b) bombastic, (c) abusive.

22 Lepidote means: (a) rabbit-like, (b) stony, (c) scaly.

23 Gimcrack means: (a) gewgaw, (b) unsafe, (c) glittering.

24 Lachrymose means: (a) unhappy, (b) tearful, (c) dismal.

25 Depict means: (a) gloat, (b) glean, (c) describe.

26 Impuissant means: (a) smelly, (b) powerless, (c) powdery.

27 Cricoid means: (a) ring-shaped, (b) flower, (c) mineral.

28 Frenetic means: (a) speedy, (b) frenzied, (c) acute.

29 Grosgrain means: (a) illegal alcohol, (b) computer language, (c) fabric.

30 Kapok means: (a) fibre, (b) china clay, (c) guard.

31 Transmogrify means: (a) change shape, (b) send, (c) translate.

32 Crepuscular means: (a) crinkled, (b) diseased skin, (c) dim.

33 Jejune means: (a) uninteresting, (b) worthless, (c) yellowed.

34 Inchoate means: (a) outraged, (b) imperfectly formed, (c) speechless.

35 Frambesia means: (a) shrub,

(b) yaws, (c) card game.

36 Treponema means: (a) spirochetes, (b) worms, (c) beetles.

37 Tantalum means: (a) Greek king, (b) metallic element, (c) spinning wheel.

38 Deflagarate means: (a) lose air, (b) burn suddenly, (c) criticize.

39 Evagation means: (a) wandering, (b) losing fluid, (c) reducing fat.

40 Gabelle means: (a) musical instrument, (b) tax, (c) form of torture.

41 Galant means: (a) style of music, (b) polite, (c) chivalrous.

42 Monotroch means: (a) solitude, (b) wheelbarrow, (c) one-handed.

43 Pholas means: (a) piddock, b) philabeg, (c) phillipsite

44 Rogation means: (a) ploughing, (b) asking, (c) forgiving.

45 Procerity means: (a) tallness, (b) propinquity, (c) celerity.

46 Quey means: (a) heifer, (b) hairstyle, (c) strange.

47 Perstringe means: (a) to reduce, (b) to constrain, (c) to subtract.

48 Peduncle means: (a) relative, (b) flower part, (c) architectural term.

49 Passim means: (a) everywhere, (b) peaceful, (c) rarely.

50 Passus means: (a) canto, (b) footstep, (c) shoe.

A nswers to Quiz 144, HISTORY

1. Edward VII. 2. Bosworth Field. 3. Lord Louis Mountbatten. 4. Henry II. 5. Catherine Parr. 6. Spain. 7. George IV. 8. Robert Baden-Powell. 9. Henry. 10. Rasputin. 11. Farmer George. 12. Queen Anne. 13. Prussian. 14. Alexander the Great. 15. George V. 16. James I (James VI of Scotland). 17. Edward (later Edward II). 18. Anne Boleyn. 19. Philip II. 20. Edward II. 21. 1936. 22. Robert Walpole. 23. Clarence. 24. Stephen. 25. He drowned. 26. Mrs Wallis Simpson. 27. Three. 28. Napoleon Bonaparte. 29 James I. 30. Jane Seymour. 31. George VI. 32. Abraham Lincoln. 33. Julius Caesar. 34. No one. 35. Duke of Wellington. 36. Lady Jane Grey. 37. King John. 38. Joan of Arc. 39. Catherine of Aragon. 40. General Gordon. 41. II. 42. The Terrible. 43. James. 44. William Pitt. 45. George. 46. Tutankhamen. 47. Francis Drake. 48. Architect. 49. The McDonalds. 50. Edward.

QUIZ 146 | Current Affairs

HARD – LEVEL THREE

1 Which terrorist organization kidnapped and murdered the Italian prime minister Aldo Moro?

2 Which prime minister resigned after the Yom Kippur War?

3 Which nun founded the Missionaries of Charity in 1950?

4 Name the senator who investigated communist activity.

5 Who were the US-backed rebels during the Afghan War?

6 Where was the protest in 1960 of 20,000 blacks against passlaws which lead to a police massacre?

7 Which South African president removed the ban on the ANC?

8 Who ran for president against Ronald Reagan in 1981?

9 Name the US-backed movement in the Angolian Civil War.

10 Which area did Israel agree to return to Egypt after the Camp David Accords?

11 How did the Pakistani president Zia Ul-Haq die?

12 Which dissident writer was the first Soviet citizen to be expelled by the government?

13 Name the Eastern European organization founded to coordinate economic policies?

14 Which African head of state became an emperor in 1976?

15 Name the West German terrorist organization who were active in the early 1970s.

16 Who sentenced Salman Rushdie to death for his Satanic Verses?

17 Who was the first president of Israel?

18 Which political party did Indira Gandhi lead?

19 Who was Soviet foreign minister under Gorbachev?

20 What accusation forced Ferdinand Marcos to leave the Philippines?

21 Which British king died in 1952?

22 Who is the head of the Zulu-based Inkatha Freedom Party?

23 Who commanded the Allied Forces during the Gulf War?

24 Which Chinese Nationalist Party leader was driven out of China by the Communists?

25 In which country were the Sandinistas based?

26 What was the Exxon Valdez involved in?

27 When was the Anglo–Irish agreement drawn up?

28 Which disease of cattle caused friction between Britain and her European partners?

29 Who was the first president of Kenya?

30 Who succeeded de Gaulle as French president?

31 What measures, introduced in Northern Ireland in August 1971, led to riots in Republican areas?

32 Where is ETA based?

33 Which political party did

Menachem Begin lead?

34 When was the Hungarian uprising?

35 Who founded Pakistan?

36 Which US president broke off diplomatic relations with Cuba?

37 Who was the leader of the Al Fatah guerrilla movement?

38 Which is the main launching site for US space missions?

39 Who was the Iraqi foreign minister during the Gulf War?

40 Which political party does Helmut Kohl lead?

41 Which town was the birthplace of the Solidarity movement?

42 When was the Berlin Wall built?

43 What was the name of the Greenpeace ship blown up in Auckland Harbor?

44 Which former UN general secretary was accused of German intelligence activities during World War II?

45 Which Canadian prime minister proposed the Constitution Act, which gave Canada complete independence?

46 Who was president of the EC from 1985 to 1995?

47 Who succeeded Menachem Begin as prime minister of Israel?

48 Name the ferry that capsized out side the port of Zeebrugge in 1987, killing 186 people?

49 When did the USA withdraw its troops from Vietnam?

50 Where are the headquarters of the Council of Europe?

A nswers to Quiz 145, Words

1. (a) Eastern prince. 2. (c) sooty. 3. (b) defamation. 4. (c) gourd. 5. (a) pregnant. 6. (b) part of a church. 7. (c) sickness. 8. (a) opera text. 9. (b) howling. 10. (c) flower ovary. 11. (b) hat. 12. (b) hidden. 13. (c) humped. 14. (b) flash. 15. (b) temporary ban. 16. (a) blink. 17. (b) artificial body part. 18. (b) deputy. 19. (b) marsh. 20. (c) cell division. 21. (b) bombastic. 22. (c) scaly. 23. (a) gewgaw. 24. (b) tearful. 25. (c) describe. 26. (b) powerless. 27. (a) ring-shaped. 28. (b) frenzied. 29. (c) fabric. 30. (a) fibre. 31. (a) change shape. 32. (c) dim. 33. (a) uninteresting. 34. (b) imperfectly formed. 35. (b) yaws. 36. (a) spirochetes. 37. (b) metallic element. 38. (b) burn suddenly. 39. (a) wandering. 40. (b) tax. 41. (a) style of music. 42. (b) wheelbarrow. 43. (a) piddock. 44. (b) asking. 45. (a) tallness. 46. (a) heifer. 47. (b) to constrain. 48. (b) flower part. 49. (a) everywhere. 50. (a) canto.

Q_{UIZ} 147 Islands

HARD - LEVEL THREE

1 Which is the world's largest island?

2 Which island, to the south of Corsica, once belonged to the House of Savoy?

3 What was the Malagassy Republic renamed as 1975?

4 On which island does the famous yachting venue of Cowes lie?

5 From which island did the tailless Manx cat originate?

6 By what name was Taiwan formerly known?

7 By whatname is the holiday resort of Kerkira better known?

8 Which island is infamously linked with the Mafia?

9 What is the large island found in the Gulf of Tongkin?

10 By what name does Argentina, refer to the Falkland Islands?

11 Which group of islands would you find north of Crete?

12 Which island lies off the southern tip of India?

13 The ownership of which island is contested by Turkey and Greece?

14 Which islands lie north-east of Cuba?

15 What is the capital of the Philippines?

16 On which 'island' would you relax in Brooklyn, New York?

17 Which island, south of Java, has a festive name?

18 Who was the most famous,

though unwilling, resident of the Isle of Elba?

19 Which book of the Bible was written on the island of Patmos?

20 Which island has been referred to as 'The Pearl of the Antilles'?

21 What is the English name for the Isles Normandes?

22 The island of Sjelland contains the capital of a European country. Name both the country and the capital.

23 The map of Italy looks like a boot kicking a ball. Which island forms the ball?

24 Which island was ceded to France by Genoa in 1768?

25 Which famous peninsula juts into the Black Sea?

26 On which island does the Chinese Nationalist Government hold power?

27 On which island do Malaysia and Indonesia meet?

28 Which group of islands would you find due south of the Bay of Bengal?

29 Of which island group is Mindanao a part?

30 Of which island is Colombo the capital?

31 On which island would you find Larnaka?

32 Which group of islands would you find north-east of Madagascar?

33 Off which continent would you

find the Galapagos Islands?

34 On which island would you find Suffolk?

35 With which island state do you associate Maui and Oahu?

36 Is Nova Scotia an island?

37 The island of New Guinea is split into two halves. One half is Irian Jaya. Name the other half?

38 By what name were the Hawaiian Islands formerly known?

39 What name is given to a large group of islands?

40 Of what island group is Okinawa a part?

41 Where would you find Kodiak Island?

42 Which country in the Persian Gulf between Qatar and Saudi Arabia is actually an archipelago?

43 Which country lies next to Haiti?

44 What is the capital of Haiti?

45 On which island do Haiti and the Dominican Republic exist side by side?

46 Between which pair of islands does the Windward Passage run?

47 What interest did the USA have in Guantanamo, Cuba?

48 Where does the mainland of Great Britain rank in the world's ten largest islands?

49 Which island has a name implying that it suffers from strong winds?

50 The Virgin Islands belong to two countries. Which are they?

Answers to Quiz 146, CURRENT AFFAIRS

1. The Red Brigades. 2. Golda Meir. 3. Mother Teresa. 4. Joseph McCarthy. 5. Mujahedin. 6. Sharpeville, a suburb of Johannesburg. 7. F.W. de Klerk. 8. Jimmy Carter. 9. UNITA. 10. Sinai. 11. In a plane crash which was thought to be sabotage. 12. Aleksandr Solzhenitsyn. 13. COMECON. 14. Jean-Bedel Bokassa. 15. The Bader-Meinhof gang. 16. Ayatollah Khomeini. 17. Chaim Weizmann. 18. The Congress Party. 19. Eduard Shevardnadze. 20. Election fraud. 21. George VI. 22. Chief Mangosuthu Buthelezi. 23. Norman Schwarzkopf. 24. Chiang Kai-Shek. 25. Nicaragua. 26. A major oil-spill off the coast of Alaska in 1989. 27. 1985. 28. BSE. 29. Jomo Kenyatta. 30. Georges Pompidou. 31. Internment. 32. The Basque Country in northern Spain. 33. The Likud Party. 34. 1956. 35. Mohammed Ali Jinnah. 36. Dwight Eisenhower. 37. Yasir Arafat. 38. Cape Canaveral. 39. Tariq Aziz. 40. The Christian Democratic Party. 41. Gdansk. 42. 1961. 43. Rainbow Warrior. 44. Kurt Waldheim. 45. Pierre Trudeau. 46. Jacques Delors. 47. Ytzhak Shamir. 48. Herald of Free Enterprise. 49. 1973. 50. Strasbourg.

Quiz 148 | People

HARD – LEVEL THREE

1 Who was seduced by the god Zeus in the shape of a swan?

2 Which Greek hero was vulnerable only at his heel?

3 Of which country was Chang Kai-Shek head of state?

4 Which romantic legendary figure later became plain Aircraftsman Ross?

5 Who said:"Die, my dear doctor, that is the last thing I shall do"?

6 Holmes had his Watson, but who was aided by Dr Petrie?

7 Pheidippides was famous as the originator of which race?

8 Who wrote Paradise Lost?

9 Who was the hero of The Catcher in the Rye?

10 Who united Germany by a policy of 'blood and iron'?

11 Which Georgian ran Stalin's secret police?

12 Which queen fought against the Roman invaders of Britain?

13 Name the Roman god of the sea?

14 Which Roman presided over the trial of Jesus.

15 Name the 19th-century French artist who was famous for his small stature?

16 Whose painting portrays the destruction of Guernica?

17 In which story by J. D. Salinger did Seymour Glass kill himself?

18 Who was the youngest member of J. D. Salinger's fictional Glass family?

19 Who is the odd one out of the Gandhi family: Mohondas, Indira, Sanjay, and Rajiv.

20 Name the Greek cyclops.

21 Who was the evil Norse god?

22 Who was the wife of the Indian hero Rama?

23 Which famous doctor was created by Boris Pasternak?

24 Who was the brother of the Anglo-Saxon chieftain Hengist?

25 Who was the Scottish mathemati cian who invented logorithms?

26 Who was the first Chancellor of post-war West Germany?

27 In the Bible two people are given credit for killing the Philistine Goliath. The most famous was David, who was the other?

28 The skeleton of a man called Yehohanan was discovered in Israel in 1968. What was his unfortunate distinction?

29 For what was Joseph Grimaldi famous?

30 By what name did Archibald Leach find fame?

31 Mr Austerlitz and Miss McMath became partners under other names. What were they?

32 Who was the director of the 1968 film Romeo and Juliet?

33 Who was responsible for inventing dynamite and gelignite?

34 Who pioneered the pneumatic

tyres fitted to the Model T Ford?

35 Which Spaniard had delusions of knightly glory?

36 Which explorer was known as 'Il Millioni'?

37 Who was famous for going over Niagara Falls in a barrel?

38 What was unusual about the hanging of John 'Babacombe' Lee?

39 Aleksandr Solzhenitsyn wrote a novel about a day in the life of one man. Who was he?

40 Which Chinese philosopher wrote The Analects?

41 Which Indian political and religious leader defied the British by making salt?

42 Which king of Egypt rejected the old gods and initiated a new form of sun worship?

43 Who was 'mad, bad and dangerous to know'?

44 He was severely disabled and had a speech impediment but became emperor of Rome. Who was he?

45 Who was popularly known as 'The Virgin Queen'?

46 Who brought the Christmas tree to the British?

47 How was Admiral Nelson's body preserved following his death at the Battle of Trafalgar?

48 Who reputedly fell in love with his own reflection?

49 Which legendary ladies were named Medusa, Stheno, and Euryale?

50 Who assassinated Jean Paul Marat?

1. Greenland. 2. Sardinia. 3. Madagascar. 4. The Isle of Wight. 5. The Isle of Man. 6. Formosa. 7. Corfu. 8. Sicily. 9. Hainan. 10. The Malvinas. 11. The Cyclades. 12. Sri Lanka. 13. Cyprus. 14. The Bahamas. 15. Manila. 16. Coney island. 17. Christmas Island. 18. Napoleon Bonaparte. 19. The Revelation of Saint John. 20. Cuba. 21. The Channel Islands. 22. Denmark. Copenhagen. 23. Sicily. 24. Corsica. 25. The Crimea. 26. Taiwan. 27. Borneo. 28. The Andaman Islands (and Nicobar Islands). 29. The Philippines. 30. Sri Lanka. 31. Cyprus. 32. The Seychelles. 33. South America. 34. Long Island. 35. Hawaii. 36. No, not quite. 37. Papua. 38. The Sandwich Islands. 39. An archipelago. 40. The Ryukyu islands. 41. The Gulf of Alaska. 42. Bahrain. 43. The Dominican Republic. 44. Port au Prince. 45. Hispaniola. 46. Haiti and Cuba. 47. It was used as a military base. 48. No. 8. 49. Fuerteventura. 50. The USA and the UK

QUIZ 149 Pot Luck

HARD - LEVEL THREE

1 How many googols make a googolplex?

2 What have an outcast group in Japan and a Basque separatist organization got in common?

3 The statue of Eros in Piccadilly Circus, London, commemorates a Victorian reformer. Who was he?

4 What's Ngorogoro national park's explosive connection?

5 Everyone has heard of the 'waters of Babylon' but which river ran through the city?

6 Soweto, in South Africa, is not an African word. What does it mean?

7 In which film did Gene Kelly dance with an umbrella?

8 What explanation did W. C. Fields give when found reading the Bible on his deathbed?

9 By what name was wartime English broadcaster William Joyce better known?

10 By what name was the European Union originally known?

11 Which Egyptian leader precipitated the Suez Crisis?

12 Name the Israeli parliament.

13 In which country did the Boxer Rebellion take place?

14 What is collagen?

15 What, according to Dante, was the inscription at the entrance to Hell?

16 Who is traditionally considered to have founded Taoism?

17 Apart from its religious merit, what special distinction does The Diamond Sutra possess?

18 What distinction do Edward V and Edward VIII share?

19 Who was the famous queen of the Iceni?

20 Which emperor made his horse a Roman consul?

21 What impossible building task were the Hebrews set by their Egyptian captors?

22 What is natron used for?

23 What is the more polite name for the act of ritual suicide known as hara kiri?

24 What instrument was the precursor of the trombone?

25 Where was the composer Frederick Delius born?

26 Which appropriately named English painter killed his father?

27 Which French mathematician died in a duel at the age of 21?

28 Which religious group worship the Ethiopian emperor Haile Selassie?

29 Would you drink a Molotov cocktail?

30 What did Howard Carter discover in 1922?

31 What inflammatory act did Marinus van der Lubbe commit in 1933?

32 Which Georgian became known as Uncle Joe?

33 What were kulaks?

34 What notable event took place at Appomattox Court House in 1865?

35 What are the people who follow the teachings of a Zoroaster called.

36 Which Spanish naval disaster was commanded by the Duke of Medina Sidonia?

37 For what military blunder was General Galtieri of Argentina responsible?

38 By what name did Siddartha Gautama become well known?

39 For which literary work did Sei Shonagon become famous?

40 Who said: 'Speak softly and carry a big stick'?

41 In which country would you find guerrillas of the Shining Path?

42 In which country did the Red Army Faction operate?

43 What happened at the Battle of Actium in 31BC?

44 Which English MP was a member of the Hellfire Club?

45 Whose execution prompted Voltaire's remark that the English occasionally shoot an admiral to encourage the others?

46 Why would a Basenji make a poor watchdog?

47 Which pigment does the cuttlefish secrete?

48 What is a haiku?

49 What is a malapropism?

50 Who wrote Six Characters in Search of an Author?

1. Leda. 2. Achilles. 3. Taiwan. 4. Lawrence of Arabia. 5. Lord Palmerston. 6. Commissioner Nayland Smith. 7. The marathon. 8. John Milton. 9. Holden Caulfield. 10. Bismark. 11. Beria. 12. Boudicca. 13. Neptune. 14. Pontius Pilate. 15. Toulouse Lautrec. 16. Pablo Picasso. 17. A Perfect Day for Bananafish. 18. Franny. 19. Sanjay Gandhi. All the others were assassinated. Sanjay died in a plane crash. 20. Polyphemus. 21. Loki. 22. Sita. 23. Dr Zhivago. 24. Horsa. 25. Napier. 26. Konrad Adenauer. 27. Elhanan. 28. He was the only person known from forensic evidence whose death was caused by crucifiction. 29. He was one of the great clowns of all time. 30. Cary Grant. 31. Fred Astaire and Ginger Rogers. 32. Bernardo Bertolucci. 33. Alfred Nobel. 34. Harvey Firestone. 35. Don Quixote. 36. Marco Polo. 37. Captain Webb. 38. The trap failed to operate on three occasions and in the end Lee's sentence was commuted to life imprisonment. 39. Ivan Denisovitch. 40. Confucius. 41. Mahatma Gandhi. 42. Akhenaton (Amenhotep IV). 43. Lord Byron. 44. Claudius. 45. Elizabeth I of England. 46. Prince Albert. 47. In a barrel of brandy. 48. Narcissus. 49. The gorgons. 50. Charlotte Corday.

QUIZ 150 | Classical Music

HARD - LEVEL THREE

1 What is the type of German opera of the 18th century called where songs are interspersed with dialogue?

2 How many strings does a cello have?

3 Who orchestrated Pictures at an Exhibition?

4 "The Polovtsian Dances" are part of which opera?

5 Who wrote the "Egmont Overture"?

6 Which nationality was Béla Bartók?

7 Which instrument does Anne-Sophie Mutter perform on?

8 Which musical work is the Young Person's Guide to the Orchestra based on?

9 Which orchestral work is based on A Thousand and One Nights, and who wrote it?

10 The "Ode to Joy" is part of which musical work?

11 How many symphonies did Bruckner write?

12 Who wrote the "Reformation Symphony"?

13 Which word describes a vocal and orchestral work telling a sacred story without dramatic effects?

14 What is a bass viola also called?

15 Who wrote the "German Requiem"?

16 Which musical work is "Anitra's Dance" part of?

17 How many semitones are there in a scale?

18 Who created a catalogue of Mozart's music?

19 Which composer established the 12-tone technique of Serial Music?

20 Who composed "My Fatherland"?

21 Which family does the English horn belong to?

22 How many symphonies did Brahms write?

23 Riccardo Muti is the director of which opera house?

24 Who composed The Creation?

25 What is the difference between an interval and a chord?

26 On a piano, what are the strings struck by?

27 In which work would you find a secion entitled "Fortuna Imperatrix Mundi"?

28 By what other name is Mendelssohn's "Hebrides Ouverture' also known?

29 What do you call an interval of eight full tones?

30 Mendelssohn's "Wedding March" is part of which musical work?

31 Who wrote the opera "Russlan and Ludmilla"?

32 Which composer was regarded as the architect of impressionism?

33 Which instrument was Fritz Kreisler famous for?

34 Which was Richard Wagner's only comic opera?

35 Which type of instrument did Henry Steinway build?

36 Who wrote In the Steppes of Central Asia?

37 What type of singing voice is Elisabeth Schwarzkopf known for?

38 In a tempo direction, what does 'assai' mean?

39 What is unusual about Beethoven's Eighth Symphony?

40 Which country does the polonaise come from?

41 Which instrument does Narciso Yepes perform on?

42 Who wrote "Till Eulenspiegel's Merry Pranks"?

43 What type of singing voice is Dame Janet Baker known for?

44 What is the name given to Beethoven's Fifth Piano Concerto?

45 What is a sarabande?

46 Who wrote "The Swan of Tuonela"?

47 Which three of Verdi's operas are based on plays by Shakespeare?

48 What is the title of Schubert's Fourth Symphony?

49 Which instrument did Arthur Grumiaux perform on?

50 What type of instrument is a sousaphone?

A nswers to Quiz 149, Pot Luck

1. A googol googols. 2. They are both called Eta. 3. The Earl of Shaftesbury. 4. It lies inside an enormous extinct volcanic crater. 5. The Euphrates. 6. South-west townships. 7. Singing in the Rain. 8. 'I'm looking for loopholes.' 9. Lord Haw Haw. 10. The Common Market. 11. President Nasser. 12. The Knesset. 13. China. 14. A protein in fibrous connective tissue. 15. 'Abandon all hope, you who enter here!' 16. Lao-tzu. 17. It was the world's first printed book. 18. They were Britain's only kings since William the Conqueror not to have been crowned. 19. Boudicca. 20. None. It is a story told of Caligula with no historical basis. 21. To make bricks without straw. 22. The mummification of corpses. 23. Seppuku. 24. The sackbut. 25. Bradford, Yorkshire. 26. Richard Dadd. 27. Evariste Galois. 28. Rastafarians. 29. No; it's a petrol bomb. 30. The tomb of Tutankhamen. 31. He set fire to the Reichstag. 32. Joseph Stalin. 33. Prosperous peasants in Czarist Russia. 34. The surrender of Robert E. Lee to Ulysses S. Grant. 35. Parsses. 36. The Spanish Armada. 37. He occupied the Falkland Islands but was heavily defeated in the ensuing war. 38. Buddha. 39. The Pillow Book of Sei Shonagon. 40. Teddy Roosevelt. 41. Peru. 42. West Germany. 43. Octavian defeated Mark Antony. 44. John Wilkes. 45. Admiral Byng's. 46. They cannot bark. 47. Sepia. 48. A traditional Japanese poem having a fixed form of 5-7-5 syllables. 49. The ludicrous misuse of a word, especially by confusion with one of a similar sound. 50. Luigi Pirandello.

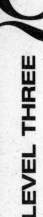

QUIZ 151 Wars & Battles

HARD - LEVEL THREE

1 During the conflict in North America, who was defeated in the Seven Years' War?

2 Which country did France declare war on in 1792?

3 Which army did Napoleon defeat at Austerlitz in 1805?

4 Which two towns saw the first battles of the American Revolution?

5 During the Korean War, which major powers supported the North Koreans?

6 During which war did the Battle of Edgehill take place?

7 The Thirty Years' War was fought on which main issue?

8 Which army was defeated in the Second Battle of Bull Run?

9 Where was the Spanish Armada fought?

10 Name the coalition, headed by Germany, Italy, and Japan, during World War II?

11 Who were the Central Powers in World War I?

12 Where was the first battle in the American Civil War?

13 In which year did the USA enter World War I?

14 Who commanded the Afrika Korps in North Africa?

15 What did the Russian February Revolution achieve?

16 When did the Vietnam War start?

17 In which year did the USA start sending troops to Vietnam?

18 Which was the opposing branch of Russian socialism that was in conflict with the Bolsheviks?

19 Which general led the Union army in the Battle of Fair Oaks?

20 In which year did the Battle of Trafalgar take place?

21 The French Revolution started during the reign of which king?

22 Which treaty ended the Seven Years' War?

23 During the American War of Independence, where did the British troops finally surrender?

24 Where was Robert E. Lee's army defeated on July 3 1863?

25 In which war was poison gas first used successfully?

26 Which part of Egypt was captured in the Six Day War?

27 What was the codename of the US bombing campaign during the Vietnam War?

28 Name the major offensive on South Vietnamese cities in 1968.

29 Which war did the Treaty of Vereeniging end?

30 Which state was created as a result of the First Balkan War?

31 Which German provoked the Franco-Prussian War?

32 What was the aim of the Boxers during their uprising in 1900?

33 During which war did Hannibal invade Italy?

34 Which commander led Union troops toward Richmond?

35 Who were the three colonial powers in North America at the start of the Seven Years' War?

36 During the Napoleonic Wars, who was defeated at Friedland?

37 During which war did the Battle of Lutzen take place?

38 Where did the Confederate Army surrender?

39 Which French king was captured during the Battle of Poitiers?

40 What was the location of a major evacuation of British and French troops by ship and boat in 1940?

41 Which war started on the Jewish Holy Day of Atonement in 1973?

42 During which battle were tanks first used?

43 Which were the disputed areas in the Russian–Japanese War?

44 In which year did the Russian Revolution begin and what name was given to the day?

45 When was the Boer War?

46 What did the Balkan League try to achieve?

47 Which city was destroyed during the Third Punic War?

48 During which war did the Battle of Sluys take place?

49 What was the name of the peninsula in the Dardanelles that British troops tried to capture in World War I?

50 What was the location of Henry V's victory over an army of French knights in 1415?

A nswers to
Quiz 150, CLASSICAL MUSIC

1. Singspiel. 2. Four. 3. Maurice Ravel. 4. Prince Igor. 5. Ludwig van Beethoven. 6. Hungarian. 7. The violin. 8. Abdelazar by Henry Purcell. 9. Sheherezade by Rimsky-Korsakov. 10. Beethoven's Ninth Symphony. 11. Nine. 12. Felix Mendelssohn-Bartholdy. 13. Oratorio. 14. Viola da gamba. 15. Johannes Brahms. 16. Peer Gynt Suite No.1. 17. 12. 18. Ludwig von Koechel. 19. Anton Schoenberg. 20. Bedrich Smetana. 21. The oboe family. 22. Four. 23. La Scala in Milan. 24. Joseph Haydn. 25. An interval is the simultaneous sounding of two pitches; a chord requires three or more pitches to be played at the same time. 26. Felt hammers. 27. Carmina Burana. 28. Fingal's Cave 29. An octave. 30. The incidental music to A Midsummer Night's Dream. 31. Mikhail Glinka. 32. Claude Debussy. 33. The violin. 34. Die Meistersinger von Nürnberg. 35. The piano. 36. Aleksandr Borodin. 37. Soprano. 38. Very. 39. It has no slow movement. 40. Poland. 41. The guitar. 42. Richard Strauss. 43. Mezzo-soprano. 44. 'Emperor'. 45. A stately court dance of the 17th and 18th centuries. 46. Jean Sibelius. 47. Falstaff, Otello, and Macbeth. 48. The 'Tragic'. 49. The violin. 50. A brass instrument similar in range to the tuba.

QUIZ 152 Crime

HARD - LEVEL THREE

1 What were stocks used for?

2 What was a gallows?

3 What did it mean if criminals were 'transported'?

4 What was the rack?

5 What punishment was inflicted on Guy Fawkes?

6 Is it true that criminals used to have to pay for their keep in prison?

7 What was the iron maiden?

8 What does the expression 'to let the cat out of the bag' refer to?

9 What fate befell Anne Boleyn?

10 What was strange about the execution of John 'Babacombe' Lee?

11 What happened to people who refused to plead in a criminal case?

12 What was a ducking stool used for?

13 What title was given to Matthew Hopkins?

14 Who were the tricoteuses?

15 What happened to the prankster Til Eugenspiel?

16 What official body was appointed by the Roman Catholic Church to root out heresy?

17 What was Alcatraz?

18 Which gang were the chief opponents of the Kray twins?

19 What was Al Capone finally convicted of?

20 What were the full names of Bonnie and Clyde?

21 What were pilliwinks?

22 How did Sitting Bull die?

23 Who tried to steal the British Crown jewels?

24 For what crime is Charles Manson infamous?

25 What crime was Lizzie Borden suspected of?

26 Who was the first murderer to be caught by wireless telegraphy?

27 Who were the Moors murderers?

28 What was a tawse?

29 Of what crime was Dreyfus falsely accused?

30 Who was known as the Demon Barber of Fleet Street?

31 What mythical character was punished by having his liver repeatedly torn out by eagles yet magically renewed itself each day?

32 What was keel hauling?

33 What, at least in stories, was the traditional punishment meted out by pirates to their captives?

34 What is the name for the Muslim legal code which prescribes severe punishments for crime?

35 Which country used the 'death of a thousand cuts'?

36 In which country could a promi nent man order a guilty subordi nate to disembowel himself?

37 In which country was the knout used as an instrument of punishment?

38 What punishment, inflicted upon Captain Jenkins, sparked off a war?

39 What was so bad about being made Keeper of the White Elephants by the King of Siam?

40 How are criminals executed in modern Thailand?

41 In which country is the electric chair a method of execution?

42 What was the Gulag?

43 There are many accounts of crucifixion, but how many crucified bodies have ever been discovered?

44 Which Roman slave was crucified after leading a slave rebellion?

45 What was the strappado?

46 What is 'falaka'?

47 For what crime was Socrates punished?

48 Who had to push a stone uphill for ever?

49 What was the name given to the practice of making a criminal prove his innocence by carrying a red-hot bar of metal in his bare hands?

50 What was Bridewell famous for?

Answers to Quiz 151, WARS & BATTLES

1. France. 2. Austria. 3. The Austro-Russian army. 4. Lexington and Concord. 5. Russia and China. 6. The English Civil War. 7. The predominance of Protestantism and Catholicism. 8. The Unionists. 9. The English Channel and the North Sea. 10. Axis. 11. Germany, Austria-Hungary, and Turkey. 12. Bull Run, on the Potomac river. 13. 1917. 14. Erwin Rommel. 15. The abdication of czar Nicholas II. 16. 1954. 17. 1961. 18. The Mensheviks. 19. George B. McClellan. 20. 1805 21. Louis XVI. 22. The Treaty of Paris. 23. In Yorktown. 24. Gettysburg. 25. World War I. 26. Sinai. 27. Rolling Thunder. 28. The Tet Offensive. 29. The Boer War. 30. Albania. 31. Otto von Bismarck. 32. To drive the foreign community out of China. 33. The Second Punic War. 34. Ulysses S. Grant. 35. Britain, France, and Spain. 36. The Russians. 37. The Thirty Years' War. 38. Appomattox in Virginia. 39. John II. 40. Dunkirk. 41. The Yom Kippur War. 42. The Battle of the Somme, fought in 1916. 43. Manchuria and Korea. 44. In 1905 The day became known as Bloody Sunday. 45. 1899–1902. 46. To drive Turkey out of Europe. 47. Carthage. 48. The Hundred Years' War. 49. Gallipoli. 50. Agincourt

QUIZ 153 Science

1 What shape is an amoeba?

2 Name the steroid hormones produced by the ovaries?

3 Which particle is described with the words 'charm' and 'strange'?

4 What is a particle carrying a charge of negative electricity?

5 Which colorless and tasteless inert gas emits a bright-red glow when conducting electricity?

6 If you mixed saltpetre (75%), sulphur (10%), and charcoal (15%), what would you get?

7 What explosive chemical is also used as to treat heart disease?

8 What is the medical name for a severe pain in the chest associated with a lack of supply of blood to the heart?

9 What medical name is often given to the pit of the stomach?

10 What is the medical name for the small tube projecting from the large intestine?

11 What is the name for the fine, powder-like material produced by the anthers of seed plants?

12 What happens to atmospheric pressure as altitude increases?

13 Name the lines on a weather map that connect points of equal atmospheric pressure?

14 Which branch of science deals with the atmosphere of a planet?

15 What is a low-lying cloud formation occurring in horizontal layers with rounded summits?

16 What name is given to the rapid decrease in atmospheric pressure?

17 What is the name for a reinforced spherical deep-diving chamber?

18 What do we call the substance that hardens and strengthens the cell walls of plants?

19 Name the condition in which a body part thickens and hardens?

20 What is the process by which organisms of different species cohabit to their mutual advantage?

21 What is special about the temperature −459.67° Fahrenheit?

22 What is the name given to the inevitable and steady deterioration of a system?

23 Who wrote Principia Mathematica?

24 Who was the first scientist to predict the return of a comet?

25 Find a word which is commonly used in pathology, dentistry, and mathematics.

26 What name is given to a stony mass found in the stomach?

27 Who was the first scientist to use a telescope to study the stars?

28 Who proposed that the Earth revolves around the sun?

29 Name the Greco-Egyptian mathematician whose theories were upset by Copernicus?

30 Who invented cathode ray tubes?

31 Who invented the miner's safety

lamp?

32 Which American invented the machine-gun?

33 For what is William Henry Fox Talbot famous?

34 Which inventor operated from laboratories at Menlo Park and West Orange?

35 Who did Edison compete with to invent the light bulb?

36 Who developed the revolver?

37 Which American developed vulcanized rubber?

38 What have the first adding machine and The Naked Lunch got in common?

39 Which nation is credited with the invention of the wheelbarrow?

40 In which year do you think the glass mirror was invented: 567 bc, ad 1278, or ad 1563?

41 The Dewar vessel was the precursor of which common household object?

42 What is nitric acid used for?

43 What class of organic compounds is obtained from meat and eggs?

44 By what other name was the Smilodon known?

45 Which gas was discovered by Joseph Priestly?

46 What is hypoxia?

47 The compound sold as Malathion is used for what purpose?

48 What is 'absolute alcohol'?

49 By what common name is diacetylmorphine known?

50 Name a group of nerve cells that form a nerve centre?

1. Imprisoning people by their ankles. 2. The structure from which criminals were hanged. 3. They were sent overseas as a punishment. 4. An instrument of torture on which people were stretched. 5. He was hanged, drawn, and quartered. 6. Yes. 7. A human-shaped box with spikes on the inside. 8. The cat o' nine tails: it was a type of whip much used on ships which was kept in a sack when not in use. 9. She was beheaded. 10. Three times. The equipment would not work. His sentence was commuted to life imprisonment. 11. They were 'pressed' by being placed under a wooden board on which weights were piled. 12. Trying witches. 13. Witchfinder General. 14. Women who sat knitting beside the guillotine. 15. He was hanged. 16. The Inquisition. 17. A notoriously tough US prison. 18. The Richardsons. 19. Tax evasion. 20. Bonnie Parker and Clyde Barrow. 21. Finger crushers. 22. He was shot by a Native American policeman. 23. Colonel Blood. 24. The murder of Sharon Tate. 25. The murder of her parents. 26. Dr Crippen. 27. Ian Brady and Myra Hindley. 28. A leather strap formerly used to punish Scottish schoolchildren. 29. Treason. 30. Sweeney Todd. 31. Prometheus. 32. Dragging a condemned man under the keel of a ship. 33. Walking the plank. 34. Sharia. 35. China. 36. Japan. 37. Russia. 38. His ear was cut off. 39. Financial ruin keeping them. 40. By machine gun. 41. USA. 42. Russian political prison camps. 43. Only one. 44. Spartacus. 45. Hanging. 46. Beating the soles of the feet (especially done in Turkey). 47. Corrupting the youth of Athens. 48. Sisyphus. 49. Trial by ordeal. 50. It was a women's prison.

QUIZ 154 World War II

HARD - LEVEL THREE

1 The invasion of which country precipitated World War II?

2 What name did the Germans give to the annexation of Austria?

3 With whom did Hitler negotiate a Non-Aggression Pact prior to his invasion of Poland?

4 What does the German expression Blitzkrieg mean?

5 Which German general was mainly responsible for applying the principles of Blitzkrieg?

6 The British had tried to negotiate a settlement with Hitler. What was this policy called?

7 What were German submarines called?

8 Which British liner was sunk by the Germans early in the war?

9 Apart from Germany, which other country attacked Poland?

10 On which date did Britain and France declare war on Germany?

11 On November 30 1939 the Soviets carried out an attack on which country?

12 When did Churchill become British prime minister?

13 From where was the British Expeditionary Force evacuated?

14 In which battle did the Luftwaffe pit itself against the RAF?

15 Which of the major countries in the war suffered no civilian casualties?

16 The USA and Great Britain suffered an almost identical number of military casualties in the conflict. How many?

17 Which country bore the heaviest military and civilian losses?

18 Who commanded the Soviet military forces?

19 Which Japanese admiral planned the attack on Pearl Harbor?

20 What nickname was given to the German V-1 rocket bomb?

21 What was the name of the French government which collaborated with the Germans?

22 Who led the Free French?

23 Who was leader of the Italian fascists during the war?

24 In which theater of operations was Rommel the German commander?

25 Which scientist was chiefly responsible for the German rocket bomb programme?

26 Why was the letter V used when naming rocket bombs?

27 What was a PIAT used for?

28 The Russians had a rocket weapon, named after a girl, which is still in use in some parts of the world. What is it called?

29 What was a Nebelwerfer?

30 What was regarded as spooky about the explosion of a V-2?

31 Give the US and British names of the underwater detection systems similar in operation to RADAR?

32 What weapon was chiefly used against submerged submarines?

33 What was the purpose of 'degaussing'?

34 What was the code name given to the German invasion of the USSR?

35 Which Soviet city was subjected to a 900-day siege?

36 What was a T34?

37 What stopped the German advance into Russia?

38 Did the Germans occupy Moscow?

39 What event brought the USA into the war?

40 What name was given to groups of German U-boats operating together?

41 Who commanded the U-boats?

42 Who commanded the Luftwaffe?

43 What name was given to Rommel's force in North Africa?

44 What symbol were Jews forced to wear to distinguish them from 'Aryans'?

45 What was the name given to the illegal trade in rationed goods?

46 What was the purpose of the Einsatzgruppen?

47 Who carried out the task of unifying the French Resistance organizations?

48 Who was the German commander in charge of the attack on Stalingrad?

49 What did Paulus finally do that was against Hitler's orders?

50 What was the codename given to the Normandy landings?

1. It has no fixed shape. 2. Oestrogen. 3. The quark. 4. An electron. 5. Neon. 6. Gunpowder. 7. Nitroglycerine. 8. Angina pectoris. 9. The solar plexus. 10. The appendix. 11. Pollen. 12. It decreases. 13. An isobar. 14. Meteorology. 15. Stratocumulus. 16. The bends. 17. A bathysphere. 18. Lignin. 19. Sclerosis. 20. Symbiosis. 21. It represents absolute zero. 22. Entropy. 23. Sir Isaac Newton. 24. Edmund Halley. 25. Calculus. 26. A gastrolith. 27. Galileo Galilei. 28. Copernicus. 29. Ptolemy. 30. William Crookes. 31. Humphrey Davy. 32. Gatling. 33. The invention of photographic processes. 34. Thomas Edison. 35. Sir Joseph Swan. 36. Samuel Colt. 37. Charles Goodyear. 38. Two men, each called William Seward Burroughs, were responsible for them. 39. The Chinese. 40. 1278. 41. The thermos flask. 42. The production of explosives. 43. Proteins. 44. The sabre-toothed tiger. 45. Oxygen. 46. A deficiency in the amount of oxygen reaching body tissues. 47. An insecticide. 48. Ethyl alcohol containing no more than 1% water. 49. Heroin. 50. Ganglion.

Quiz 155 Books

1 The character Natty Bumpo has two nicknames, one English and the other French. What are they?

2 What scandalous tale was written by Lucius Apuleius?

3 What Richard Adams was devoted to the adventures of rabbits?

4 What was the name of Bradbury's tale of an evil traveling fair?

5 Which of Anthony Burgess's novels concerned Christianity?

6 Who wrote "Breakfast at Tiffany's"?

7 What is the name of the series of novels by Anthony Powell?

8 Name David Lodge's novel concerning a catastrophe at a well-known British institution.

9 Sinclair Lewis wrote which novel about an evangelical preacher?

10 What dangerous-sounding novel was written by Laclos?

11 Who wrote the novels in which the spy George Smiley appears?

12 Which professor wrote a novel apparently opposing cannibalism.

13 In which Graham Greene novel did he describe small-time crooks at a seaside resort?

14 Which F. Scott Fitzgerald hero had a past cloaked in mystery?

15 Which of C. Isherwood's Berlin characters was noted for her emerald green nail polish?

16 Who wrote "Cider with Rosie"?

17 What was the real name of Ettrick Shepherd?

18 Which of Stephen King's characters used psychokinetic powers to gain revenge?

19 Ruth Prawer Jhabvala had parents of two nationalities but was born in a third country. Name them.

20 Who created the detective Lord Peter Wimsey?

21 Which Nigerian novelist wrote "The Famished Road"?

22 Which American scholar wrote a series of books entitled "The Masks of God"?

23 Which Robert Louis Stevenson novel used characters based on Robin Hood?

24 What name was given to a series of four books by Lawrence Durrell set in Egypt?

25 What event was dramatized in "The Night Runners of Bengal"?

26 What was Bram Stoker's job when he wrote "Dracula"?

27 What brief book did Stephen Hawking write?

28 In which science fiction novel, written by which scientist, do we read of an intelligent cloud?

29 Who wrote a book entitled "The Unbearable Lightness of Being"?

30 Who wrote the book in which Mrs Robinson appears?

31 In which book are monks murdered by a poisoned book?

32 In a J.D. Salinger book a story is

dedicated 'For Esme'. What is the rest of the dedication?

33 Which novel, in the form of two diaries, tells the story of a girl held prisoner by an entomologist?

34 Which Frenchman wrote about a revolution in New York?

35 Who wrote "The Naked Ape"?

36 Who created Captain Nemo?

37 Who wrote "Ethics"?

38 Who wrote "Utopia"?

39 For what literary work is Cellini chiefly remembered?

40 Name the US town made famous by Garrison Keillor.

41 Which science fiction story tells the story of a laboratory mouse and a mentally subnormal human?

42 Who wrote "Games People Play"?

43 Which Asimov novel states the Three Laws of Robotics?

44 What was the name of the walking, carnivorous plants created by John Wyndham?

45 In which Norman Mailer novel is the protagonist mummified?

46 A book called "The English Governess at the Siamese Court" was turned into which musical?

47 Which novel, with a Chinese connection, was written by Simone de Beauvoir?

48 Which Graham Greene novel was set in French Vietnam?

49 Who wrote "The Descent of Man"?

50 Who wrote: 'The mind is its own place, and in itself can make a heav'n of hell, a hell of heav'n'?

Answers to Quiz 154, WORLD WAR II

1. Poland. 2. Anschluss. 3. Joseph Stalin. 4. Lightning war. 5. Guderian. 6. Appeasement. 7. U-boats. 8. SS Athenia. 9. USSR. 10. September 3, 1939. 11. Finland. 12. May 10 1940. 13. Dunkirk. 14. The Battle of Britain. 15. The USA. 16. About 300,000. 17. The USSR. 18. Georgi Zhukov. 19. Admiral Yamamoto. 20. Doodlebug. 21. Vichy. 22. General de Gaulle. 23. Benito Mussolini. 24. North Africa. 25. Werner von Braun. 26. It stood for Vergeltungswaffen (Vengeance Weapons). 27. It was an anti-tank weapon. 28. Katyusha (Katie). 29. A German multi-barreled rocket launcher. 30. The rocket traveled faster than sound so it was heard only after it had exploded. 31. ASDIC and SONAR. 32. Depth charges. 33. It prevented ships from setting off magnetic mines. 34. Operation Barbarossa. 35. Leningrad. 36. It was the main type of Russian battle tank. 37. The Russian winter. 38. No. 39. The bombing of Pearl Harbor by the Japanese. 40. Wolf packs. 41. Admiral Doenitz. 42. Goering. 43. The Afrikacorps. 44. A yellow Star of David. 45. The black market. 46. Extermination of the Jews. 47. Jean Moulin. 48. Paulus. 49. Surrender. 50. Operation Overlord.

Q UIZ 156 | Pot Luck

HARD – LEVEL THREE

1 In which constellation would you find the star Bellatrix?

2 In Ancient Greece, games were held in Delphi every four years in honor of Apollo. What were they called?

3 Which country's national flag has two horizontal stripes, one red and one white of the same width?

4 What type of animal is a pangolin?

5 During the Hundred Years War, in which battle did the English capture John the Good?

6 What is the basic unit of currency in Korea?

7 Which composer wrote the ballet Appalachian Spring?

8 What is the capital of Laos?

9 Who became Spanish prime minister in 1975, following General Franco's death?

10 Which Austrian engineer designed the VW Beetle?

11 What can you examine with an otoscope?

12 Which hormone, produced by the adrenal cortex, regulates the salt and water balance in the body?

13 Jakob Grimm (of the Brothers Grimm) had a profession aside from writing. What was it?

14 What is etymology?

15 What do Jews celebrate on Rosh Hashanah?

16 What type of animal is an ichneumon?

17 What do you call a left-hand page of a book?

18 The ranunculus is a type of wild flower. By what name is it more commonly known?

19 Who directed the film Bugsy Malone?

20 Which period in prehistory saw the disappearance of dinosaurs?

21 In which country does the Atacama desert lie?

22 Which president succeeded Andrew Johnson?

23 Who wrote the opera Tancredi?

24 Of which Frankish dynasty was Pepin the Short king?

25 Which is Carlo Collodi's most famous piece of literature?

26 Who won the Nobel Peace Prize in 1983?

27 Which city in northern Italy is famous for its white marble?

28 Which invention is René Laënnec famous for?

29 What are cumulonimbus clouds composed of?

30 Jonas Salk developed the first vaccine against which disease?

31 Which two groups were fronted by Grace Slick?

32 On which river is Stuttgart situated?

33 Who wrote the novel Zorba the Greek?

34 Who did Paul von Hindenburg succeed as leader of the Weimar

Republic?

35 What do you call the positively charged particles within the nucleus of an atom?

36 What is the unit for measuring sound intensity?

37 In which organ is the Bowman's capsule situated?

38 Where are the Comoro Islands situated?

39 Who plays the part of Charles Smithson in the film "The French Lieutenant's Woman"?

40 Which artist painted "The Funeral at Ornans"?

41 What is the warm surface current off the western coast of South America which occurs every 4 to 12 years?

42 Who wrote the music to the TV series "Twin Peaks"?

43 The Mosquito Coast is divided between which two countries?

44 What does the stratum corneum consist of?

45 What is the name of the dry, dusty wind that originates in the Sahara and blows north toward the Mediterranean?

46 Which South American volcano erupted in 1985 killing over 20,000 people?

47 How are you most likely to catch trichinosis?

48 What is the capital of Azerbaijan?

49 Who directed the film Back to the Future?

50 What did Urban II bring about by his sermon at Clermont?

Answers to Quiz 155, Books

1. Hawkeye and La Longe Carabine. 2. The Golden Ass. 3. Watership Down. 4. Something Wicked This Way Comes. 5. Kingdom of the Wicked. 6. Truman Capote. 7. A Dance to the Music of Time. 8. The British Museum is Falling Down. 9. Elmer Gantry. 10. Les Liaisons Dangereuses. 11. John le Carré. 12. Malcolm Bradbury wrote Eating People is Wrong. 13. Brighton Rock. 14. The Great Gatsby. 15. Sally Bowles. 16. Laurie Lee. 17. James Hogg. 18. Carrie. 19. Britain, Poland, and Germany. 20. Dorothy L. Sayers. 21. Ben Okri. 22. Joseph Campbell. 23. The Black Arrow. 24. The Alexandria Quartet. 25. The Indian Mutiny. 26. He was touring manager to the actor Henry Irving. 27. A Brief History of Time. 28. The Black Cloud by Fred Hoyle. 29. Milan Kundera. 30. The Graduate by Charles Webb. 31. The Name of the Rose. 32. With Love and Squalor. 33. The Collector. 34. Project for a Revolution in New York by Allain Robbe-Grillet. 35. Desmond Morris. 36. Jules Verne. 37. Spinoza. 38. Sir Thomas More. 39. The Life of Benvenuto Cellini. 40. Lake Woebegon. 41. Flowers for Algernon. 42. Eric Berne. 43. I, Robot. 44. Triffids. 45. Ancient Evenings. 46. The King and I. 47. The Mandarins. 48. The Quiet American. 49. Charles Darwin. 50. John Milton, Paradise Lost.

QUIZ 157 | Places

HARD - LEVEL THREE

1 Which town did Tel Aviv merge with in 1950?

2 Which waterway connects the Southern Atlantic and Pacific Oceans?

3 Where is the St. George's Channel?

4 Which sea is Bombay situated at?

5 Which river flows along the German-Polish border?

6 Of which country is Guayaquil the largest city?

7 Which stretch of water lies between Iceland and Greenland?

8 What is the capital of Uruguay?

9 What river is Montreal situated on?

10 What is the predominant religion in Nepal?

11 In which country would you pay in forint?

12 Where is Wilkes Land?

13 Which South American country achieved independence from Spain in 1824?

14 In which mountain range is Lake Titicaca situated?

15 On which river is Warsaw situated?

16 Which country does Gotland belong to?

17 Which country does Ethiopia form its eastern border with?

18 Which island group does Rhodes belong to?

19 At which sea is Palermo situated?

20 Which US state is St Paul the capital of?

21 On which Hawaiian island is Honolulu situated?

22 Which desert occupies parts of Botswana, Namibia, and northern South Africa?

23 What is the name of the islands situated at the western entrance of the English Channel, to the south-west of England?

24 On which sea is Baku situated?

25 Which two countries does the Brenner Pass connect?

26 What is the capital of Angola?

27 Where would you find the ancient city of Knossos?

28 Which is the lowest point on the Earth?

29 On which sea is Murmansk situated?

30 In which city is the cathedral of St. John the Divine?

31 Of which country was Zaire a colony before it became independent in 1960?

32 Which countries does the Gobi Desert occupy?

33 On which river is Toulouse situated?

34 Which country does the island of Bornholm belong to?

35 At which sea is Darwin situated?

36 Which capital city is laid out in the shape of an aeroplane?

37 What is the capital of Byelorussia?

318

38 What is the name of the water way between Alaska and eastern Siberia?

39 Where does the river Ganges rise?

40 What is the East German town of Meissen famous for?

41 Which countries does Paraguay have borders with?

42 Between which two lakes are the Niagara Falls?

43 Which US state lies between Indiana and Pennsylvania?

44 Which is the highest peak of the Andes?

45 In which country can the former kingdom of Ashanti be found now?

46 What is Bechuanaland now called?

47 Which island lies at the entrance to the Gulf of Mexico?

48 Which is the world's smallest independent state?

49 Of which country is Maputo the capital?

50 Where would you find the Koutoubya Mosque?

A nswers to Quiz 156, Pot Luck

1. Orion. 2. The Pythian Games. 3. Indonesia's. 4. A scale-covered anteater. 5. The Battle of Poitiers. 6. The won. 7. Aaron Copland. 8. Vientiane. 9. Adolfo Suarez Gonzales. 10. Ferdinand Porsche. 11. The eardrum. 12. Aldosterone. 13. He was a philologist. 14. A branch of linguistics that investigates . the origin and development of words. 15. New Year. 16. A large mongoose. 17. A verso. 18. Buttercup. 19. Alan Parker. 20. The cretaceous. 21. Chile. 22. Ulysses S. Grant. 23. Gioacchino Rossini. 24. The Carolingians. 25. Pinocchio. 26. Lech Walesa. 27. Carrara. 28. The stethoscope. 29. A mixture of water droplets and ice. 30. Polio. 31. Jefferson Airplane and Jefferson Starship. 32. The Neckar. 33. Nikos Kazantzakis. 34. Friedrich Ebert. 35. Protons. 36. The decibel. 37. The kidneys. 38. In the Indian Ocean between the east African coast and Madagascar. 39. Jeremy Irons. 40. Gustave Courbet. 41. El Niño. 42. Angelo Badalamenti. 43. Nicaragua and Honduras. 44. Mainly dead skin cells. 45. Sirocco. 46. The Nevado del Ruiz in Colombia. 47. By eating raw or undercooked meat, especially pork. 48. Baku. 49. Robert Zemeckis. 50. The first Crusade.

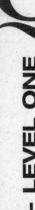

Quiz 158 | Horse Racing

HARD - LEVEL ONE

1 Which is the oldest British flat classic race?

2 How many winners did Gordon Richards ride in the 1947 season?

3 Which jockey riding Shergar in 1981 won in his first Derby ride?

4 Which jockey won the Prix de l'Arc de Triomphe from 1985 to 1987 on three different horses?

5 Where did Britain's first evening meeting take place?

6 Who rode Henbit, Nashwan and Erhaab to Derby victories?

7 Which horse, in 1977, became the first to win the Mackeson and Hennessy in the same season?

8 Which course celebrated 100 years of racing in July 1987?

9 Who was the first woman to ride a winner over fences in Britain?

10 In 1925 at Windsor, bookmakers went on strike. Against what?

11 Where was the Derby held during the two World Wars?

12 On which course in Australia is the Melbourne Cup run?

13 Which jockey had most Classic wins before Lester Piggott?

14 Which was the first racecourse equipped with a photo-finish camera?

15 On which horse did Princess Anne win her first flat race?

16 Diomed was the first winner of which great race?

17 Which race came first, the 1000 Guineas or 2000 Guineas?

18 What is Dick Hern's real first name?

19 Which gossip columnist was owner of My Purple Prose?

20 Where is the Happy Valley racecourse?

21 What is the first name of Peter Scudamore's father?

22 In betting, how much is a monkey?

23 In which Surrey town is Sandown racecourse?

24 Lester Piggott shares his birthday with which annual event?

25 In which country did Steve Donoghue ride his first winner?

26 What is the real first name of Richard Dunwoody?

27 Son of a famous father, who had his first winner at Kempton in 1978?

28 In his 1990 comeback which horse gave Lester Piggott his first winner?

29 How many individual bets make up a Yankee?

30 How many Grand Nationals did Desert Orchid win?

31 In 1990 Mr Frisk set a record time in which major race?

32 Which Earl of Derby gave his name to the race?

33 To a year each way, when was Red Rum's third Grand National win?

34 Where is the Lincoln Handicap

320

held?

35 Which three races make up the English Triple Crown?

36 How did 19th century jockey Fred Archer die?

37 Which Irish rider won the Prix de L'Arc de Triomphe four times?

38 To two years each way, when did Lester Piggott first win the Derby?

39 Which classic race was sponsored by Gold Seal from 1984-92?

40 Who rode Devon Loch in the sensational 1956 Grand National?

41 What colour was Arkle?

42 How long is the Derby?

43 Sceptre managed to win how many classics outright in a season?

44 Shergar won the 1981 Derby by a record of how many lengths?

45 Which National Hunt jockey retired in 1993 with most ever wins?

46 What was the nickname of Corbiere?

47 Who rode Nijinsky to victory in the Derby?

48 In which decade was the Prix de L'Arc de Triomphe first run?

49 Who triumphed in the Oaks on Ballanchine and Moonshell?

50 Which horse was National Hunt Champion of the Year four times in a row from 1987 on?

Answers to Quiz 157, PLACES

1. Jaffa. 2. The Strait of Magellan. 3. Between Ireland and Wales. 4. The Arabian Sea. 5. Oder. 6. Ecuador. 7. The Denmark Strait. 8. Montevideo. 9. The St. Lawrence. 10. Hinduism. 11. Hungary. 12. Antarctica. 13. Peru. 14. The Andes. 15. The Vistula. 16. Sweden. 17. Somalia. 18. The Dodecanese. 19. The Tyrrhenian Sea. 20. Minnesota. 21. Oahu. 22. The Kalahari. 23. The Isles of Scilly. 24. The Caspian Sea. 25. Austria and Italy. 26. Luanda. 27. Crete. 28. The Dead Sea. 29. The Barents Sea, part of the Arctic Ocean. 30. New York. 31. Belgium. 32. Mongolia and north China. 33. The Garonne. 34. Denmark. 35. The Timor Sea. 36. Brasilia. 37. Minsk. 38. The Bering Strait. 39. In the Himalayas. 40. Porcelain. 41. Brazil, Bolivia, and Argentina. 42. Lake Ontario and Lake Erie. 43. Ohio. 44. The Aconcagua. 45. Ghana. 46. Botswana. 47. Cuba. 48. Vatican City. 49. Mozambique. 50. Marrakesh.

QUIZ 159 | Pop Music

QuIZ 159

HARD - LEVEL THREE

1 Who recorded the album "Hounds Of Love"?

2 Who was the organist with The Doors?

3 What was the name of Paul McCartney's group after the break-up of the Beatles?

4 Who wrote the musical "Candide"?

5 Which song contains the words 'Behind the shelter in the middle of a roundabout the pretty nurse is selling poppies from a tray'?

6 What was Abba's first US hit single?

7 Who wrote the piece "In the Mood"?

8 Which original Queen album contains the song "Bohemian Rhapsody"?

9 Who sang the title song to the film "Hello Dolly"?

10 Which ragtime song was used in the film "The Sting"?

11 Which song contains the words 'Take me on a trip upon your magic swirlin' ship, my senses have been stripped'?

12 On which original Dire Straits album is the song 'Walk of Life"?

13 From which musical comes the song "Mr Mistoffelees"?

14 What was Madonna's first hit?

15 Who sang the title song to the film "What's New Pussycat"?

16 In which year did Elvis Presley die?

17 Which Carole King album topped the charts in 1971 and went on to sell over 15 million copies?

18 Who wrote the score to the musical "Evita"?

19 Who was the singer of the Eurythmics?

20 Which song contains the words 'Sitting on a sofa on a Sunday afternoon, going to the candidates' debate'?

21 Who wrote the song "The Times They are a-Changin"?

22 What was the theme song to the film "Flashdance"?

23 In which musical can you find the song "Food, Glorious Food"?

24 On which Fleetwood Mac album is the song "Go Your Own Way"?

25 Who wrote the operetta 'The Mikado"?

26 Who preceded Phil Collins as lead singer of Genesis?

27 What was the title of the first Beatles single?

28 Who wrote the score to the musical "Kiss Me Kate"?

29 Which song contains the words 'Beelzebub has a devil for a son'?

30 Who wrote the song "This Land is Your Land"?

31 From which musical does the song "There's no Business like Show Business" come from?

32 Who was the lead singer of The Police?

322

33 Who played the king in the film musical "The King and I"?

34 Who made the single "Peggy Sue"?

35 Which was Bon Jovi's first top ten hit?

36 Who sang the theme song to the James Bond film "Goldfinger"?

37 For which type of music was Bob Marley famous?

38 Who made the album "Tubular Bells"?

39 Who made the recording "Banana Boat Song"?

40 Who brought out the album "The Joshua Tree"?

41 Which song contains the words 'My father was a tailor, he sewed my new blue jeans'?

42 Who was the lead singer of T. Rex?

43 From which musical does the song "All I Ask of You" come ?

44 Which Parisian singer was known for songs like "Non, je ne regrette rien"?

45 Which was Elton John's first US top 10 hit?

46 Who wrote the music to the film musical "Gigi"?

47 Which two singers had a massive hit in 1985 with the remake of "Dancing in the Street"?

48 Through which film did Meat Loaf become a success?

49 Who is the singer of U2?

50 Who first performed the rock opera Tommy?

Answers to Quiz 158, HORSE RACING

1. St Leger. 2. 269. 3. Walter Swinburn. 4. Pat Eddery. 5. Hamilton. 6. Willie Carson. 7. Bachelor's Hall. 8. Wolverhampton. 9. Jane Thorne. 10. Betting tax. 11. Newmarket. 12. Flemington Park. 13. Frank Buckle. 14. Epsom. 15. Gulfland. 16. Derby. 17. 2000 Guineas in 1809. 18. William. 19. Nigel Dempster. 20. Hong Kong. 21. Michael. 22. £500. 23. Esher. 24. Guy Fawkes Night. 25. France. 26. Thomas. 27. Walter Swinburn, Jnr. 28. Nicholas. 29. 11. 30. One. 31. Grand National. 32. 12th. 3 1977. 34. Doncaster. 35. 2,000 Guineas, Derby, St Leger. 36. Committed suicide. 37. Pat Eddery. 38. 1954. 39. The Oaks. 40. Dick Francis. 41. Bay. 42. 1 mile 4. furlongs. 43. Four. 44. Ten. 45. Peter Scudamore. 46. Corky. 47. Lester Piggott. 48. 1920s. 49. Frankie Dettori. 50. Desert Orchid.

QUIZ 160 Football

HARD - LEVEL ONE

1 Which Rio-based club is named after a Portuguese navigator?

2 Which Japanese city is home to Grampus Eight?

3 For which national team does Abedi Pele play?

4 On which day of the week do the Spanish usually play football?

5 Which shirt number do Italian clubs reserve for their star player?

6 Which Dutch side play their games in the Philips Stadium?

7 Which Spanish team did Gary Lineker play for?

8 Which country was in three of the first four European finals?

9 Which city is home to Racing Club and River Plate?

10 At which ground do the Republic of Ireland play home games?

11 Which former goalie coached both Juventus and Lazio?

12 In which European country are the headquarters of UEFA?

13 Which French side did Trevor Steven play for?

14 Where did Aston Villa win the European Cup in 1982?

15 Where in France is the ground known as Le Stadium?

16 Which Serie A club is based on the island of Sardinia?

17 In which stadium was the final of the 1992 Olympic tournament?

18 In what year was the first ever European Cup match played?

19 Argentina's Maradona played for which club during 1992–93?

20 Independiente are a leading club in which country?

21 Which side beat Arsenal in the 1995 European Cup Winners' Cup with a goal in the last minute of extra time?

22 In which country was the 1992 European Championship staged?

23 Name the the beaten finalists in the 1994 World Cup final?

24 The quickest goal in a World Cup tournament was scored by Bryan Robson against who in 1982?

25 Which country became the first to win the World Cup three times?

26 Which Spanish side did Howard Kendall once manage?

27 Which was the first British team to lift the European Cup after a penalty shoot-out?

28 Alfredo di Stefano played international football for three countries – Argentina, Spain and which other country?

29 Which item of kit was made compulsory by FIFA in 1990?

30 Who is the only player to score a hat-trick in a World Cup final?

31 What colour did the legendary keeper Lev Yashin play in?

32 Which striker was known as the Octopus in his own country?

33 Bobby Robson left which club to

join Barcelona?

34 Oscar Ruggeri became the highest capped player for which country?

35 Who had the final kick of the 1994 World Cup Final?

36 In which decade did Bayern Munich first win the UEFA Cup?

37 Former Italian prime minister Silvio Berlusconi took over which club?

38 Thomas Ravelli became the most capped player for which country?

39 The stadium the Monumental is in which country?

40 Which Dutchman came with Muhren to Ipswich in the 80s?

41 Alfredo di Stefano played for Argentina, Spain and which other country?

42 Before 1994 when did Brazil last win the World Cup?

43 The club Feyenoord is based in which city?

44 Which club play at the Bernabeu Stadium?

45 Who scored England's winner against Belgium in Italia 90?

46 What colour are Germany's shorts?

47 How old was Maradona when he first played for Argentina?

48 Who captained Italy in the 1994 World Cup Final?

49 Gullit, Van Basten and Rijkaard lined up at which non-Dutch club?

50 Which country does Stefan Schwartz play for?

Answers to Quiz 159, Pop Music

1. Kate Bush. 2. Ray Manzarek. 3. Wings. 4. Leonard Bernstein. 5. 'Penny Lane'. 6. 'Waterloo'. 7. Glenn Miller. 8. A Night at the Opera. 9. Louis Armstrong. 10. 'The Entertainer'. 11. 'Mr Tambourine Man'. 12. Brothers in Arms. 13. Cats. 14. 'Holiday'. 15. Tom Jones. 16. 1977. 17. Tapestry. 18. Andrew Lloyd Webber. 19. Annie Lennox. 20. 'Mrs Robinson'. 21. Bob Dylan. 22. 'What a Feeling'. 23. Oliver! 24. Rumours. 25. Gilbert and Sullivan. 26. Peter Gabriel. 27. 'Love Me Do'. 28. Cole Porter. 29. 'Bohemian Rhapsody'. 30. Woody Guthrie. 31. Annie Get Your Gun. 32. Sting. 33. Yul Brynner. 34. Buddy Holly. 35. 'You Give Love a Bad Name'. 36. Shirley Bassey. 37. Reggae. 38. Mike Oldfield. 39. Harry Belafonte. 40. U2. 41. 'The House of the Rising Sun'. 42. Marc Bolan. 43. Phantom of the Opera. 44. Edith Piaf. 45. 'Your Song'. 46. Frederick Loewe. 47. Mick Jagger and David Bowie. 48. The Rocky Horror Picture Show. 49. Bono. 50. The Who.

Q UIZ 161 Games

1 Name the Japanese board game played with black and white 'stones'?

2 In card games, what is the meaning of 'finesse'?

3 What is shogi?

4 Which Greek games were held in honor of the god Apollo?

5 What, in the context of games, is the meaning of the word 'rubber'?

6 What is Hoyle?

7 What is bezique?

8 What is hare and hounds?

9 What is fan tan?

10 What is shuffleboard?

11 In which game would you 'castle'?

12 What is the object of the game called knights?

13 What popular children's prank was called Knock Down Ginger?

14 With which festival do you associate the custom of Trick or Treat?

15 Who won the 1996 Wimbledon's men's singles tennis championship?

16 In which sporting event would a competitor wear the maillot jaune?

17 With which sport do you associate the expression 'slam dunk'?

18 How many men form a team in Australian football?

19 What is the difference between fives and squash?

20 What is the Irish game that vaguely resembles hockey?

21 In which country is golf thought to have originated?

22 For what sporting achievement is James Naismith remembered?

23 Where did chess originate?

24 How do you keep the score in a game of cribbage?

25 In which game might you attempt a carom?

26 The game of quoits is traditionally, though not necessarily, associated with a method of travel. What is it?

27 The Chinese name for table tennis is 'ping pong'. True or false?

28 In poker which of these hands is worth the most: (a) royal flush, (b) full house, or (c) four of a kind?

29 In which country did canasta originate?

30 In which country did badminton originate?

31 Which children's game uses a whip?

32 Which toy has Satanic connections?

33 Which sport uses a jack?

34 By what other name is the game of petanque known?

35 What form of roulette can have fatal consequences?

36 Which game, played on a chess board, goes by different names in the UK and the USA?

37 What is jokari?

38 What is a slalom?

39 With which sport do you associ

ate the Cresta Run?

40 Which of these is not a martial art: Tae Kwon Do, Wing Chun, or Basho?

41 Which country won the Euro 96 soccer competition?

42 The Japanese play a gambling game on a vertical pinball machine. What is its name?

43 In which sport would you find gutta percha used?

44 How do you croquet an opponent's ball?

45 What is a roquet shot?

46 What did the word croquet originally mean?

47 Which game is divided into 'chukkers'?

48 What is buzkashi?

49 The polka used to be a very popular dance. What does the name mean?

50 Edson Arantes do Nascimento was a famous Brazilian soccer player. By what name was he better known?

1. Vasco da Gama. 2. Nagoya. 3. Ghana. 4. Sunday. 5. Ten. 6. PSV Eindhoven. 7. Barcelona. 8. USSR. 9. Buenos Aires. 10. Lansdowne Road. 11. Dino Zoff. 12. Switzerland. 13. Marseille. 14. Rotterdam. 15. Toulouse. 16. Cagliari. 17. Nou Camp. 18. 1955. 19. Seville. 20. Argentina. 21. Zaragoza. 22. Sweden. 23. Italy. 24. France. 25. Brazil. 26. Atlético Bilbao. 27. Liverpool. 28. Colombia. 29. Shin guard. 30. Geoff Hurst. 31. Black. 32. Faustino Asprilla. 33. Porto. 34. Argentina. 35. Roberto Baggio. 36. 1990s. 37. AC Milan. 38. Sweden. 39. Argentina. 40. Frans Thijssen. 41. Colombia. 42. 1970. 43. Rotterdam. 44. Real Madrid. 45. David Platt. 46. Black. 47. 16. 48. Franco Baresi. 49. AC Milan. 50. Sweden.

QUIZ 162 Pop Music

HARD - LEVEL THREE

1 Who joined Pink Floyd in 1968 after Syd Barrett left the group?

2 Who wrote the score to the musical "Guys and Dolls"?

3 Which jazz musician brought out the album "Touchstone"?

4 Who composed the soundtrack for the film "One Trick Pony"?

5 Which group did Pete Seeger and Lee Hays form in 1948?

6 Who originally recorded the Simply Red hit "If You Don't Know Me by Now" in 1972?

7 On which Simple Minds album is the song "The Belfast Child"?

8 Which musical contains the song "You'll Never Walk Alone"?

9 Ernie Evans was a pop sensation in the early 1960s. How was he better known?

10 Which singer was born Gordon Matthew Sumner?

11 Who wrote the theme to the film Dangerous Liaisons?

12 Which Spanish opera star did Freddie Mercury sing duets with?

13 Who wrote the USA for Africa song "We Are the World"?

14 Who wrote the song "I Get a Kick out of You"?

15 Which group released the album "Communiqué"?

16 Which instrument does Joe Henderson play?

17 Who released a cover version of the old Platters song "Smoke Gets in Your Eyes" in 1974?

18 Which musical does "Life Upon the Wicked Stage"come from?

19 Paul McCartney released an arrangement of which nursery rhyme in 1972?

20 With which song did Steve Miller top the charts in 1982?

21 Who wrote "A Harlem Symphony"?

22 On which John Lennon album is the song "Number Nine Dream"?

23 Who sang the theme tune to the film Endless Love?

24 Who wrote the Janis Joplin hit "Me and Bobby McGee"?

25 Which musical the song "I Don't Know How to Love Him" come from?

26 Which singer released the album Spanish Train and Other Stories?

27 Who was the musician, known for his electronic experiments, who played with Roxy Music from 1971 to 1973?

28 On which Foreigner album is the song "Hot Blooded"?

29 Which teen band did Alan and Derek Longmuir belong to?

30 Which jazz musician brought out the album Perfect Machine?

31 What was the name of Elvis Costello's backing group?

32 In 1988 Phil Collins had a hit with "Groovy Kind of Love". Who recorded this song originally?

33 Which Belgian jazz guitarist, born in 1910, originated from a gypsy family?

34 Which Chubby Checker hit was re-released in 1975?

35 What does Miles Davis play?

36 Who recorded the theme song of the James Bond film "The Living Daylights"?

37 Which group backed Tony Sheridan in the early 60s?

38 Who composed the song "Strangers in the Night"?

39 From which musical does the song "We Said We Wouldn't Look Back" come?

40 Who recorded the "Hot Buttered Sou"l album in 1969?

41 Chet Atkins was responsible for creating which style of music?

42 Which singer recorded the album "Songs in the Key of Life"?

43 Which jazz musician wrote the song "Crawlin' Kingsnake"?

44 The Paul McCartney song "We All Stand Together"appeared on the soundtrack of which cartoon film?

45 Which guitarist replaced Eric Clapton in the Yardbirds in 1965?

46 Who wrote the theme tune for the film "Grease"?

47 "I'll Never Fall in Love Again" is a song from which musical?

48 In which film did Bing Crosby sing his song "White Christmas"?

49 By what name were Bill Medley and Bobby Hatfield better known?

50 Who sang the theme tune to the film "Arthur"?

Answers to Quiz 161, GAMES

1. Go. 2. Playing of a card in a suit when one holds a non-sequential higher card. 3. Japanese board game. 4. The Pythian games. 5. A series of games of which two out of three, or three out of five, must be won. 6. A book of rules for card games and other indoor games. 7. A card game similar to pinochle that is played with a deck of 64 cards. 8. A game in which one group of players leaves a trail of paper scraps for another group to follow. 9. A Chinese betting game. 10. A game in which disks are slid towards one of two usually triangular targets. 11. Chess. 12. To swap pieces of two colors from one side of the board to the other in the least number of 'knight' moves. 13. Knocking on someone's front door and running away. 14. Hallowe'en. 15. Richard Krajicek. 16. The Tour de France. 17. Basketball. 18. Eighteen. 19. In fives the players use their hands to hit the ball. 20. Hurling. 21. Scotland. 22. He invented basketball. 23. India. 24. By moving pegs along a board full of holes. 25. Billiards. 26. Passenger ships. 27. True. 28. Royal flush. 29. Uruguay. 30. India. 31. Spinning tops. 32. The Diabolo. 33. Bowls. 34. Boules. 35. Russian roulette. 36. Draughts/checkers. 37. A game that involves hitting a ball on elastic with a bat. 38. An event where the contestants weave in and out of a series of posts. 39. Bobsleigh. 40. Basho. 41. Germany. 42. Pachinko. 43. Golf; to make balls. 44. By hitting your ball when the two are in contact. 45. To hit another player's ball in croquet. 46. A shepherd's crook. 47. Polo. 48. An Afghan game in which mounted players struggle for possession of a headless calf. 49. A Polish woman. 50. Pele.

 Quiz 163 | Pot Luck

1 What does the Latin tag Nil desperandum mean?

2 In the city name Washington DC, what do the letters DC stand for?

3 Which of the tropics is north of the equator?

4 In which direction do tornadoes usually spin in the northern hemisphere?

5 Only two flowering plants grow in Antarctica. One is a relative of the carnation, what is the other?

6 How much of the Earth's ice is found in Antarctica?

7 Where is the deepest point in the oceans?

8 In ad 582 Paris experienced a shower of what was thought to be blood. What was it?

9 There is a fungus that can use jet fuel as a source of food. True or false?

10 What is the definition of the 'minimum lethal dose' of a toxin?

11 What is hypermertropia?

12 Why is a wound in your tongue far more painful than a wound of the same size on your back?

13 What percentage of the body's energy is consumed by the brain?

14 A British scientist once successfully used Coca Cola as a replacement for oil in a car. True or false?

15 When did Native Americans first get the vote?

16 Which was the first country to give the vote to women?

17 By what title was Augustina Domonech better known?

18 Which Irish adventurer tried to steal the British crown jewels?

19 What is alliteration?

20 What is the bony substance in a tooth just beneath the enamel?

21 What is a lectern?

22 What is the oldest alloy?

23 Why does a helium balloon rise in air?

24 What is a molecule?

25 Why can there never be a perfect vacuum?

26 Why is carbon monoxide so dangerous?

27 What is a 'mother lode'?

28 What is a saskatoon?

29 What is pemmican?

30 By what other name is the kinkajou known?

31 By what nickname is the American Stars and Stripes flag often known?

32 Which English leader's body was exhumed and hanged after his death?

33 What is the name of the race of dwarfs whose magic ring was stolen from them by Siegfried?

34 In the Nibelungen, which queen of Iceland was defeated by Siegfried?

35 What is the name for a Russian carriage drawn by three horses

abreast?

36 What was a charabanc?

37 What was a travois?

38 'He was a Jeanne d'Arc, a saint. He was a martyr. Like many martyrs, he held extreme views.' Who was Ezra Pound describing?

39 St. George survived the dragon but, according to tradition, what fate eventually befell him?

40 Where did Albert Schweitzer establish his hospital?

41 Who won the Nobel Prize for Peace in 1989?

42 What is an andiron?

43 What is a trephine?

44 Where would you find the stratosphere?

45 What is a galley proof?

46 What, in railway terms, is a caboose?

47 Who was the founder of Presbyterianism?

48 For what is Matthew Vassar famous?

49 Giuseppi Garibaldi lived in the USA before becoming an Italian hero. What trade did he follow?

50 Who wrote the book "Death in Venice"?

Answers to Quiz 162, Pop Music

1. Dave Gilmour. 2. Frank Loesser. 3. Chick Corea. 4. Paul Simon. 5. The Weavers. 6. Harold Melvin and The Blue Notes. 7. Street Fighting Years. 8. Carousel. 9. Chubby Checker. 10. Sting. 11. George Fenton. 12. Montserrat Caballe. 13. Michael Jackson and Lionel Richie. 14. Cole Porter. 15. Dire Straits. 16. Saxophone. 17. Bryan Ferry. 18. Showboat. 19. 'Mary Had a Little Lamb'. 20. 'Abracadabra'. 21. Spike Hughes. 22. Walls and Bridges. 23. Diana Ross and Lionel Richie. 24. Kris Kristofferson. 25. Jesus Christ Superstar. 26. Chris de Burgh. 27. Brian Eno. 28. Double Vision. 29. The Bay City Rollers. 30. Herbie Hancock. 31. The Attractions. 32. The Mindbenders. 33. Django Reinhardt. 34. 'Let's Twist Again'. 35. Trumpet. 36. A-HA. 37. The Beatles. 38. Bert Kaempfert. 39. Salad Days. 40. Isaac Hayes. 41. The Nashville Sound. 42. Stevie Wonder. 43. John Lee Hooker. 44. Rupert the Bear. 45. Jeff Beck. 46. Barry Gibb. 47. Promises Promises. 48. Holiday Inn. 49. The Righteous Brothers. 50. Christopher Cross.

Quiz 164 | Kid's TV

HARD - LEVEL THREE

1 What is the longest running children's TV programme?

2 What did the letters in "TISWAS" stand for?

3 Who was the "Saturday Girl" on "Multi-Coloured Swap Shop"?

4 Which series was a children's predecessor of "Monty Python"?

5 Which village's postmistress is called Mrs Goggins?

6 What was "Fingermouse" made from?

7 Who fought against Bulk and Texas Pete?

8 Who presented his own "Cartoon Time" and "Cartoon Club"?

9 Which three singers from "Rainbow" were given their own series?

10 Which show ended ruefully with "Bye bye, everybody, bye bye"?

11 Which show was first presented by Emma Forbes and Andi Peters?

12 Which 1970s ecologists had their own TV series?

13 Which family had a daily help called Mrs Scrubbitt?

14 Which magazine programme had a mascot called Murgatroyd?

15 What sort of animal was Parsley in "The Herbs"?

16 Who had magical adventures and lived at 52 Festive Road?

17 Which pre-school programme

was the first programme on BBC2?

18 Which former "Blue Peter" presenter's mother is Gloria Hunniford?

19 Who were Andy Pandy's two best friends?

20 In which 1980s/1990s series did Robin of Islington and Little Ron appear?

21 How many programmes had "Blue Peter" by their anniversary in May 1997?

22 Which pre-school characters live in Home Hill?

23 Who presented the first series of "Live and Kicking"?

24 What were the Teenage Mutant Hero Turtles called?

25 What was the name of the alien discovered, by Mike, in a wardrobe?

26 Who is the postmistress of Greendale?

27 What sort of creature is Children's BBC's Otis?

28 In which US state is "Sweet Valley High" set?

29 Which spacecraft was flown by Steve Zodiac?

30 Which character did Susan Tully play in "Grange Hill"?

31 Which comedian wrote the theme music for "Supergran"?

32 Where would you find Hugh, Pugh, Barney McGrew, Cuthbert,

Dibble and Grubb?

33 Who numbered Barnabas, Willy and Master Bate in his crew?

34 Who did Captains White, Blue, Grey and Magenta deal with?

35 Which "historical" series included Barrington, Rabies and Little Ron?

36 What sort of creature is Dilly?

37 How many legs did the Famous Five have on TV?

38 Where is the teenage drama series "Sweat" set?

39 In which show would you find Dump-Pea?

40 In "Rag, Tag and Bobtail" what was Tag?

41 What is "Fablon" called on "Blue Peter"?

42 What did every contestant win on "Crackerjack"?

43 Who was the longest-lasting presenter of "Rainbow"?

44 The cartoon series about Willy Fogg was based on which book?

45 What sort of animal said, "I'm just a big silly old Hector"?

46 What day of the week was "The Woodentops" originally broadcast?

47 In "The Herbs" what were schoolteacher Mr Onion's pupils called?

48 Which characters live in Springfield?

49 Who has presented "How" and "How 2"?

50 What was Huckleberry Hound's favourite song?

A nswers to Quiz 163, Pot Luck

1. Never despair. 2. District of Columbia. 3. Tropic of Cancer. 4. Anticlockwise. 5. Grass. 6. Nine-tenths. 7. The Marianas Trench. 8. Red dust blown up from the Sahara. 9. True. The Kerosene fungus. 10. The smallest amount needed to kill a guinea pig weighing 250g (9oz) within four days. 11. Longsightedness. 12. The touch receptors on the tongue are 100 times denser than those on the back. 13. 20%. 14. True. 15. 1924. 16. New Zealand, in 1893. 17. The Maid of Zaragoza. 18. Colonel Blood. 19. Using the same letter or sylla- ble several times in rapid succession. 20. Dentine. 21. A reading desk. 22. Bronze. 23. Helium is much lighter than air. 24. The smallest part of any substance that can exist and still exhibit all its properties. 25. The container of the vacuum gives off tiny traces of vapor which destroy the it. 26.Combines with haemoglobin in blood, eliminating oxygen. 27. The main source of ore in a region. 28. A shrub of north-west North America. 29. A Native American food pre- pared from meat, fat and berries. 30. The honey bear. 31. Old Glory. 32. Oliver Cromwell. 33. Nibelung. 34. Brunhild. 35. Troika. 36. A large bus. 37. A frame slung between trailing poles, pulled by a dog or horse. 38. Adolf Hitler. 39. He was martyred. 40. Lambarene. 41. The Dalai Lama. 42. A support used for holding up logs in a fireplace. 43. A surgical instrument used to cut out disks of bone. 44. Above the troposphere and below the mesosphere. 45. A proof taken from composed type. 46. The last car on a freight train, with kitchen and sleeping facilities. 47. John Calvin. 48. He advocated higher educa- tion for women and endowed Vassar College. 49. He was a candle maker. 50. Thomas Mann.

Q_{UIZ} 165 Pot Luck

HARD - LEVEL THREE

1 Which gas shares its name with Superman's home planet?

2 In politics, to whom does the expression "Father of the House" refer?

3 On which island is Wall Street?

4 What was the name of Welsh hero Prince Llewelyn's dog?

5 What is the study of fluids moving in pipes?

6 What type of person studies the relationship between living organisms and their environment?

7 What was George Washington's wife first name?

8 Which English town is an anagram of ancestral?

9 Where, in Baker Street, did Sherlock Holmes live?

10 What does the word "Bolshoi" mean?

11 In mythology, who was banished by his son Jupiter?

12 Which London borough is the "G" in GMT?

13 Where in London is the Royal Opera House?

14 What is Eric Clapton's middle name?

15 How many dancers feature in a *pas de deux*?

16 Which William wrote a poem about daffodils?

17 What was the name of the World War I ace nicknamed "The Red Baron"?

18 Who is Lady Antonia Fraser's father?

19 Who invented frozen food?

20 What unit is used to measure the gas we use in our homes?

21 What title did Harold Macmillan take?

22 Which monarch founded Eton College?

23 Which Shakespeare play is in three parts?

24 What is a mordant?

25 Which "ology" is the art of ringing bells?

26 How was Achilles killed?

27 Which king was Queen Elizabeth II's grandfather?

28 Which precinct does Ed McBain write about?

29 Who wrote the novel "Dr Zhivago"?

30 Who was prime minister of Britain at the outbreak of World War II?

31 Whom did Margaret Thatcher replace as leader of the Tory party?

32 Who hit a golf shot on the moon?

33 Which dog show was first held in Islington in 1891?

34 What does "Honi soit qui mal y pense" mean?

35 In which "ology" were Freud and Jung active?

334

36 What acid gives nettles their sting?

37 Which king was nicknamed "Farmer George"?

38 Who was the last Briton to win the men's singles at Wimbledon?

39 On which peninsula is the city of Sevastopol situated?

40 Which word goes after piece and before times to make two new words?

41 What was SHAPE?

42 Who was the Greek muse of dance?

43 Which rock guitarist prophetically said, "When you're dead you're made for life"?

44 In which country is Puccini's "Turandot" set?

45 Which country did "Kaiser Bill" rule?

46 What colour of ballet shoes did Hans Christian Andersen write about?

47 What was Mrs Gaskell's first name?

48 Which British newspaper is nicknamed "The Thunderer"?

49 What according to Scott McKenzie did you wear in your hair in San Francisco?

50 After 1928, women over what age were given the vote?

1. Blue Peter. 2. Today Is Saturday Watch And Smile. 3. Sarah Greene. 4. Do Not Adjust Your Set. 5. Greendale. 6. Paper. 7. SuperTed. 8. Rolf Harris. 9. Rod, Jane and Freddy. 10. Sooty. 11. Live and Kicking. 12. The Wombles. 13. The Woodentops. 14. Magpie. 15. Lion. 16. Mr Benn. 17. Play School. 18. Caron Keating. 19. Teddy and Looby Loo. 20. Maid Marian and her Merry Men. 21. 3000. 22. The Teletubbies. 23. Andi Peters, Emma Forbes. 24. Leonardo, Michaelangelo, Raphael, Donatello. 25. Angelo. 26. Mrs Goggins. 27. Aardvark. 28. California. 29. Fireball XL5. 30. Suzanne Ross. 31. Billy Connolly. 32. Trumpton. 33. Captain Pugwash. 34. The Mysterons. 35. Maid Marian and her Merry Men. 36. Dinosaur. 37. 12. 38. Australia. 39. "Poddington Peas". 40. Mouse. 41. Sticky back plastic. 42. Crackerjack pencil. 43. Geoffrey Hayes. 44. Around the World in Eighty Days. 45. Dog. 46. Friday. 47. The Chives. 48. The Simpsons. 49. Fred Dinenage. 50. Clementine.

Around the UK

HARD - LEVEL THREE

1 Which county did Huntingdonshire become part of in 1974?

2 What is High Wycombe famous for manufacturing?

3 Which atomic energy establishment used to be called Windscale?

4 Which two London boroughs begin with E?

5 Which seaside resort is on the Fylde?

6 What is the low-lying area of East Anglia called?

7 Which city was a Roman fortress called Deva and retains its medieval walls?

8 How many tunnels under the Mersey link Liverpool to the Wirral?

9 In which northern city is the National Railway Museum?

10 The Ribble is the chief river of which county?

11 In which city is the University of East Anglia?

12 Which county is Thomas Hardy associated with?

13 Which part of Oxford is famous for motor car manufacture?

14 Which Devon port has a famous Hoe?

15 Which county is also known as Salop?

16 Which Isle has Needles off its west coast?

17 Where would you find the 18th-century Assembly Rooms and Royal Crescent?

18 Which county does not exist: North, South, East or West Yorkshire?

19 In which town is the shopping complex, the Metro Centre?

20 Where would you find the Backs and the Bridge of Sighs?

21 Alphabetically what is the last county?

22 In which Metropolitan county are Trafford and Tameside?

23 In which National Park is Scafell Pike?

24 On which bank of the Thames is the City of London?

25 Consett is associated with the processing of which two metals?

26 Which city is served by Speke airport?

27 Which county lies between the North Sea and Greater London?

28 What is Lindisfarne also known as?

29 In which county is Hadrian's Wall?

30 From which London station are there trains direct to the continent through the Channel Tunnel?

31 How many faces has the clock on Big Ben's tower?

32 In which port were Dickens and Brunel both born?

33 In which London building is the Lord Mayor's banquet held?

34 Which Womble was named after the town on the Isle of Mull?

35 Which Channel Island is famous for having no cars?

36 Where is Beaumaris Castle?

37 Girton and Newnham are colleges of which university?

38 Where in London is the Lutine Bell?

39 Bryher is part of which islands?

40 Which Hills divide England and Scotland?

41 Cumbernauld is near which British city?

42 Which Sea joins the St George's Channel and the North Channel?

43 In which county is Chequers, the Prime Minister's country residence?

44 What is England's second largest cathedral?

45 Which Firth lies between south west Scotland and north west England?

46 Where is The Cathedral Church of St Michael, consecrated in 1962?

47 Which Leicestershire town is famous for its pork pies?

48 What are the canals in Cambridge called?

49 In which county is the southern end of the Pennine Way?

50 Which Roman road shares its name with a type of fur?

A nswers to
Quiz 165, Pot Luck

1. Krypton. 2. The longest-serving MP. 3. Manhattan. 4. Gelert. 5. Hydraulics. 6. Ecologist. 7. Martha. 8. Lancaster. 9. 221B. 10. Big. 11. Saturn. 12. Greenwich. 13. Covent Garden. 14. Patrick. 15. Two. 16. Wordsworth. 17. Baron von Richthofen. 18. Lord Longford. 19. Clarence Birdseye. 20. Therms. 21. Earl of Stockton. 22. Henry VI. 23. Henry VI. 24. A substance used to fix colours in dyeing. 25. Campanology. 26. By an arrow in his heel. 27. George V. 28. The 86th Precinct. 29. Boris Pasternak. 30. Neville Chamberlain. 31. Edward Heath. 32. Alan Sheppard. 33. Crufts. 34. Evil to him who evil thinks it. 35. Psychology. 36. Formic acid. 37. George III. 38. Fred Perry. 39. The Crimea. 40. Meal. 41. Supreme Headquarters Allied Powers in Europe. 42. Terpsichore. 43. Jimi Hendrix. 44. China. 45. Germany. 46. Red. 47. Elizabeth. 48. The Times. 49. Flowers. 50. 21.

Q UIZ 167 | Leisure

FOR ANSWERS SEE QUIZ NO 168

HARD - LEVEL THREE

1 Fountains Abbey is in which county?

2 In which museum would you see Constable's "Haywain"?

3 In what activity would you make a banjo cable or a leaf rib?

4 What moves when a chess player moves two pieces in one move?

5 Where would you go to see the Battle of the Flowers?

6 What would you have if you were a collector of Coalport?

7 How many tricks make up a grand slam in bridge?

8 What is the Viking Centre in York called?

9 What is the national game of the Basques?

10 In which seaside resort is Frontierland?

11 What is the value of the ace in baccarat?

12 What is the practice of creating replicas of animals from their dead skins called?

13 Which Cluedo weapon is nearest the beginning of the alphabet?

14 What is the minimum number of players in a game of bezique?

15 The aim is to knock down how many pins in a game of skittles?

16 What was the name of the first Rolls-Royce?

17 What is Brighton Pier called?

18 Which Essex town is famous for its Oyster Festival?

19 The Eurotunnel Exhibition Centre is nearest which port?

20 In pottery what is slip?

21 What is numismatics?

22 Alfred Wainwright wrote books on which leisure activity?

23 How many wheels are there normally on a skateboard?

24 In which month is the London-to-Brighton Veteran Car Run?

25 Where did bonsai gardens originate?

26 What would you be doing if you practised a strathspey and a pas de basque?

27 What is the practice of formal handwriting called?

28 In knitting what does psso mean?

29 In which city would you be if you went to the Fitzwilliam Museum?

30 What do British stamps not have on them which most other stamps do?

31 In which city is the National Railway Museum?

32 What is the maximum number of players in a game of poker?

33 Which game takes its name from the Chinese for sparrow?

34 How many pieces are on a chess board at the start of a game?

35 Which card game derives its name from the Spanish word for basket?

36 Which stately home is sometimes called the Palace of t

the Peak?

37 In which county would you visit Sissinghurst Gardens?

38 In which museum is the "Mona Lisa"?

39 How did Canterbury Cathedral announce it would emulate St Paul's in 1997?

40 In which city is Tropical World, Roundhay Park?

41 In which French château is there a Hall of Mirrors?

42 Which Suffolk Hall hosts days where Tudor life is re-created in great detail?

43 The Bluebell Railway straddles which two counties?

44 What does "son et lumiere" mean?

45 What do you use to play craps?

46 How many dominoes are there in a double-six set?

47 How many different topics are there in a game of Trivial Pursuits?

48 In which month would you go to watch Trooping the Colour?

49 Where in Paris would you go to see Napoleon's tomb?

50 In which county is Whipsnade Park Zoo?

A nswers to Quiz 166, AROUND THE UK

1. Cambridgeshire. 2. Furniture. 3. Sellafield. 4. Ealing, Enfield. 5. Blackpool. 6. The Fens. 7. Chester. 8. Two. 9. York. 10. Lancashire. 11. Norwich. 12. Dorset. 13. Cowley. 14. Plymouth. 15. Shropshire. 16. Isle of Wight. 17. Bath. 18. East. 19. Gateshead. 20. Cambridge. 21. Worcestershire. 22. Greater Manchester. 23. Lake District. 24. North. 25. Iron, steel. 26. Liverpool. 27. Essex. 28. Holy Island. 29. Northumberland. 30. Waterloo. 31. Four. 32. Portsmouth. 33. The Guild Hall. 34. Tobermory. 35. Sark. 36. Anglesey. 37. Cambridge. 38. Lloyd's of London. 39. Scillies. 40. Cheviots. 41. Glasgow. 42. Irish Sea. 43. Buckinghamshire. 44. York Minster. 45. Solway Firth. 46. Coventry. 47. Melton Mowbray. 48. The Backs. 49. Derbyshire. 50. Ermine Street.

QUIZ 168 | Celebrities

HARD - LEVEL THREE

1 Who are the parents of Fifi Trixiebelle, Peaches and Pixie?

2 What is the profession of Princess Stephanie of Monaco's husband?

3 Who is Tiggy Legge-Bourke nanny to?

4 What is the name of Earl Spencer's former model wife?

5 What is the first name of the crown prince of Spain?

6 Before their resignations in 1996 who did Patrick Jephson and Steve Davies work for ?

7 Who is heir to the throne of Monaco?

8 Which "Baywatch" star married Tommy Lee?

9 What were the two married names of the late Jacqueline Bouvier?

10 On which Caribbean island did Princess Diana spend her first Christmas after the Queen announced she should divorce Prince Charles ?

11 Which actress/model gave birth to twins at the age of 44 on November 30th, 1995?

12 What nickname was given to the group of artists which included Dean Martin, Frank inatra and Peter Lawford ?

13 Which former playboy is Annette Bening married to?

14 Which one-time Hollywood pair have a daughter called Dakota ?

15 Maria Mapls is the wife of which famous property tycoon?

16 Which actress is the wife of Simon MacCorkindale?

17 What is the name of the daughter of "Catwoman" Eartha Kitt?

18 Which Man United football star's name was linked with Dani Behr?

19 Who was Athina Roussel's multi-millionairess mother?

20 What is the first name of Michael Caine's wife?

21 From which US state does model Jerry Hall come?

22 Who was Mrs Larry Fortensky until early 1996?

23 Who is Lady Helen Taylor's mother?

24 Who was widowed in 1990 when her husband's boat lost control?

25 What colour is jet setter Ivana Trump known for wearing?

26 Which southern French resort holds a yearly film festival?

27 Which film star is Mrs Carlo Ponti?

28 Which actress won a legal battle against Random House in 1996 ?

29 Which actress/model advertises Revlon Flex hair products?

30 Which crown did actress/model Mary Stavin receive in the 1970s?

31 Which country shares its name with Kim Basinger's daughter?

32 Who are the parents of Prince Michael Jr?

33 What is the son of Jemima and Imran Khan called?

34 Who was the famous sister of Lee Radziwill Ross?

35 In what field is Tommy Hilfiger a famous name?

36 Who is the son-in-law of the 17th Duke of Norfolk?

37 Carlos Leon has a famous daughter; who is the child's mother?

38 What colour dress did Paula Yates wear to marry Bob Geldof?

39 Who was Liz Taylor's eighth husband?

40 What type of clothes would you buy from Janet Reger?

41 Which Viscount attended Elton John's 50th birthday dressed as a lion?

42 In which field is Patrick Cameron famous?

43 Which fashion house does Stella Tennant model for?

44 What was Princess Diana's stepmother's first name?

45 Which couple advertised Quorn before their very public split?

46 Which Cindy's divorce settlement was reputedly in the region of £50 million?

47 Which MP's children are called Annabel, Alexandra and Rupert?

48 Who married Jennifer Flavin as his third wife?

49 Who is Tara Newley's famous mother?

50 Who was the late Hector Barrantes?

Answers to Quiz 167, LEISURE

1. North Yorkshire. 2. National Gallery. 3. Knitting. 4. Castle, King. 5. Jersey. 6. China. 7. 13. 8. Jorvik. 9. Pelota. 10. Morecambe. 11. One. 12. Taxidermy. 13. Candlestick. 14. Two. 15. Nine. 16. Silver Ghost. 17. Palace Pier. 18. Colchester. 19. Folkestone. 20. Liquid clay. 21. Study and collection of coins. 22. Fell walking. 23. Four. 24. November. 25. China. 26. Scottish dancing. 27. Calligraphy. 28. Pass slipped stitch over. 29. Cambridge. 30. The name of the country. 31. York. 32. Eight. 33. Majong. 34. 32. 35. Canasta. 36. Chatsworth. 37. Kent. 38. The Louvre. 39. Charge for admission. 40. Leeds. 41. Versailles. 42. Kentwell. 43. East and West Sussex. 44. Sound and light. 45. Dice. 46. 28. 47. Six. 48. June. 49. Les Invalides. 50. Bedfordshire.

QUIZ 169 Sci-Fi

HARD - LEVEL THREE

1   Which character was described as "part man, part machine, all cop"?

2   Who played the part of the rebel princess in "Star Wars"?

3   "2001: A Space Odyssey" was based on a short story by whom?

4   What was the first of the man and monkey conflict films?

5   What planet did long-eared Mr Spock come from?

6   "Judge Dredd" was based on the character from which comic?

7   Which director said, "I'm embarrassed and ashamed that I get paid for doing this"?

8   In which film did Jane Fonda "do her own thing" in the 40th century?

9   What was the Fahrenheit reading in Truffaut's 1960s film?

10   Which hero has been portrayed by Christopher Reeve and Kirk Alyn?

11   Who was the star of "The Terminator" films?

12   Which rock band did the score for the 1970s romp "Flash"?

13   Where was Darth Vader based in "Star Wars"?

14   In which film did Bruce Willis play a time-travelling criminal?

15   Which creatures mutated in "Them"?

16   In which film did Claude Rains star as someone who was not seen?

17   Which rock star played Newton in "The Man Who Fell To Earth"?

18   In which film does Charlton Heston think he is Earth's last survivor?

19   Which vehicles set out to devour Paris?

20   In which film are people terminated at the age of 30?

21   In titles, which words go before "Stood Still" and "Caught Fire"?

22   Robbie The Robot and Dr Morbius appear in which film?

23   "Alien" posters said that "in space no one can hear you" do what?

24   In the 1953 film how many fathoms did the Beast come from?

25   "How I Learned To Stop Worrying And Love The Bomb" is known by what shorter title?

26   Which veteran actor played Ben (Obi-Wan) Kenobi?

27   In which 1960s film does rocket radiation activate flesh-eating zombies?

28   Which Roddy featured in the "Ape" series?

29   Who is the female companion of Flash Gordon?

30   In "The Incredible Shrinking Man" which creature does the man fight off with a needle?

31   In "Doctor Who" what does TARDIS stand for?

32   Which programme began with the control voice saying "There is

342

nothing wrong with your television set"?

33 In which series did scientist Dr Sam Beckett appear?

34 What was the Six Million Dollar Man's previous occupation?

35 In which sci-fi series did Joanna Lumley and David McCallum star?

36 What was unusual about Drs Peter Brady and Daniel Westin?

37 Which time traveller came by flying saucer to 1980s London?

38 Which adventurer, trapped in ice, thawed out in 1966?

39 What was Steve Zodiac's spacecraft?

40 Where were the Robinson family lost in the 1960s series?

41 What is Doctor Who always called in the series?

42 Which series has had Eartha Kitt in the role of Catwoman?

43 Who played Jamie in "Doctor Who" and Joe Sugden in "Emmerdale"?

44 What were Captain Kirk's two Christian names?

45 How was Diana Prince better known?

46 What did "A" stand for in the name of the 1960s series?

47 What was special about the Man from Atlantis, Mark Harris?

48 Which 11th-century wizard became trapped in the 20th century?

49 What was Doomwatch?

50 Who travelled in "The Liberator" fighting The Federation?

1. Paula Yates and Bob Geldof. 2. Racing driver. 3. Princes William and Harry. 4. Victoria. 5. Felipe. 6. The Princess of Wales. 7. Prince Albert. 8. Pamela Anderson. 9. Kennedy, Onassis. 10. Barbuda. 11. Jane Seymour. 12. Rat Pack. 13. Warren Beatty. 14. Don Johnson and Melanie Griffith. 15. Donald Trump. 16. Susan George. 17. Kitt. 18. Ryan Giggs. 19. Christina Onassis. 20. Shakira. 21. Texas. 22. Elizabeth Taylor. 23. The Duchess of Kent. 24. Princess Caroline of Monaco. 25. Gold. 26. Cannes. 27. Sophia Loren. 28. Joan Collins. 29. Cindy Crawford. 30. Miss World. 31. Ireland. 32. Michael Jackson and Debbie Rowe. 33. Sulaiman. 34. Jackie Kennedy-Onassis. 35. Clothes design. 36. David Frost. 37. Madonna. 38. Scarlet. 39. Larry Fortensky. 40. Underwear. 41. Linley. 42. Hairdressing. 43. Chanel. 44. Raine. 45. Julia and Will Carling. 46. Costner. 47. Michael Heseltine. 48. Sylvester Stallone. 49. Joan Collins. 50. Fergie's Argentinian polo-playing step father.

Quiz 170 Pot Luck

FOR ANSWERS SEE QUIZ NO 171

HARD - LEVEL THREE

1 Which moor is named after the county town of Cornwall?

2 Who laid the foundation stone at Coventry Cathedral?

3 In which city was Stephane Grappelli born?

4 Who had a No. 1 in the 60s with "Everlasting Love"?

5 Which tennis player was given the name "Ice Man" by the press?

6 Who cleaned at the Crossroads Motel?

7 Which does fibrin cause the blood to do?

8 What name links a former "EastEnders" actor and a radio DJ?

9 In which county are England's highest cliffs?

10 What is the Russian word for citadel?

11 In which century was George Frederick Handel born?

12 Which sportsman wrote the autobiography "Unleashed"?

13 What is John Gielgud's first name?

14 Who was the first female presenter of "Busman's Holiday"?

15 What is the Pentateuch?

16 In which sitcom did Sandra Hennessey appear?

17 What was the name of the first cloned sheep?

18 Which school did Billy Bunter go to?

19 Who wrote the books on which "The Jewel in the Crown" was based?

20 Who has advertised Brut, Patrick boots, Shredded Wheat and Sugar Puffs?

21 Allurophobia is a fear of what?

22 What do the letters P.S. stand for at the end of a letter?

23 Whose last words were "That was a great game of golf, fellas"?

24 In the Chinese calendar which year follows the year of the tiger?

25 Who was the first person to captain, coach and manage England at cricket?

26 Who was King of the Huns from 406 to 453?

27 What word can go after "tar" and before "gent"?

28 With which sport is Willie Wood connected?

29 In which decade of the 20th century was Eric Clapton born?

30 Which actor played the only Dirty Dozen member to survive?

31 In medical terms, what are you if you are "DOA"?

32 In which crisis, in 1956, did England become involved?

33 What does Anno Domini mean?

34 Which Neil Diamond song was a No. 1 for UB40?

35 In which city is the area of Toxteth?

36 Who was the vocalist on Gary Moore's hit "Parisienne Walkways"?

37 In the farce, where did Charley's Aunt come from?

38 Over which sea was Glenn Miller lost?

39 Where is Britain's most southerly mainland point?

40 Which song title links Go West and Blondie?

41 What do W and S stand for in W.S. Gilbert's name?

42 Tony Doyle is connected with which sport?

43 In which century was Leonardo da Vinci born?

44 What was invented by Lewis E. Waterman?

45 Who wrote the novel "Emma"?

46 In which German town was "Auf Wiedersehen Pet" set?

47 Which birthstone is linked to January?

48 In which decade was the series "Agony" screened for the first time?

49 How is the General Purpose (GP) Vehicle commonly known?

50 Which poem begins, "Is there anybody there? said the Traveller"?

Answers to Quiz 169, SCIENCE FICTION

1. Robocop. 2. Carrie Fisher. 3. Arthur C. Clarke. 4. Planet Of The Apes. 5. Vulcan. 6. 2000 A.D. 7. Steven Spielberg. 8. Barbarella. 9. 451. 10. Superman. 11. Arnold Schwarzenegger. 12. Queen. 13. The Death Star. 14. Twelve Monkeys. 15. Ants. 16. The Invisible Man. 17. David Bowie. 18. The Omega Man. 19. Cars. 20. Logan's Run. 21. The Day the Earth. 22. Forbidden Planet. 23. Scream. 24. 20,000. 25. Dr Strangelove. 26. Alec Guinness. 27. The Night of the Living Dead. 28. McDowall. 29. Dale Arden. 30. Spider. 31. Time And Relative Dimensions In Space. 32. The Outer Limits. 33. Quantum Leap. 34. Astronaut. 35. Sapphire and Steel. 36. Invisible. 37 . Dominick Hide. 38. Adam Adamant. 39. Fireball XL5. 40. Space. 41. The Doctor. 42. Batman. 43. Frazer Hines. 44. James Tiberius. 45. Wonder Woman. 46. Andromeda. 47. Half man, half fish. 48. Catweazle. 49. Government department. 50. Blake's Seven.

Quiz 171 Pop Music

HARD - LEVEL THREE

1 Who was lead singer with Style Council?

2 Who sang with Dave Dee, Beaky, Mick and Tich?

3 How many of The Walker Brothers were related to each other as brothers?

4 Which group backed Lulu on the original "Shout"?

5 Which group featured Dave Gilmour and Roger Waters?

6 Which day did The Boomtown Rats not like?

7 What was Take That's first No 1?

8 Which Irish supergroup started life known as Feedback?

9 Who was the Who's original drummer?

10 Which group formed their own label Dep International?

11 Merrill, Jay, Wayne, Jimmy and Donny made up which group?

12 Which group made the album "Crisis? What Crisis"?

13 Which Kinks hit starts, "Dirty old river, must you keep rolling..."?

14 Which group was led by Phil Lynott?

15 Paul Jones and Mike D'Abo both sang lead with which group?

16 Justin Hayward and Denny Laine were members of which group?

17 Which group opened the Wembley Stadium section of Live Aid?

18 Wet, Wet, Wet come from which country?

19 Which group sang about Horace Wimp?

20 How were The Jacksons credited on their early hits?

21 Whose first top ten single was "The Eton Rifles" in 1979?

22 Which group used the main theme from the 1812 Overture in their first single hit?

23 Which Simply Red album contained "For Your Babies"?

24 Which glam group asked "Metal guru, is it you?"?

25 Which group wanted to "Take It To The Limit"?

26 Which group had the original hit with "Love Is All Around"?

27 Who thought that "Life Is A Minestrone"?

28 Gary and Martin Kemp were members of which group?

29 Which group had seven consecutive top four hits until the release of "The Medal Song"?

30 What was Queen's first hit?

31 What was Michael Jackson's 1995 Christmas No. 1?

32 What was coupled with "Maggie May" on Rod Stewart's single?

33 Which singer co-wrote "Evergreen"?

34 Reclusive Syd Barrett was a founder of which supergroup?

35 In which state was Elvis Presley born?

36 Which album has Bowie with a red lightning flash design on his face?

37 Which Elton John song starts "She packed my bags last night pre-flight"?

38 In which country was Mark Knopfler born?

39 Whose albums include "Diamonds and Pearls" and "Symbol"?

40 In the 90s who got into legal battle with Sony over his contract?

41 Which Gibb brother's song gave Diana Ross a No. 1?

42 What role did Madonna portray in the film "Dick Tracy"?

43 On the cover of "Thriller" Jackson is leaning on which elbow?

44 Which guitarist was "Unplugged" in 1992?

45 Which vocal harmony group backed Elvis from the mid 50s?

46 Who appeared as the Acid Queen in the film "Tommy"?

47 Roger Taylor was a member of which supergroup?

48 Which reggae superstar was given a state funeral in Jamaica?

49 Which Michael Jackson album first included "Don't Stop 'Til You Get Enough"?

50 Which superstar produced music for the 1989 "Batman" film?

Answers to Quiz 170, POT LUCK

1. Bodmin Moor. 2. Queen Elizabeth II. 3. Paris. 4. Love Affair. 5. Bjorn Borg. 6. Amy Turtle. 7. Clot. 8. Mike Reid. 9. Devon. 10. Kremlin. 11. 17th. 12. Jack Russell. 13. Arthur. 14. Sarah Kennedy. 15. First five books of the Old Testament. 16. "The Liver Birds". 17. Dolly. 18. Greyfriars. 19. Paul Scott. 20. Kevin Keegan. 21. Cats. 22. Postscript. 23. Bing Crosby. 24. Rabbit. 25. Ray Illingworth. 26. Attila. 27. "Tan". 28. Bowls. 29. 40s. 30. Charles Bronson. 31. Dead On Arrival. 32. The Suez Crisis. 33. In the year of our Lord. 34. "Red Red Wine". 35. Liverpool. 36. Phil Lynott. 37. Brazil. 38. English Channel. 39. Lizard Point. 40. "Call Me". 41. William Schwenck. 42. Cycling. 43. 15th. 44. Fountain Pen. 45. Jane Austen. 46. Dusseldorf. 47 Garnet. 48. 1970s. 49. Jeep. 50. "The Listeners".

Quiz 172 | TV Times

HARD - LEVEL THREE

1 What is the first name of Kavanagh QC?

2 What is the mascot for "The Great Antiques Hunt"?

3 Patrick Moore is famous for playing which musical instrument?

4 In which county was "Where the Heart Is" set?

5 What is Rab C. Nesbitt's wife called?

6 Henry Sandon became famous on which TV show?

7 Who did the Simpsons replace as TV's longest-running cartoon family in 1997?

8 What is the name of the infirmary in "Bramwell"?

9 Who is Jennifer Paterson's cooking partner?

10 Which female doctor succeeded Beth Glover in "Peak Practice"?

11 What is the fictional village where "Heartbeat" is set?

12 What is the profession of the chief characters in "This Life"?

13 Which actor is the son of Nigel Davenport and Maria Aitken?

14 Which role did Harry Enfield play in "Men Behaving Badly"?

15 What did the ARP warden call Mainwaring in "Dad's Army"?

16 Which children's TV character lives in Pontypandy?

17 Which detective has a dog called Snowy?

18 Who is the comedienne mother of the actress Suzy Aitchison?

19 n which decade was "Hi-De-Hi" first set?

20 Which comedian began his show with a shop-window illusion?

21 Where was Dot Cotton living before she returned to Walford in 1997?

22 Who was the blondest person on "Shooting Stars"?

23 Who was Reginald Perrin's boss?

24 Whose catchphrase in "Drop the Dead Donkey" was "I'm not here"?

25 Who plays the title role in "Dr Quinn: Medicine Woman"?

26 In which show would you find PC Goody?

27 Where would you find the Simpsons other than in "The Simpsons"?

28 In which series would you find Benton Fraser?

29 Which Geoff Hamilton series was first shown after his death?

30 Who left "Blue Peter" in 1996 and presented "Songs of Praise"?

31 Who was dubbed TV's Mr Sex?

32 Which drama/comedy was set in St Elgius Hospital?

33 What was Zoë's job in "May to December"?

34 In "Lovejoy" what was Tinker's surname?

35 Which ex-breakfast TV presenter has had a nightly show on Sky 1?

348

36 Where were the first three series of "Animal Hospital" based?

37 Who drew the animated titles sequence for "Yes Minister"?

38 What was the job of the heroes of "Common as Muck"?

39 Who was the most successful act on "The Big Time"?

40 Which city is "Casualty"'s Holby said to be?

41 What was the nickname of Sam Malone of "Cheers"?

42 In which month does the "Children in Need" appeal normally take place?

43 Who was the undertaker in "Dad's Army"?

44 Whose children included Primrose, Petunia, Zinnia and Montgomery?

45 Who was the sports commentator on "The Day Today"?

46 Who was Detective Sergeant Andy Crawford's father-in-law?

47 Which House was the surgery for Drs Finlay and Cameron?

48 Who was the third Doctor Who?

49 In the early 60s what was Radio 2 known as?

50 Which TV marriage began with "Happy Ever After" in 1969?

Answers to Quiz 171, Pop Music

1. Paul Weller. 2. Dozy. 3. None of them. 4. Luvvers. 5. Pink Floyd. 6. Monday. 7. Pray. 8. U2. 9. Keith Moon. 10. UB40. 11. The Osmonds. 12. Supertramp. 13. Waterloo Sunset. 14. Thin Lizzy. 15. Manfred Mann. 16. The Moody Blues. 17. Status Quo. 18. Scotland. 19. Electric Light Orchestra. 20. Jackson Five. 21. Jam. 22. The Move. 23. Stars. 24. T. Rex. 25. The Eagles. 26. The Troggs. 27. 10cc. 28. Spandau Ballet. 29. Culture Club. 30. Seven Seas of Rye. 31. "Earth Song". 32. "Reason To Believe". 33. Barbra Streisand. 34. Pink Floyd. 35. Mississippi. 36. Aladdin Sane. 37. "Rocket Man". 38. Scotland. 39. Prince. 40. George Michael. 41. "Chain Reaction". 42. Breathless Mahoney. 43. Left. 44. Eric Clapton. 45. The Jordanaires. 46. Tina Turner. 47. Queen. 48. Bob Marley. 49. Off The Wall. 40. Prince.

QUIZ 173 | Pot Luck

HARD - LEVEL THREE

1   In which Welsh county is the Gower Peninsula?

2   What was first put into £1 notes in 1940?

3   Who were defending champions at the 1966 football World Cup?

4   Who was the first American president to be assassinated?

5   Which city in the book of Genesis is still in existence?

6   What did the City of London and 32 metropolitan boroughs become in 1965?

7   What did Ian Beale train to be in the early "EastEnders" episodes?

8   What bird is depicted over the door of the US Embassy in London?

9   Who has had hits with ELO, Cliff Richard and John Travolta?

10 In which city is Bizet's "Carmen" set?

11 In which century was Abraham Lincoln born?

12 Who wrote "Empire Of The Sun"?

13 Which children's rhyme was associated with the Black Death?

14 Who was known as the King of Swing?

15 Which character did Neil Morrissey play in "Boon"?

16 Vera Chapman played 66 times for England at which sport?

17 Which footballer's biography is "Where Do I Go from Here?"?

18 What do Johnny Mathis, Elvis Presley and Little Richard all share?

19 How did Al Capone meet his death?

20 Blue and seal-points are types of which cat?

21 Which Latin term - usually applied to legal evidence - means at first sight?

22 What is the next highest prime number above 13?

23 Which veteran rock star had a quadruple coronary heart bypass in May 1997?

24 What is Victor Gollancz particularly associated with?

25 Where did young Ben Needham mysteriously vanish in 1991?

26 Where in England was a railway station called Mumps?

27 In which decade of the 20th century was Sean Connery born?

28 Who had a lover called Mellors?

29 Which Tropic line goes through Taiwan?

30 Who had a 90s No. 1 with "Sleeping Satellite"?

31 Which London hospital took its first infant patient in 1852?

32 Which Cornish village claims to be the birthplace of King Arthur?

33 Which is the main river to flow through Hamburg?

34 Which band had a lead singer called Morrissey?

35 Who was jilted on her wedding day in "Great Expectations"?

36 What patent did Graham Bell file three hours before Elisha Gray?

37 What was the nickname given to VI Flying bombs in World War II?

38 Which common British garden creature belongs to the locust family?

39 What damaged Alexandra Palace in both 1873 and 1980?

40 Which motel provides the setting in "Psycho"?

41 In which century was David Livingstone born?

42 Which character was the transvestite in "M*A*S*H"?

43 Who was the first female presenter of "Blue Peter"?

44 What does Genghis Khan mean?

45 Who wrote the book "Clayhanger"?

46 Which ocean liner, retired in 1967, became a hotel in Long Beach?

47 Paper sized 210mm x 297mm is known by which A number?

48 If it's 12 noon GMT what time is it in Berlin?

49 For Elton John's 50th birthday party who did Janet Street-Porter go dressed as?

50 Preston is on which river?

Answers to Quiz 172, TV TIMES

1. James. 2. A bloodhound. 3. Xylophone. 4. Yorkshire. 5. Mary. 6. "Antiques Roadshow". 7. The Flintstones. 8. The Thrift. 9. Clarissa Dickson Wright. 10. Erica Matthews. 11. Aidensfield. 12. Lawyers. 13. Jack Davenport. 14. Dermot. 15. Napoleon. 16. Fireman Sam. 17. Tin Tin. 18. June Whitfield. 19. 1950s. 20. Harry Worth. 21. Gravesend. 22. Ulrika Jonsson. 23. CJ. 24. Gus Hedges . 25. Jane Seymour. 26. "The Thin Blue Line". 27. "Brookside". 28. "Due South". 29. "Paradise Gardens". 30. Diane-Louise Jordan. 31. Angus Deayton. 32. "St Elsewhere". 33. PE teacher. 34. Deal. 35. Selina Scott. 36. Harmsworth Hospital. 37. Gerald Scarfe. 38. Dustmen. 39. Sheena Easton. 40. Bristol. 41. Mayday. 42. November. 43. Fraser. 44. Ma and Pa Larkin. 45. Alan Partridge. 46. "Dixon of Dock Green". 47. Arden House. 48. Jon Pertwee. 49. The Light Programme. 50. Terry Scott and June Whitfield.

Q UIZ 174 | Sport

UIZ
174

FOR ANSWERS SEE QUIZ NO 175

HARD - LEVEL THREE

1 In darts, what is the maximum check-out score?

2 Who has won most international soccer caps for England?

3 Which country did boxer Lennox Lewis represent at the Olympics?

4 Which TV sports quiz show is hosted by Nick Hancock?

5 Faldo, Clark, James and who represented Europe in the 1995 Ryder Cup?

6 What nationality is tennis player Michael Chang?

7 A snooker player makes a break of eight points. Which three colours are potted?

8 In greyhound racing what colour does the first dog wear?

9 For what sport is Ellery Hanley famous?

10 Who won the Superbowl '96?

11 What role did Oliver McCall play in Frank Bruno's career?

12 At which Grand Prix circuit did Ayrton Senna lose his life?

13 Who was the first man to do the 100-metre breast stroke in under a minute?

14 Which football club has won the English championship the most times?

15 Where was Barry Sheene in a 175 mph crash in 1975?

16 Which twisting Grand Prix circuit is only 1.95 miles long?

17 Has croquet ever been a sport in the Olympics?

18 Which boxer used to enter the ring to Tina Turner's "Simply The Best"?

19 Name the Scottish League teams whose names end in United?

20 In Rugby Union, who is Australia's record try scorer?

21 At which venue was the 1996 B&H Masters played?

22 In speedway racing, how many laps of the track does a race consist of?

23 Apart from England which European country took part in cricket's 1996 World Cup?

24 Which world heavyweight boxer died in an air-crash in 1969?

25 Who won a 100-metre breast stroke gold in the 1980 Olympics?

26 In badminton, how many points win a single game?

27 Which trainer is known as the "Queen of Aintree"?

28 Is an own goal allowed for in the rules of hockey?

29 Which two sports take place on a piste?

30 Who only passed his UK motor bike test in February 1996?

31 Who fought Muhammad Ali in the Rumble in the Jungle?

32 Jennifer Susan Harvey is better known by what name?

33 Which Englishman scored the first 1997 Ashes century?

34 Which Italian said he could not "understand a word Dennis Wise is saying"?

35 Which Andy won rugby's Lance Todd Award in 1988 and 1990?

36 Who was skipper of Middlesbrough's 1997 FA Cup Final team?

37 Who was the female competitor excused a sex test at the 1976 Olympics?

38 Who was the first Swede to win Wimbledon's Men's Singles?

39 Who was Marvellous Marvin?

40 Who left Llanelli in 1989 to play rugby league for Widnes?

41 Who sponsored the 1997 one-day England v. Australia cricket?

42 Who won the 125th Open at Lytham?

43 Who was the first black athlete to captain Great Britain men's team?

44 Who retired in the 90s after 15 years as chairman of the FA?

45 Who is Michael Schumacher's younger racing driver brother?

46 Which Spanish player interrupted Graf's reign as women's singles champion at Wimbledon?

47 Who was the English captain of the 1980 British Lions tour?

48 Which boxer was born in Bellingham, London, on May 3 1934?

49 Which left-handed batsman has scored most runs for England?

50 Who was Leeds's manager before George Graham?

A nswers to Quiz 173, POT LUCK

1. County of Swansea (was West Glamorgan till 1996). 2. Metal strips. 3. Brazil. 4. Abraham Lincoln. 5. Damascus. 6. Greater London. 7. A chef. 8. Eagle. 9. Olivia Newton-John. 10. Seville. 11. 19th. 12. J.G. Ballard. 13. "Ring-a-ring-a Roses". 14. Benny Goodman. 15. Rocky Cassidy. 16. Hockey. 17. George Best. 18. Born same year (1935). 19. Died of syphilis. 20. Siamese. 21. Prima facie. 22. 17. 23. Rick Parfitt. 24. Publishing (Writing). 25. Greek island of Kos. 26. Oldham. 27. 30s. 28. Lady Chatterley. 29. Tropic of Cancer. 30. Tasmin Archer. 31. The Great Ormond Street Children's Hospital. 32. Tintagel. 33. The Elbe. 34. The Smiths. 35. Miss Havisham. 36. Telephone. 37. Doodlebugs. 38. The grasshopper. 39 Fire. 40. The Bates Motel. 41 19th. 42 Corporal Klinger. 43. Leila Williams. 44. Universal ruler. 45. Arnold Bennett. 46. Queen Mary. 47. A4. 48. 1 p.m. 49. Wonder Woman. 50. Ribble.

QUIZ 175 Pop Music

HARD - LEVEL THREE

1 Who had a 70s hit with "Feelings"?

2 Who had a "Pretty Good Year" in the charts in 1994?

3 Which Irish singer has made records with Clannad and Sinatra?

4 "Don't Worry" was the first solo success for which female singer?

5 Who was lead singer with the Animals?

6 Who did Nick Berry play in "EastEnders" at the time of his first No. 1?

7 Who did Marc Almond sing with for his first No. 1?

8 Who - in song - lived high on a mountain in Mexico?

9 Which group introduced Dina Carroll to the charts?

10 Who has recorded with Cliff Richard, Steve Harley and Jose Carreras?

11 Who was the "Wichita Lineman"?

12 What word added to Bells, Mink and Pearl completes group names?

13 Who was lead singer with the Bay City Rollers?

14 Which country did Aneka - who sang "Japanese Boy" - come from?

15 Who sang "Private Number" with William Bell?

16 Who was responsible for the English lyrics of "My Way"?

17 Who were Bobby, Mike, Cheryl and Jay?

18 Who did Chubby Checker sing with on the 80s twist revival single?

19 Who is Pat Boone's singing daughter?

20 Which female singer starred in the 80s video for "Ant Rap"?

21 Who was the Geno referred to in Dexy's Midnight Runners' No. 1?

22 Which Spice Girl comes from Leeds?

23 Who wrote and sang the original "Spirit In The Sky"?

24 Who took "Wonderwall" into the charts for the second time in 1995?

25 Who was the first female artist to have a No. 1 and wear an eye patch?

26 Who wrote "All By Myself"?

27 Who sang "Never On A Sunday"?

28 Who sang with Peabo Bryson on "A Whole New World"?

29 Our Cilla's "Anyone Who Had A Heart" was a cover of which singer's song?

30 Who was the guitar virtuoso who wrote "Albatross"?

31 Who had a 90s No. 1 with "Turtle Power"?

32 Who backed Desmond Dekker on "The Israelites"?

354

33 Who had a No. I with Cher, Neneh Cherry and Eric Clapton?

34 Stiltskin's "Inside" was used to advertise which product?

35 What was Mud's first No. I?

36 Who kept Oasis and "Wonderwall" off the top?

37 Who had a 80s No. I with "La Bamba"?

38 What was on the other side of Louis Armstrong's "What A Wonderful World"?

39 What was the title of Deniece Williams's 1977 No. I?

40 In which decade did Lulu first top the UK charts?

41 What in brackets is added to the title "Make Me Smile"?

42 Who had the first No. I on the Food label?

43 Which No1 contains the words "hear the beat of the tambourine"?

44 Who had a 70s No. I with "Silver Lady"?

45 What was Whitney Houston's first UK No. I?

46 Who was Procol Harum's "Whiter Shade Of Pale" vocalist?

47 Which trumpeter had two No. Is in the 50s?

48 Who had a No. I with the Fresh Prince?

49 What was on the other side of the Beatles' "We Can Work It Out"?

50 Who wrote "Love Is All Around"?

A nswers to Quiz 174, SPORT

1. 170 – two treble 20s plus bull. 2. Peter Shilton. 3. Canada. 4. They Thinks It's All Over. 5. David Gilford. 6. American. 7. Red, yellow, brown. 8. Red. 9. Rugby League. 10. Dallas. 11. Bruno beat McCall to become the WBC Heavyweight champion. 12. San Marino, Italy. 13. Adrian Moorhouse in 1987. 14. Liverpool. 15. Daytona. 16. Monaco. 17. Yes. 18. Chris Eubank. 19. Ayr and Dundee. 20. David Campese. 21. Wembley Arena. 22. Four. 23. Netherlands. 24. Rocky Marciano. 25. Duncan Goodhew. 26. 15 points. 27. Jenny Pitman. 28. Yes. 29. Fencing and skiing. 30. Eddie Kidd. 31. George Foreman. 32. Jenny Pitman. 33. Graham Thorpe. 34. Gianfranco Zola. 35. Gregory. 36. Nigel Pearson. 37. Princess Anne. 38. Bjorn Borg. 39. Marvin Hagler. 40. Jonathan Davies. 41. Texaco. 42. Tom Lehman. 43. Kris Akabusi. 44. Sir Bert Millichip. 45. Ralf. 46. Conchita Martinez. 47. Bill Beaumont. 48. Henry Cooper. 49. David Gower. 50. Howard Wilkinson.

Quiz 176 Pot Luck

1. What was a hit for Bobby "Boris" Pickett and the Crypt-Kickers?

2. What is the real name of the 90s road protestor Swampy?

3. Which former US president was born in Tampico, Illinois?

4. Which country signed the Waitangi Treaty with Britain?

5. What was the sequel to "Winnie the Pooh"?

6. What is the common name for inflamed sebaceous glands?

7. What kind of creature is a Queen Alexandra's Birdwing?

8. What returned to Piccadilly Circus in 1947 after being in hiding during the war?

9. What is the subject of Landseer's painting "The Monarch of the Glen"?

10. Which member of Queen wrote "Radio Ga Ga"?

11. What is the only English anagram of CROUTON?

12. Which English county was the home to the world's first iron bridge?

13. The Thomas Cup is awarded in which sport?

14. In woodwork, what does a tenon fit to form a joint?

15. Who was the hero of "The Camels Are Coming", published in 1932?

16. What was Tonto's horse called?

17. What is the capital of Angola?

18. Who wrote the novel "The Tenant Of Wildfell Hall"?

19. What type of skate was invented in 1760 by Joseph Merlin?

20. Which Indian cricketer was nicknamed "Little Master"?

21. In fiction, where did Tom Brown graduate to?

22. In which century was Mozart born?

23. Which character did Laurence Olivier play in "Brideshead Revisited"?

24. What revolutionary fought with Castro and eventually died in Bolivia?

25. Who wrote the First World War poem "Anthem For Doomed Youth"?

26. In Scrabble, how many points is the letter R worth?

27. Who had an 80s No. 1 with "Doctorin' The Tardis"?

28. Who was Inspector Clouseau's manservant?

29. In which Dickens novel does John Jarndyce appear?

30. Which US city felt an earthquake for 47 seconds on April 18 1906?

31. What is the background colour of the United Nations flag?

32. How old is a horse when it changes to a mare from a filly?

33. Which city is home to Britain's longest cathedral?

34 Which of the Great Lakes is the largest freshwater lake in the world?

35 The BDO is the UK governing body of which sport?

36 Which Roman road linked London to York?

37 What country are chrysanthemums native to?

38 Which former Watford chairman married Renate?

39 What was the name of the suburb in which "Crossroads" was set?

40 What happens to something if it is - literally - petrified?

41 In which century was William Shakespeare born?

42 Which Royal celebrates his birthday on June 10?

43 Who had a 60s No. I with "All Or Nothing"?

44 Which musical term means at a walking pace?

45 What does the A stand for in NATO?

46 Who was the first presenter of "Celebrity Squares"?

47 Who wrote the novel "A Clockwork Orange"?

48 Which American state is home to Dodge City?

49 In which sitcom did Sam and Mrs Wembley appear?

50 Which programme pushed "Panorama" out of its traditional 9.30 p.m. Monday slot in 1997?

Answers to Quiz 175, Pop Music

1. Morris Albert. 2. Tori Amos. 3. Bono. 4. Kim Appleby. 5. Eric Burdon. 6. Simon Wicks. 7. Gene Pitney. 8. Angelo (Brotherhood of Man). 9. Quartz. 10. Sarah Brightman. 11. Glen Campbell. 12. Blue. 13. Les McKeown. 14. Scotland. 15. Judy Clay. 16. Paul Anka. 17. Bucks Fizz. 18. Fat Boys. 19. Debby. 20. Lulu. 21. Geno Washington. 22. Mel B (Scary). 23. Norman Greenbaum. 24. Mike Flowers Pops. 25. Gabrielle. 26. Eric Carmen. 27.Lynn Cornel. 28. Regina Belle. 29. Dionne Warwick. 30. Peter Green. 31. Partners In Kryme. 32. The Aces. 33. Chrissie Hynde. 34. Levi's jeans. 35. "Tiger Feet". 36. Robson & Jerome. 37. Los Lobos. 38. "Cabaret". 39. "Free." 40. 90s. 41. "(Come Up And See Me)". 42. Blur. 43. "Dancing Queen". 44. David Soul. 45. "Saving All My Love For You". 46. Gary Brooker. 47. Eddie Calvert. 48. Jazzy Jeff. 49. "Day Tripper". 50. Reg Presley.

Quiz 177 Books

1 What was the first book in English to be printed in England?

2 Which books do castaways automatically receive on "Desert Island Discs"?

3 Who was responsible for "The Complete Hip and Thigh Diet"?

4 In which century was the "Oxford English Dictionary" started in earnest?

5 Which book had to be owned compulsorily by every member of his country's adult population?

6 Which religious sect published "The Truth That Leads to Eternal Life"?

7 Who wrote "The Hitch Hiker's Guide to the Galaxy"?

8 Which British publisher launched Penguin titles in 1935?

9 In which decade did Guinness start to publish their "Book of Records" annually?

10 Who began publishing Beatrix Potter's books in 1902?

11 Who wrote "The Thorn Birds"?

12 What was Jeffrey Archer's first successful novel?

13 Which MP's first novel went straight to No. 1 in the "Sunday Times" bestsellers list in 1994?

14 What was Jeffrey Archer's sequel to "Kane and Abel"?

15 Who wrote "The Downing Street Years"?

16 Who created the character Emma Harte?

17 Which French novelist wrote "Gigi"?

18 What was the difference between Delia Smith's 1986 "Complete Cookery Course" and her 1989 "Complete Cookery Course"?

19 Who wrote "The Female Eunuch"?

20 Which book title links Jules Verne and Michael Palin?

21 Which Roddy Doyle bestseller won the Booker Prize in 1993?

22 What was Audrey Eyton's bestselling book of the 1980s?

23 In which county was Jane Austen born?

24 What is a bibliophile?

25 What colour are the French Michelin guides?

26 Who wrote "The Godfather"?

27 Who wrote "Possession"?

28 What was the name of "Poirot's Last Case"?

29 Who also writes as Barbara Vine?

30 In which county was Catherine Cookson born?

31 Which town is the main setting for the Cadfael novels?

32 Part of whose life story is called "The Path to Power"?

33 Who wrote the biography "Frank Sinatra: An American Legend"?

34 Which alternative comedian wrote "Gridlock"?

35 What was the job of Mellors in "Lady Chatterley's Lover"?

36 Under which pseudonym does Harry Paterson also write?

37 Which comedy actress wrote "When's it Coming Out"?

38 Which Mary Wesley novel transferred to TV with Felicity Kendal and Paul Eddington?

39 Which suspense novelist was the cousin of horror movie actor Christopher Lee?

40 What is the name of Bernard Cornwell's hero, played on TV by Sean Bean?

41 Which politician wrote "A Woman's Place"?

42 Who created the detective Maigret?

43 Whose autobiography is called "Long Walk to Freedom"?

44 Who wrote the tales on which the film "The Jungle Book" was based?

45 In which country was the best seller "Wild Swans" set?

46 Where do Jackie Collins' "Wives, Husbands and Kids" live?

47 What was the name of Lord Peter Wimsey's butler?

48 What were the "Dogs of War" in Frederick Forsyth's novel?

49 Which novel by Victor Hugo became a long-running musical?

50 Whose autobiography is called "Take It Like A Man"?

A nswers to Quiz 176, POT LUCK

1. "The Monster Mash". 2. Daniel Hooper. 3. Ronald Reagan. 4. New Zealand. 5. The House at Pooh Corner. 6. Acne. 7. A butterfly. 8. Eros. 9. A stag. 10. Roger Taylor. 11. Contour. 12. Shropshire. 13. Badminton. 14. Mortise. 15. Biggles. 16. Scout. 17. Luanda. 18. Anne Brontë. 19. Roller skate. 20. Sunil Gavaskar. 21. Oxford. 22. 18th. 23. Lord Marchmain. 24. Che Guevara. 25. Wilfred Owen. 26. 1. 27. The Timelords. 28. Cato. 29. Bleak House. 30. San Francisco. 31. Light blue. 32. Four years. 33. Winchester. 34. Lake Superior. 35. Darts. 36. Ermine Street. 37. Japan. 38. Elton John. 39. King's Oak. 40. It turns to stone. 41. 16th. 42. Prince Philip. 43. Small Faces. 44. Andante. 45. Atlantic. 46. Bob Monkhouse. 47. Anthony Burgess. 48. Kansas. 49. "On the Up". 50. "Birds Of A Feather".

Q UIZ 178 | Rugby

HARD - LEVEL THREE

1 Which county play at Kingsholm?

2 Who captained Australia in the 1995 World Cup Final?

3 Which League club is nicknamed "The Wires"?

4 Whom did Will Carling describe as a "freak"?

5 Who plays at home at Welford Road?

6 Which League side play at Bury FC's ground, Gig Lane?

7 Who was the first Welshman to be sent off playing for his country at Twickenham?

8 Who played League between 1946 and 1964 and created a record for most tries in a career?

9 Where are you if you are at "Billy Williams' cabbage patch"?

10 Who captained Australia in their World Cup win in 1991?

11 Which nephew of Barry John became a Wigan player?

12 Who played for both England and New Zealand in the 1980s?

13 Which League club is nicknamed "The Chemics"?

14 Who captained England in the 1995 World Cup Final?

15 Who scored on his debut for Wales against England in 1996?

16 Who play at Thrum Hall?

17 Who kicked the winning goal in extra time in the 1995 World Cup Final for South Africa?

18 What was the previous name of London Broncos?

19 Who plays at the Stoop Memorial Ground?

20 To whom is the Lance B. Todd Memorial Trophy awarded?

21 In what year did Scotland first win at Parc des Princes?

22 Who in 1883 picked the ball up and ran with it to "discover" rugby?

23 Which two clubs play at home at Craven Park?

24 Who played for Wales in 53 consecutive games from 1967 to 1978?

25 In Union, which international team name was first used in 1924?

26 Who can win the Five Nations but not the Triple Crown?

27 Who scored most tries for Ireland in the 1991 World Cup?

28 Apart from Wigan name four teams beginning with a W who have been League champions?

29 In League, what is awarded for the BBC TV try of the season?

30 What was the Regal Trophy previously called?

31 Which country won league's World Cup from 1975 to 1995?

32 Which Scot was British Lions captain for the '93 New Zealand tour?

33 How old was Will Carling when he first captained England?

34 Which superstar singer opened the 1995 World Cup?

35 The league Lions tour of 1996 visited Fiji and New Zealand and where else?

36 On his return to union which Jonathan said, "It's a challenge I don't particularly need"?

37 Which nation has won the Grand Slam most times?

38 Where was Jeremy Guscott born?

39 Which sponsor called last orders on its sponsorship of the Welsh League?

40 Which stadium hosted the League's 1995 World Cup Final?

41 The Ranfurly Shield is contested in which country?

42 Over half of the 1997 Lions squad came from which country?

43 In which decade was the John Player/Pilkington Cup begun?

44 Which English club did Franco Botica join when he left Wigan?

45 Which Michael has scored most points for Australia

46 Which team ended Wigan's Challenge Cup record run?

47 Which team won the first match in the Super League?

48 Which was the first team in the 90s other than Bath to win the Pilkington Cup?

49 Which two countries contest the Bledisloe Cup?

50 In the 1995 World Cup who were beaten by Scotland?

Answers to Quiz 177, Books

1. The Canterbury Tales. 2. The Bible and the complete works of Shakespeare. 3. Rosemary Conley. 4. 19th. 5. Chairman Mao's Little Red Book. 6. Jehovah's Witnesses. 7. Douglas Adams. 8. Allen Lane. 9. 1960s. 10. Frederick Warne. 11. Colleen McCullough. 12. Not a Penny More, Not a Penny Less. 13. Edwina Currie. 14. The Prodigal Daughter. 15. Margaret Thatcher. 16. Barbara Taylor Bradford. 17. Colette. 18. The 1989 Course was Illustrated. 19. Germaine Greer. 20. Around the World in Eighty Days. 21. Paddy Clarke Ha Ha Ha. 22. The F-Plan Diet. 23. Hampshire. 24. A book lover. 25. Red. 26. Mario Puzo. 27. A.S. Byatt. 28. Curtain. 29. Ruth Rendell. 30. County Durham. 31. Shrewsbury. 32. Margaret Thatcher's. 33. Nancy Sinatra. 34. Ben Elton. 35. Gamekeeper. 36. Jack Higgins. 37. Maureen Lipman. 38. The Camomile Lawn. 39. Ian Fleming. 40. Sharpe. 41. Edwina Currie. 42. Georges Simenon. 43. Nelson Mandela. 44. Rudyard Kipling. 45. China. 46. Hollywood. 47. Bunter. 48. Mercenaries. 49. Les Misérables. 50. Boy George's.

QUIZ 179 Cricket

HARD - LEVEL THREE

1 What does the first C stand for in TCCB?

2 Which county did David Gower play for apart from Leicestershire?

3 Which West Indies star scored over 8,000 Test runs?

4 Which teams played in the final of cricket's World Cup in 1992?

5 Who did Ray Illingworth replace as England's chairman of selectors?

6 Which county won the Championship in 1990 and 1991?

7 What was remarkable about the 16 overs that South Africa's Hugh Tayfield bowled against England at Durban in 1957?

8 Who was England's youngest and later oldest postwar Test player?

9 Which player broke a leg in a Test series against New Zealand in 1992?

10 In 1995, Jack Russell took how many catches in a Test to create a new world record?

11 Which three counties did Ian Botham play for?

12 Which county have won the championship most times?

13 Where is Kent's cricket ground headquarters?

14 Edmonds and Emburey were the spinning duo for which county?

15 Which all-rounder took 100 wickets and scored 1000 runs between 1903 and 1926?

16 What are the Christian names of Australia's Waugh brothers?

17 Where do Middlesex play home matches?

18 On which West Indian island is Sabina Park?

19 What was the result of the 1995-96 Test series between South Africa and England?

20 Which English county has Brian Lara played for?

21 Who was the "bodyline" bowler?

22 Gloucestershire cricketers of the 1870s W. G. and E. M. had what surname?

23 Who are the only father and son to captain England?

24 Which Englishman took 19 wickets in a 1956 Test against Australia?

25 Who was bowling for Glamorgan when Sobers hit six sixes in an over?

26 How many test centuries did Geoff Boycott score for England?

27 What is the signal for a no-ball?

28 Who was selected for all World Cups from 1975 to 1995?

29 Which new county joined the championship in the 1990s?

30 Who was West Indian captain before Richie Richardson?

31 Which county entered the County Championship in 1992?

32 Which country batted first in the 1997 Ashes First Test in

England?

33 Which county did Allan Lamb play for?

34 What was Alfred Freeman's nickname?

35 Which county has its HQ at Sophia Gardens?

36 Which county did Dermot Reeve take to the championship?

37 What creature is on the Somerset badge?

38 Which pair of spinners dominated the 80s at Middlesex?

39 Which country did Martin Crowe play for?

40 What is the colour of the *Wisden Cricketers' Almanac*?

41 Which county has its HQ in Nottingham Road?

42 Which cricketer has advertised Nike boots, Dansk low-alcohol lager and Shredded Wheat?

43 Which county took to an all-chocolate strip in the 90s?

44 Which cricket personality is known as Bumble?

45 Who was the first Scotsman to captain England?

46 Who became the first Test bowler to take 19 wickets?

47 Which county did Ian Botham join on leaving Somerset?

48 Is Brian Lara a right- or left-handed batsman?

49 Which country does umpire Cyril Mitchley come from?

50 Which England fast bowler took Dylan as a middle name in honour of Bob Dylan?

A nswers to Quiz 178, RUGBY

1. Gloucester. 2. Brad Fittler. 3. Warrington. 4. Jonah Lomu. 5. Leicester. 6. Swinton. 7. Paul Ringer. 8. Brian Bevan. 9. Twickenham. 10. Nick Farr-Jones. 11. Scott Quinnell. 12. Jamie Salmon. 13. Widnes. 14. Dennis Betts. 15. Rob Howley. 16. Halifax. 17. Joel Stransky. 18. London Crusaders. 19 Harlequins. 20 .Rugby League Cup Final Man of The Match. 21. 1995. 22. William Webb Ellis. 23. Hull Kingston Rovers and Barrow. 24. Gareth Edwards. 25. The British Lions. 26. France. 27. Brian Robinson. 28. Wakefield Trinity, Warrington, Widnes, Workington Town. 29. Eddie Waring Memorial Trophy. 30. John Player Trophy. 31. Australia. 32. Gavin Hastings. 33. 22. 34. Diana Ross. 35. Papua New Guinea. 36. Davies. 37. England. 38. Bath. 39. Heineken. 40. Wembley. 41. New Zealand. 42. England. 43. 1970s. 44. Castleford. 45. Lynagh. 46. Salford Reds. 47. Paris St Germain. 48. Harlequins. 49. Australia, New Zealand. 50. Ivory Coast.

Q UIZ 180 | Pot Luck

HARD - LEVEL THREE

1. What was Disney's second animated feature film?

2. What is a glow worm as it is not a worm?

3. Where are the world headquarters of the Mormon Church?

4. Which Motown group featured Lionel Richie before he went solo?

5. What was the nickname of boxer Dave Green?

6. Which animal's name is Aboriginal and means "No drink"?

7. Which role did Phil Collins play in a stage version of "Oliver!"?

8. Which flowering plant family includes asparagus?

9. Which Irish county would you be in if you were in Tipperary?

10. Who was Muhammad Ali's first professional opponent outside the US?

11. Who wrote the children's classic "The Secret Garden"?

12. What was the nickname of Sir Arthur Travers Harris?

13. What genus and species is man classified as?

14. Which imaginary island was created in 1516 by Sir Thomas More?

15. Who had a 50s No. 1 with "The Story Of My Life"?

16. In which state was "Dynasty" set?

17. Which British school did Kurt Hahn found in the 1930s?

18. In which decade was the series "'Allo 'Allo" screened for the first time?

19. What word can go after "port" and before "seaman"?

20. In which continent is Lake Titicaca?

21. Who was asked for the bolt in the original "The Golden Shot"?

22. Which American Football team did Gavin Hastings first play for?

23. In which century was Charles Perrault collecting his fairy stories?

24. If the weather is calm what is wind force on the Beaufort scale?

25. What is the capital of Libya?

26. What was the name of the chess-playing computer that beat Kasparov?

27. Concorde and Louise Bonne are types of which fruit?

28. Who was the first winner on Wimbledon's new 1997 No. 1 court?

29. Who did Wimbledon players describe as a jellyfish?

30. What type of quadrilateral has all sides the same length but contains no right angles?

31. Which is the third film of the "Star Wars" trilogy?

32. What is the diameter in inches of a standard competition

364

dartboard?

33 Which children's programme had the sci-fi strip "Bleep and Booster"?

34 A beluga is a type of what?

35 Lent always begins on which day of the week?

36 Which royal told the press to "naff off" at the Badminton Horse Trials?

37 David Wagstaffe was the first British footballer to be shown what?

38 Which language does the word "anorak" come from?

39 Why did the catfish get its name?

40 What title did Billy Connolly give to the Village People's "In The Navy"?

41 Who wrote the novel "The Woman In White"?

42 What was the nickname of Arthur Marx?

43 In which century was Richard the Lionheart born?

44 Which US state is renowned for its Black Hills?

45 What kind a school was run by Pussy Galore?

46 Photophobia is a fear of what?

47 What relation, if any, was Pitt the Elder to Pitt the Younger?

48 Who had a 80s No. I with "Never Gonna Give You Up"?

49 Which character did Emma Samms play in "Dynasty"?

50 Which countries share the world's longest frontier?

QUIZ 181 | Movies

HARD - LEVEL THREE

1 Which Bond villain has been played by Telly Savalas and Donald Pleasence?

2 Who directed "Hustle" and "The Dirty Dozen"?

3 What was the second Bond film?

4 Which role did Jim Carrey play in "Batman Forever"?

5 In which 1997 film does Pierce Brosnan play a vulcanologist?

6 Whose film biography was called Dragon?

7 What does "Ice Cold" refer to in the John Mills film "Ice Cold in Alex"?

8 Which sport are "Kid's Return" and "Tokyo Fist" about?

9 What was the occupation of the Fugitive?

10 Which means of transport dominates in "Speed"?

11 Which 1997 Mafia film starred Al Pacino and Johnny Depp?

12 In which US city is "Metro" set?

13 What was Pierce Brosnan's second film as James Bond?

14 What was the third Die Hard film called?

15 Who played Bond girl Solitaire in "Live and Let Die"?

16 In which decade does the action of "Raiders of the Lost Ark" take place?

17 What was Oliver Stone's final Vietnam Trilogy film?

18 Which means of transport features in "The Hunt For Red October"?

19 Which country is the setting for Oliver Stone's "Platoon"?

20 Who plays the US captain escaping an Italian POW camp in Von Ryan's "Express"?

21 Who co-wrote and starred in "Cliffhanger" in 1993?

22 Which action movie is subtitled "Judgment Day"?

23 Who is the actress caught between an undercover cop and a drug dealer in "Tequila Sunrise"?

24 Which film critic's father produced "The Cruel Sea"?

25 Who directed the first three Godfather films?

26 Which 1995 film allegedly cost £1.3 million per minute screen time?

27 Which singer joined Mel Gibson for Mad Max Beyond "Thunderdome"?

28 Which city is the setting for "French Connection II"?

29 Which film's action begins with "Houston, we have a problem"?

30 Who played 007 in 1984 in "Never Say Never Again"?

31 What was Barbra Streisand character called in "Funny Girl"?

32 In which musical do Tracy Lord and CK Dexter Haven appear?

33 In which musical is "The Duelling

Cavalier" a film in the making?

34 Who sings "As Long as He Needs Me" in Oliver!?

35 Who directed "A Chorus Line"?

36 Which singer - famous for dubbing other actresses' voices - played Sister Sophia in "The Sound of Music"?

37 What was the follow-up to "Saturday Night Fever" called?

38 Who did Betty Hutton replace as Annie in "Annie Get Your Gun"?

39 What was the job of Joel Grey's character in "Cabaret"?

40 Which musical was based on a Harold Gray comic strip?

41 What instrument does Robert de Niro play in in "New York New York"?

42 Which musical does "The Ugly Duckling" come from?

43 Who sang "Moon River" in "Breakfast at Tiffany's"?

44 Which song in "Evita" was composed specially for the film?

45 How many Von Trapp children are there in "The Sound of Music"?

46 "Hopelessly Devoted to You" is sung in which movie?

47 Who are the two gangs in "West Side Story"?

48 Which character did Liza Minnelli play in "Cabaret"?

49 Which movie musical has the song "Feed the Birds"?

50 Who played Mama Rose in the 1993 movie "Gypsy"?

A nswers to Quiz 180, POT LUCK

1. Pinocchio. 2. A beetle. 3. Salt Lake City. 4. The Commodores. 5. Boy. 6. Koala. 7. The Artful Dodger. 8. Lily. 9. County Tipperary. 10. Henry Cooper. 11. Frances Hodgson Burnett. 12. "Bomber". 13. Homo sapiens. 14. Utopia. 15. Michael Holliday. 16 Colorado. 17. Gordonstoun. 18 1980s. 19. "Able". 20. South America. 21. Bernie. 22. Scotish Claymores. 23. 17th. 24. 0. 25. Tripoli. 26. Deep Blue. 27. Pears. 28. Tim Henman. 29. Gary Lineker. 30. Rhombus. 31. Return of the Jedi. 32. 18. 33. "Blue Peter". 34. Whale. 35. Wednesday. 36. The Princess Royal. 37. A red card. 38. Eskimo. 39. It has whiskers. 40. "In the Brownies". 41. Wilkie Collins. 42. "Harpo". 43. 12th. 44. South Dakota. 45. A flying school. 46. Strong light. 47. Father. 48. Rick Astley. 49. Fallon Carrington-Colby. 50. Canada and USA.

Quiz 182 Nature

HARD - LEVEL THREE

1 What do conifers have in their cones?

2 Which tree's leaves are the symbol of The National Trust?

3 Which three coniferous trees are native to Britain?

4 Which garden tree with yellow flowers has poisonous seeds?

5 What colour are the flowers of the horse chestnut tree?

6 In which country did the bonsai technique develop?

7 Which tree do we get turpentine from?

8 In which continent did the monkey-puzzle tree originate?

9 Which tree produces cobs and filberts?

10 Aspen is from which family of trees?

11 Is the wood of a coniferous tree hard or soft?

12 What is the more common name for the great maple?

13 What sort of environment do alder trees grow in?

14 Which tree is cork obtained from?

15 In which county is England's largest forest?

16 Which tree is sago obtained from?

17 Which beech tree has purplish leaves?

18 What is the Spanish chestnut also called?

19 Which tree can be English, American or Eurasian?

20 To which family does the umbrella tree belong?

21 The teak is native to which continent?

22 Which wood is used for piano keys?

23 Which maple's sap is used to make maple syrup?

24 To which family does the osier belong?

25 Which is thought to be the tallest tree in the world and one of the longest-lived?

26 Which tree produces "keys"?

27 What colour flowers does a jacaranda tree have?

28 Which tree produces the seeds from which cocoa is made?

29 To which group of trees do blue gum and red gum belong ?

30 What is the linden tree also called?

31 What is the common name for the antirrhinum?

32 Which hanging basket favourite is also called pelargonium?

33 What qualities do the flowers helichrysum and acroclinium have?

34 By what name is Solidago known?

35 What type of bell is a campanula?

36 Which yellow, pink-flushed rose was bred by Meilland in 1945?

37 Which wild flower is also known as the knapweed?

38 Which flower has rung-like leaflets?

39 What would you find in an anther on a stamen?

40 What is the common name for the plant Impatiens?

41 Which flowers are said to symbolize the Crucifixion?

42 Which flower, also called chalk plant or baby's breath, is a favourite with flower arrangers?

43 Bachelor's buttons are a variety of which yellow wild flower?

44 Which flower's seeds are pickled to make capers?

45 Which animals love nepeta, giving the latter its common name?

46 What sort of hyacinth is a muscari?

47 Which flower – Lychnis – shares its name with a fictional detective?

48 Which two flowers would you find in an orchestra?

49 Which flower gets its name from a Persian or Turkish word for turban?

50 Which plant is grown not for its flowers but for its silvery seed pods?

QUIZ 183 Pot Luck

HARD - LEVEL THREE

1 Which plant's scientific name is *Impatiens*?

2 Which Chinese city is home to the Terracotta Army?

3 What did the North West Mounted Police become in 1920?

4 Who were Roberta, Phyllis and Peter collectively known as?

5 Which drink is named after the Ethiopian city of Kaffa?

6 Who played Dot Cotton in "EastEnders"?

7 What coin was made compulsory in 1971 and illegal in 1985?

8 Which county is home to the Brecon Beacons?

9 Which King received the support of Robin Hood?

10 What is the highest UK peak south of the Scottish border?

11 In which century was Fred Astaire born?

12 Who wrote the novel "Crime and Punishment"?

13 How was Malcolm Little better known?

14 Who had a 90s No. 1 with "Pray"?

15 Which drink has "7X" as a secret formula?

16 How old was Brian Clough when he stopped playing soccer?

17 Who published "My Silent War" in the USSR in 1968?

18 In which series did Frank and Danny Kane appear?

19 Which country was the setting for "Carry On Up the Khyber"?

20 Who was the first presenter of "Give Us A Clue"?

21 What word can go after "rest" and before "hood"?

22 Which stone is used in snooker tables?

23 In song lyrics, you can bring Pearl or Rose but who can't you bring?

24 Who in 1997 became Britain's first Muslim MP?

25 In which decade did Minnie the Minx first appear in the "Beano"?

26 Alan Scotthorne was a 90s world champion in which sport?

27 Which well-known Frenchman designed Italy's flag?

28 Whose box was opened by Epimethius?

29 Which name derived from Greek means stone or rock?

30 Which team's football kit was designed by Bruce Oldfield in 1997?

31 Which wartime hero had the same name as Hilda Ogden's cat?

32 What kind of plants is the name Harry Wheatcroft linked with?

33 Which ocean are the Seychelles in?

34 What expense became compulsory for cars in 1921?

35 Which university had Sir Robin Day as a former union president?

370

36 Which decade saw the first FA Cup Final at Wembley?

37 What kind of reference book was Bradshaw's?

38 What is a butterfly larva more commonly called?

39 Which actress appeared in Woody Allen's "The Purple Rose of Cairo"?

40 Which fictional doctor lived in Puddleby-on-Marsh?

41 In which decade of the 20th century was Mikhail Gorbachev born?

42 What was Bob Marley's middle name?

43 What is the only English anagram of TOENAIL?

44 If it's 12 noon GMT what time is it in Athens?

45 Who wrote "Journey To The Centre Of The Earth"?

46 Alan Hansen joined Liverpool from which club?

47 Who had a 90s No. 1 with "Rhythm Is A Dancer"?

48 Which is the only active volcano in mainland Europe?

49 In which century was Jane Austen born?

50 On which ranch was "Bonanza" set?

A nswers to Quiz 182, NATURE

1. Seeds. 2. Oak. 3. Yew, Scots Pine, Juniper. 4. Laburnum. 5. White/cream. 6. Japan. 7. Pine. 8. South America. 9. Hazel. 10. Poplar. 11. Soft. 12. Sycamore. 13. Wet. 14. Cork oak. 15. Northumberland. 16. Palm. 17. Copper beech. 18. Sweet chestnut. 19. Elm. 20. Magnolia. 21. Asia. 22. Ebony. 23. Sugar maple. 24. Willow. 25. Redwood. 26. Ash. 27. Blue/violet. 28. Cacao. 29. Eucalyptus. 30. Lime. 31. Snapdragon. 32. Geranium. 33. Everlasting. 34. Golden Rod. 35. Canterbury bell. 36. Peace. 37. Cornflower. 38. Jacob's ladder. 39. Pollen. 40. Busy Lizzie. 41. Passion flower. 42. Gypsophila. 43. Buttercups. 44. Nasturtium. 45. Cats (Catmint). 46. Grape hyacinth. 47. Campion. 48. Viola, Bugle. 49. Tulip (tuliban). 50. Honesty.

Q UIZ 184 | Television

1 Who presented "Crimewatch UK" with Nick Ross prior to Jill Dando?

2 Who were the two regulars on Gary Lineker and David Gower's teams in "They Think It's All Over"?

3 Who is the priest played by Stephen Tomkinson in "Ballykissangel"?

4 Who replaced Botham and Beaumont on "A Question of Sport"?

5 Who had a late-night chat show when Channel 5 was launched?

6 Who left "Blue Peter" to join the "Clothes Show" team?

7 Who is known as "Mr Trick Shot"?

8 Who starred as Blanco in "Porridge"?

9 Which TV star's first record release was "Extremis"?

10 What is the "Baywatch" star Pamela Anderson's son called?

11 Who were the stars of "A Close Shave"?

12 Who wrote "The Singing Detective" and "Pennies From Heaven"?

13 Which actress is married to John Thaw?

14 Who co-starred with Adam Faith in "Love Hurts"?

15 Who is Anthea Turner's TV presenter sister?

16 Who left "Peak Practice" for "Bliss"?

17 Whose TV wife was played by Teri Hatcher?

18 Who was known as the Green Goddess?

19 Who first presented the weather on BBC's "Breakfast Time"?

20 Who was known as the Galloping Gourmet?

21 Who became resident cook on GMTV in spring 1997?

22 Who first presented "The Antiques Roadshow" in 1981?

23 Who are team captains in Bob Holness's "Call My Bluff"?

24 Who hosted the retrospective quiz show "Backdate"?

25 Which TV star was flown in from the US to introduce the Spice Girls' first live UK performance?

26 Who is dubbed the King of Swing during election campaigns?

27 Who replaced Anthea Turner on GMTV's breakfast couch?

28 Who is Beverley Callard's actress daughter?

29 Who first presented "Nine O'Clock Live" on GMTV?

30 Which actress is married to the playwright Jack Rosenthal?

31 What is the favoured transport of the Two Fat Ladies TV cooks?

32 Jamiroquai's Jay Kay composed the theme music for coverage of which sport new to TV in 1997?

33 In '97 who was voted sexiest woman on TV by *Radio Times* readers?

34 What are the first names of the Doctors Bramwell in the TV series?

35 Which show pits Merton v. Hislop with Deayton as referee?

36 Whose characters included Marcel Wave and Sid Snot?

37 In which sci-fi series did the red-suited Kochanski appear?

38 Which US actor accompanied Martin Bell on his election campaign?

39 What was the name of Nick's first wife in "Heartbeat"?

40 In which area of London was the "Ab Fab" Monsoon household?

41 Who co-wrote "Yes Minister" with Jonathan Lynn?

42 Which series featured the Carol Hathaway/Doug Ross saga?

43 Who was on a desert island as a "Girl Friday" in the mid-90s?

44 In which American state is "Northern Exposure" set?

45 What was the Job in "No Job For A Lady"?

46 Who was Conservative MP for Haltemprice?

47 What were Les Dawson and Roy Barraclough's old gossips called?

48 Which planet was Mork from?

49 In which series was business conducted at the Winchester?

50 "Laverne and Shirley" was a spin-off from which 70s US series?

A nswers to Quiz 183, Pot Luck

1. Busy Lizzy. 2. Xian. 3. Royal Canadian Mounted Police. 4. The Railway Children. 5. Coffee. 6. June Brown. 7. The decimal halfpenny. 8. Powys. 9. Richard I. 10. Snowdon. 11. 19th. 12. Fyodor Dostoevsky. 13. Malcolm X. 14. Take That. 15. Coca-Cola. 16. 29. 17. Kim Philby. 18. "The Paradise Club". 19. India. 20. Michael Aspel. 21. "Rain". 22. Slate. 23. Lulu. 24. Mohammed Sarwar. 25. 50s. 26. Angling. 27. Napoleon. 28. Pandora's. 29. Peter. 30. Norwich City's. 31. Rommel. 32. Roses. 33. The Indian Ocean. 34. Tax discs. 35. Oxford. 36. 1920s. 37. Railway timetable. 38. Caterpillar. 39. Mia Farrow. 40. Dr Doolittle. 41. 30s. 42. Nesta. 43. Elation. 44. 2 p.m. 45. Jules Verne. 46. Partick Thistle. 47. Snap. 48. Mount Vesuvius. 49. 18th. 50. The Ponderosa.

QUIZ 185 Pot Luck

HARD - LEVEL THREE

1 Which captain of Darwin's ship HMS "Beagle" became governor of New Zealand?

2 What was W. H. Auden's first name?

3 Who had the word "Skytrain" printed on one side of his aircraft?

4 What source of light is used in producing a hologram?

5 Which Bond movie was a hit for Sheena Easton?

6 Who classified the elements into the periodic table?

7 Where in Canada is the world's second-largest French-speaking city?

8 Which character did Clark Gable play in "Gone With the Wind"?

9 Which tsar conquered Kazan and Siberia in the 16th century?

10 What name is given to a plant which dies down at the end of the growing season?

11 In which year did Britain abandon the gold standard?

12 Which Italian artist included Halley's comet in a fresco of the Nativity?

13 Which object took almost seven hours to rise from the Solent?

14 Which "Dad's Army" actor was married to Hattie Jacques?

15 What name is given to the genetic make-up of an individual?

16 Where did chess originate in the second century AD?

17 What happened to the main character "Metamorphosis"?

18 What style of music was pioneered by jazzmen Charlie Parker and Dizzy Gillespie?

19 Which 18th-century priest discovered that plants absorb air?

20 Cecil Beaton won Oscars for his designs for which two films?

21 In the rhyme, what is Friday's child?

22 What is the name given to the religious leader of a synagogue?

23 Which two countries fly supersonic passenger aircraft?

24 What did Mahatma Gandhi train to become?

25 Where would you find an avenue of sphinxes?

26 Which instrument did Lionel Hampton introduce to jazz?

27 Who played the Riddler in "Batman Forever"?

28 Who was the last prisoner to be held at Spandau?

29 Which rock star, known as "Slowhand", received an OBE in 1995?

30 Which theme from a film did the BBC use for the 1984 Olympics?

31 What is the main language spoken in Chile?

32 In which Shakespeare play do we meet two grave diggers?

33 Which Eastern religion includes

374

the caste system?

34 Who was king of England from 1413 to 1422?

35 What animal lives in a drey?

36 In which African country is the city of Bulawayo?

37 On which river do Rochester, Chatham and Gillingham stand?

38 Which queen started a nursing service for soldiers?

39 In which sport was Sir Donald Bradman famous?

40 Who said, "I never had any problems with drugs, only with policemen"?

41 In the Bible, name the son who Abraham was asked to sacrifice?

42 Who was the last Roman Catholic king of England?

43 What sort of bird is a Cinnamon Norwich?

44 Winnipeg is the capital of which Canadian province?

45 Of which country was Aldo Moro prime minister?

46 At which battle was Richard III killed?

47 Who wrote the operetta "Bitter Sweet" and the play "Private Lives"?

48 What do we call a group of bishops?

49 Which country does a car come from if it shows CDN as the international registration letters?

50 What part of the body would be affected if you suffered from myopia?

Answers to Quiz 184, TELEVISION

1. Sue Cook. 2. Rory McGrath, Lee Hurst. 3. Peter Clifford. 4. Ally McCoist, John Parrott. 5. Jack Docherty. 6. Tim Vincent. 7. John Virgo. 8. David Jason. 9. Gillian Anderson. 10. Brandon. 11. Wallace and Gromit. 12. Dennis Potter. 13. Sheila Hancock. 14. Zoë Wanamaker. 15. Wendy Turner. 16. Simon Shepherd. 17. Superman's. 18. Diana Moran. 19. Francis Wilson. 20. Graham Kerr. 21. Ross Burden. 22. Hugh Scully. 23. Alan Coren, Sandi Toksvig. 24. Valerie Singleton. 25. Jennifer Aniston. 26. Peter Snow. 27. Fiona Phillips. 28. Rebecca Callard. 29 .Lorraine Kelly. 30. Maureen Lipman. 31. Motorbike and sidecar. 32. Grand Prix racing. 33. Helen Mirren. 34. Eleanor, Robert. 35. "Have I Got News For You?". 36. Kenny Everett. 37. "Red Dwarf". 38. David Soul. 39. Kate. 40. Holland Park. 41. Anthony Jay. 42. "ER". 43. Joanna Lumley. 44. Alaska. 45. MP. 46. Alan B'Stard. 47. Cissie and Ada. 48. Ork. 49. "Minder". 50. "Happy Days".

QUIZ 186 | Pop Music

HARD - LEVEL THREE

1 How are Messrs Hodges and Peacock better known?

2 "It's four o'clock and we're in trouble deep" comes from which Everly Brothers song?

3 What relation was Sonny to Cher in their single-making days?

4 Pepsi and Shirlie provided backing vocals for which superstar group?

5 What was the first Eurythmics top ten single back in 1983?

6 What little animal did Nina and Frederick sing about?

7 Which duo were made up of Paul and Art?

8 Whom did Diano Ross duo with on "Endless Love"?

9 Which TV show gave Peters and Lee their first break?

10 Who did Elton John sing with on his first British No 1?

11 What were the first names of the Ofarims?

12 Which artist did Brian and Michael sing about?

13 What was The Pipkins' only hit?

14 According to Peter and Gordon, to know you is to do what?

15 "It Takes Two" featured Tammi Terrell and who else?

16 Which duo has spent most weeks in the UK single charts?

17 Who were respectable in 1987?

18 How many of duo Miki and Griff were female?

19 Which duo had a No 1 with "Would I Lie To You"?

20 Which duo comprised Marc Almond and David Ball?

21 Who produced Ike and Tina Turner's "River Deep Mountain High"?

22 Which male/female singing duo had 16 weeks at No 1 in 1978?

23 According to "Tears for Fears", what did everyone want to rule?

24 Which duo charted with the "The Skye Boat Song"?

25 Which duo appeared in drag in an Abba tribute?

26 Who partnered Pearl Carr in the 1959 Eurovision Song Contest?

27 Who charted with "(I Wanna Give You) Devotion"?

28 How many girls in the duo Everything But the Girl?

29 Which Simon and Garfunkel song starts "I'm sitting in a railway station"?

30 How are Christopher Lowe and Neil Tennant better known?

31 Which all-girl group included Michael Steele?

32 Which country did A-Ha come from?

33 Mike D'Abo and Paul Jones sang with which group?

34 Tony McCarroll was the only non-family member of which group?

35 What was Blondie's first No. 1?

36 Who has had hits featuring Duane Eddy, Max Headroom and Tom Jones?

37 Which 60s group charted with "Tell Me When"?

38 What was the surname of Luke and Matt of Bros?

39 Who were Sarah Dullin, Siobhan Fahey and Keren Woodward?

40 Who was lead singer with Amen Corner?

41 What was in brackets in the title of Chic's "Dance Dance Dance"?

42 Which group featured Stewart "Woody" Wood?

43 Which group made records about an Arnold and an Emily?

44 Roger McGuinn and David Crosby were in which 60s band?

45 What was Wet Wet Wet's first No. 1?

46 Which 60s group featured Demis Roussos and Vangelis?

47 Thin Lizzy came from which country?

48 Steve Marriott and Ronnie Lane were in which band?

49 Which group were responsible for "Chirpy Chirpy Cheep Cheep"?

50 In the 60s who did the Roulettes back?

A nswers to
Quiz 185, Pot Luck

1. Robert Fitzroy. 2. Wystan. 3. Sir Freddie Laker. 4. Laser. 5. For Your Eyes Only. 6. Mendeleyev. 7. Montreal. 8. Rhett Butler. 9. Ivan the Terrible. 10. Herbaceous. 11. 1931. 12. Giotto. 13. The Mary Rose. 14. John Le Mesurier. 15. Genotype. 16. India. 17. Turned into an insect. 18. Bebop. 19. Stephen Hales. 20. Gigi and My Fair Lady. 21. Loving and giving. 22. Rabbi. 23. France and Great Britain. 24. Lawyer. 25. Luxor, Egypt. 26. Vibraphone. 27. Jim Carrey. 28. Rudolf Hess. 29. Eric Clapton. 30. Chariots of Fire. 31. Spanish. 32. Hamlet. 33. Hindu. 34. Henry V. 35. Squirrel. 36. Zimbabwe. 37. The Medway. 38. Queen Alexandra. 39. Cricket. 40. Keith Richard. 41. Isaac. 42. James II. 43. Canary. 44. Manitoba. 45. Italy. 46. Battle of Bosworth. 47. Noel Coward. 48. Bench. 49. Canada. 50. Eyes.

Q UIZ 187 | Pot Luck

HARD - LEVEL THREE

1 When a cow stands up, which legs does it get up on first?

2 Who sang "On the good ship Lollipop"?

3 According to the proverb, what is the better part of valour?

4 When driving a car in Britain what is the hand signal for turning left?

5 In ads, what were you using if your fingers did the walking?

6 From which London railway station do you normally travel to Bristol?

7 In which film is the Harry Lime theme?

8 Which American city is named after a British prime minister?

9 Where would you find a dead man's handle?

10 How is Concetta Franconeri better known?

11 On which river does swan-upping take place?

12 Which country lies immediately east of Iraq?

13 Which London building is nicknamed 'Ally Pally'?

14 Who claimed that "History is Bunk"?

15 In which English city is the cathedral known as 'Paddy's Wigwam'?

16 From which port was the bulk of the British Expeditionary Force in France evacuated in 1940?

17 Which architect designed New York's Guggenheim Museum?

18 Who wrote "Gulliver's Travels"?

19 In which city was General Gordon put to death?

20 What kind of animal is a pipistrelle?

21 According to the proverb which fruit tastes sweetest?

22 What was the name for the ancient Egyptian good luck charm in the shape of a beetle?

23 Who was depicted in "Spitting Image" as a slug?

24 Who said "Father, I cannot tell a lie"?

25 By what name do we often call nitrous oxide?

26 In German fable who sold his soul to Mephistopheles?

27 What do Bluebell, the Watercress, and the Severn Valley all have in common?

28 What is Freddie Starr's real name?

29 Which sport did David Duckham play?

30 What is the unit of currency in Iran?

31 If libel is a written defamation, what is oral defamation?

32 Which pianist had hits with "Side Saddle" and "Roulette"?

33 Which word can go after jumbo and before black?

34 What name was given to the

mediaeval warlike expeditions to the Holy Land?

35 In which year was the first manned space flight?

36 In Canada, of which province is St John's the capital?

37 Which animal's name literally means "earth pig"?

38 Who was the first major criminal to be arrested as a result of the use of radio?

39 Who made their screen debut in "Puss In Boots"?

40 Which dance is usually performed to "Orpheus in the Underworld"?

41 Who played the part of Mrs Wembley in "On The Up"?

42 According to the proverb what makes Jack a dull boy?

43 Of which flower is ox-eye a type?

44 In Britain which is the ultimate court of appeal?

45 Which country did tennis-playing sisters Katerina and Manuela Maleeva come from?

46 Amritsar is a holy city for the followers of which religion?

47 What are ink-caps, death caps and puffballs all types of?

48 Which country was once called New France?

49 What does the second E in the acronym ERNIE stand for?

50 What is the wife of a marquis called?

A nswers to Quiz 186, POP MUSIC

1. Chas and Dave. 2. Wake Up Little Suzie. 3. Husband. 4. Wham! 5. Sweet dreams (are made of this). 6. Donkey. 7. Simon and Garfunkel. 8. Lionel Richie. 9. Opportunity Knocks. 10. Kiki Dee. 11. Esther and Abi. 12. L. S. Lowry. 13. Gimme Dat Ding. 14. Love you. 15. Marvin Gaye. 16. Everly Brothers. 17. Mel and Kim. 18. One. 19. Charles and Eddie. 20. Soft Cell. 21. Phil Spector. 22. John Travolta and Olivia Newton-John. 23. The World. 24. Roger Whittaker, Des O'Connor. 25. Erasure. 26. Teddy Johnson. 27. Nomad. 28. One. 29. Homeward Bound. 30. Pet Shop Boys. 31. Bangles. 32. Norway. 33. Manfred Mann. 34. Oasis. 35. "Heart Of Glass". 36. Art Of Noise. 37. Applejacks. 38. Goss. 39. Bananarama. 40. Andy Fairweather-Low. 41. "Yowsah Yowsah Yowsah". 42. The Bay City Rollers. 43. Pink Floyd. 44. The Byrds. 45. "With A Little Help From My Friends". 46. Aphrodite's Child. 47. Ireland. 48. The Small Faces. 49. Middle of the Road. 50. Adam Faith.

Q UIZ 188 | World Tour

HARD - LEVEL THREE

1 What is the largest office building in the USA?
2 Which wind blows from the Sahara to southern Italy?
3 Which Canadian island has Victoria as its capital?
4 Which country has the time zones Eastern, Central, Mountain and Pacific?
5 In which ocean are the Maldives?
6 Which US state is known as the Lone Star State?
7 In which country is Cotopaxi, the world's highest volcano?
8 How do the Argentinians refer to the Falkland Islands?
9 What is the USA's oldest educational institution called?
10 What did the Mason Dixon Line divide in the USA?
11 Which country has most neighbouring countries?
12 The Keys are islands off which US state?
13 Darwin is the capital of which Australian state?
14 Which river flows over the Victoria Falls?
15 Which two territories joined together to form Tanzania?
16 On which river are Quebec and Montreal?
17 Where are the US gold reserves?
18 In which country is the Mekong Delta?
19 Which capital is on the Moskva river?
20 Which river divides the USA and Mexico?
21 Where is Madison Square Garden?
22 How was Botswana known immediately prior to independence?
23 In which country is the world's highest waterfall?
24 Which US island was a registration point for immigrants until 1954?
25 Which of the world's highest mountains between India and China is not in the Himalayas?
26 How is Byzantium and Constantinople now known?
27 What is the second largest state of the US?
28 Tierra del Fuego is off which country?
29 Fuerteventura is in which island group?
30 Which is the highest mountain in North America?
31 What do Washington, Basildon and Cwmbran have in common?
32 What is the fault in San Francisco called?
33 What is the world's longest mountain range?
34 What is the third largest US state after Alaska and Texas?
35 Which country has IS as its international registration letters?

36 Where is Transylvania?

37 What is a sea containing many islands called?

38 What colour is the Bakerloo line on the London Underground map?

39 Orly airport is near which city?

40 What is the capital of Tasmania?

41 In Austria what is the Grossglockner?

42 Where are Waverley and Haymarket stations?

43 Where is the administrative HQ of Hampshire?

44 How was British Honduras subsequently known?

45 On which river is the Kariba Dam?

46 Herm is one of which group of islands?

47 Which South American country was named after Venice?

48 What is the capital of the US state of Ohio?

49 In which East Anglian town is the Greene King brewery based?

50 Which of the Cinque Ports has six letters in its name?

Answers to Quiz 187, Pot Luck

1. Back. 2. Shirley Temple. 3. Discretion. 4. Turning your right arm in a circle. 5. Yellow Pages. 6. Paddington. 7. The Third Man. 8. Pittsburgh. 9. In an electric train, tube train. 10. Connie Francis. 11. The Thames. 12. Iran. 13. Alexandra Palace. 14. Henry Ford. 15. Liverpool. 16. Dunkirk. 17. Frank Lloyd Wright. 18. Jonathan Swift. 19. Khartoum. 20. A bat. 21. Forbidden fruit. 22. The scarab. 23. Kenneth Baker. 24. George Washington. 25. Laughing gas. 26. Faust. 27. Railways. 28. Freddie Starr. 29. Rugby Union. 30. The rial. 31. Slander. 32. Russ Conway. 33. Jet. 34. The Crusades. 35. 1961. 36. Newfoundland. 37. Aardvark. 38. Dr Crippen. 39. Tom & Jerry. 40. Can-can. 41. Joan Sims. 42. All work and no play. 43. Daisy. 44. House of Lords. 45. Bulgaria. 46. Sikh. 47. Mushrooms or toadstools. 48. Canada. 49. Equipment. 50. Marchioness.

QUIZ 189 | Pot Luck

HARD - LEVEL THREE

1 Which novel is about a boy called Billy Casper who trains a hawk?

2 Martina Navratilova won most doubles trophies with which partner?

3 With what is Threadneedle Street associated?

4 In which art has Beryl Grey achieved fame?

5 Who lives in a kraal?

6 Whose real name was Ronald Wycherly?

7 What colour is angelica?

8 With which country is the famous soldier Robert Clive associated?

9 What happens in a vortex?

10 To which section of the orchestra does the tuba belong?

11 In the song, who stuck a feather in his hat called macaroni?

12 What was the first Ealing Comedy?

13 What is the county town of Shropshire?

14 In which sporting event does the winning team move backwards?

15 What is a fandango?

16 Eau-de-nil is a shade of what colour?

17 Which revolution began in 1917?

18 Who is said to have introduced the habit of smoking into this country?

19 After seven which is the next highest prime number?

20 In boxing at what weight do you fight if you weigh over 12 stone 7 pounds?

21 Who wrote the novel "Jane Eyre"?

22 Until the country's recent division, what was the capital of Yugoslavia?

23 Which drink is known as eau-de-vie?

24 In which country were turkeys first found?

25 What is a carillon?

26 How many moves are there in a chess game in which White opens and wins with Fool's Mate?

27 In which month each year is Battle of Britain week?

28 In a bullfight who kills the bull?

29 What size of bottle is a magnum?

30 What is David Frost's middle name?

31 Which book of the Bible tell us about the creation of the world?

32 What is a lacuna?

33 Edible, blue and hermit are all types of which creature?

34 Who played Thomas A Becket to Peter O'Toole's Henry II?

35 In which country is Waterloo, site of the Napoleonic battlefield?

36 In which play does Miss Prism appear?

37 Where is the metatarsal arch?

382

38　Which Beatles song was the theme for "Read All About It"?

39　On a map, which places are joined by a contour?

40　In the song, which official is waiting "for me and my gal"?

41　What is pulchritude?

42　Which film comedians are associated with the phrase, "That's another fine mess you got me in"?

43　Which creature's song refers to a final speech or performance?

44　Which letter of the alphabet is used to describe a soft lead pencil?

45　Who was nicknamed the Brown Bomber?

46　In which country were there originally mandarins?

47　Who or what are Effingham, Grenville, Benbow and Collingwood?

48　For which sport is Gordon Pirie remembered?

49　What was Buddy Holly's real first name?

50　Which of Shakespeare's plays involves a pound of flesh?

A nswers to Quiz 188, World Tour

1. The Pentagon. 2. Sirocco. 3. Vancouver. 4. USA. 5. Indian. 6. Texas. 7. Ecuador. 8. Las Malvinas. 9. Harvard. 10. States with and without slavery. 11. China (16). 12. Florida. 13. Northern Territory. 14. The Zambesi. 15. Tanganyika, Zanzibar. 16. St Lawrence. 17. Fort Knox. 18. Vietnam. 19. Moscow. 20. Rio Grande. 21. New York. 22. Bechuanaland. 23. Venezuela. 24. Ellis Island. 25. K2. 26. Istanbul. 27. Texas. 28. Argentina. 29. Canaries. 30. McKinley. 31. They are all new towns. 32. San Andreas Fault. 33. Andes. 34. California. 35. Iceland. 36. Romania. 37. Archipelago. 38. Brown. 39. Paris. 40. Hobart. 41. Mountain. 42. Edinburgh. 43. Winchester. 44. Belize. 45. Zambesi. 46. Channel Islands. 47. Venezuela. 48. Columbus. 49. Bury St Edmunds. 50. Romney.

QUIZ 190 Movies

FOR ANSWERS SEE QUIZ NO 191

HARD - LEVEL THREE

1 Off which island is "Jaws" set?

2 Who played Harrison Ford's father in "Indiana Jones and the Last Crusade"?

3 Who is the cop battling with terrorists in "Die Hard"?

4 Which films are about the Corleone family?

5 What is Christopher Reeve's most famous role?

6 Who directed "Broken Arrow"?

7 In "Towering Inferno", what was Paul Newman?

8 Which was the first Bond movie?

9 Where was the Beverly Hills Cop based?

10 Who was Bad in Spaghetti Westerns?

11 Which was the first of the "Indiana Jones" films?

12 Which hero did Mel Gibson play in "Braveheart"?

13 In which city is "The Untouchables" set?

14 Who was involved in the writing of "Rocky" and "Rambo"?

15 Which was the first Bond film with Roger Moore?

16 Who played the starring role in "Last of the Mohicans"?

17 Who directed "Lawrence of Arabia"?

18 Which film starred Harrison Ford as an ex-CIA man?

19 For what did Kevin Costner win an Oscar in "Dances with Wolves"?

20 Which was George Lazenby's only Bond film?

21 Who starred as Jake La Motta in "Raging Bull"?

22 Which Clint Eastwood film won an Oscar for Gene Hackman?

23 Who played Bonnie to Warren Beatty's Clyde?

24 Who co-starred with Michael Douglas in "Romancing the Stone"?

25 What was the memorable, and at that time innovative, scene in "Bullitt"?

26 Which Bond film had the song "Nobody Does It Better"?

27 In which film did John Wayne win his only Oscar?

28 Which movie preceded "Magnum Force" and "The Enforcer"?

29 Who plays "Rob Roy"?

30 Who plays Miss Moneypenny?

31 In which film does Robert De Niro ask "are you talkin' to me?"?

32 Who wrote the book on which "The Russia House" was based?

33 Whom was the Jackal trying to assassinate in " The Day of the Jackal"?

34 Which president is being referred to in "All the President's Men"?

35 Who won an Oscar for "The Accused"?

36 Where does the action of "Predator" take place?

37 What is Hitchcock said to have used for the blood in "Psycho"?

38 Which three actors have each played Hannay in "The 39 Steps"?

39 Who played the role of Donald Woods in "Cry Freedom"?

40 What sort of establishment is the setting for "The China Syndrome"?

41 For which film did the reviewer write "Enough to make you kick the next pigeon you come across"?

42 What relation is Carter to Cain in "Raising Cain"?

43 On whose novel is the Sissy Spacek film "Carrie" based?

44 Who play the getaways in the remake of "The Getaway"?

45 What is the relationship between Tippi Hedren and Melanie Griffith?

46 What does Bridget Fonda advertise for and get Jennifer Jason Leigh?

47 In which classic film do Mrs Danvers and Maxim de Winter appear?

48 Whose "Fatal Attraction" to Glenn Close cost him dear?

49 For which film did Steven Spielberg win his first Oscar as Director?

50 Who were the first performers to win the Best Actor and Actress Oscars in the same film after Henry Fonda and Katharine Hepburn in 1981?

Answers to Quiz 189, POT LUCK

1. Kestrel for a Knave, by Barry Hines (Kes). 2. Pam Shriver. 3. Bank of England. 4. Ballet (dance). 5. A Zulu. 6. Billy Fury. 7. Green. 8. India. 9. Everything swirls around. 10. Brass. 11. Yankee Doodle. 12. Passport to Pimlico. 13. Shrewsbury. 14. Tug of war. 15. Dance. 16. Green/blue-green. 17. Russian Revolution. 18. Sir Walter Raleigh. 19. Eleven. 20. Heavyweight. 21. Charlotte Brontë. 22. Belgrade. 23. Brandy. 24. North America. 25. Set of bells. 26. 7. 27. September. 28. Matador. 29. Holds two ordinary bottles. 30. Paradine. 31. Genesis. 32. A space. 33. Crab. 34. Richard Burton. 35. Belgium. 36. The Importance of Being Earnest. 37. In your foot. 38. Paperback Writer. 39. Places of the same height. 40. The parson. 41. Beauty. 42. Laurel and Hardy. 43. Swan. 44. B. 45. Joe Louis. 46. China. 47. British admirals. 48. Long-distance running. 49. Charles. 50. The Merchant of Venice.

Quiz 191 Pot Luck

1 The River Ganges is a holy place for the followers of which religion?

2 What is the name for the home of an eagle?

3 Where was Robbie Burns born in Ayrshire?

4 Which Shakespearian play takes place in Illyria?

5 Which two leaders had a meeting in the Brenner Pass in World War II?

6 Tom Thumb, Tennis Ball and Winter Density are all types of what?

7 Which flower is particularly associated with Mary, the Madonna?

8 On which Yorkshire moor was a battle fought on July 2nd, 1644?

9 Which music hall comedian was known as the "Cheeky Chappie"?

10 In which industry was Lord Nuffield a pioneer?

11 Which word describes architecture dating from the time of James I?

12 What word describes the minimum number of members on a committee in attendance for it to reach valid decisions?

13 Who composed the "Thunder and Lightning" Polka?

14 Which war was fought in the Far East from 1950 to 1953?

15 What type of animal is a Kerry Blue?

16 In which year was the evacuation of Dunkirk?

17 Which German pianist took a walk in the Black Forest in the 1960s?

18 What does an anemometer measure?

19 What is a filbert?

20 Which strait links the Black Sea and the Sea of Marmara?

21 What does a lexicographer write or make?

22 What was the name of the prison in "Porridge"?

23 Who or what live in a holt?

24 Which city was once known as Eboracum?

25 In 1915, which British liner was sunk by a German submarine?

26 "Match of the Day" has been used as a TV title for soccer and which other sport?

27 By what name is mid-Lent Sunday popularly known?

28 In ads, what is Homepride's head chef called?

29 Of the Seven Wonders of the World, where was the Colossus?

30 Which gorge is crossed by the Clifton suspension bridge?

31 What are Steadman triples, Plain Bob Caters and Gransire triples?

32 What kind of animal is a chamois?

33 In which African country is the

386

city of Ibadan?

34 Which part of the body would be affected by astigmatism?

35 For what is Oberammergau famous?

36 Which city is the administrative headquarters of Cumbria?

37 Which actress/dancer's real name was Virginia McMath?

38 Where in your body is the frontal bone?

39 On which day does the Church celebrate Jesus entering Jerusalem?

40 Which Berlin hit advertised a car?

41 Who wrote "The Dancing Years" and "King's Rhapsody"?

42 What is the collective noun to describe a number of nightingales?

43 With which holy city is the name Zion associated?

44 Which Scandinavian animals are famous for running over cliffs?

45 Before he became a disciple of Jesus, what was Matthew's job?

46 What does road sign with a white capital letter R on a green background indicate?

47 Boswell wrote the biography of which famous writer?

48 Ophelia appears in which Shakespeare play?

49 To what does the adjective crepuscular refer?

50 In Australia, what animal is a jumbuck?

A nswers to Quiz 190, MOVIES

1. Long Island. 2. Sean Connery. 3. Bruce Willis. 4. The Godfather. 5. Superman. 6. John Woo. 7. The architect. 8. Dr No. 9 Detroit. 10. Lee Van Cleef. 11. Raiders of the Lost Ark. 12. William Wallace. 13. Chicago. 14. Stallone. 15. Live and Let Die. 16. Daniel Day-Lewis. 17. David Lean. 18. Patriot Games. 19. Directing. 20. On Her Majesty's Secret Service. 21. De Niro. 22. Unforgiven. 23. Faye Dunaway. 24. Kathleen Turner. 25. Car chase. 26. The Spy Who Loved Me. 27. True Grit. 28. Dirty Harry. 29. Liam Neeson. 30. Lois Maxwell. 31.Taxi Driver. 32. John Le Carré. 33. Charles de Gaulle. 34. Richard Nixon. 35. Jodie Foster. 36. South America. 37. Chocolate sauce. 38. Robert Donat, Kenneth More, Robert Powell. 39. Kevin Kline. 40. Nuclear power plant. 41. The Birds. 42. Twin brother. 43. Stephen King's. 44. Alec Baldwin and Kim Basinger. 45. Mother and daughter. 46. Single White Female. 47. Rebecca. 48. Michael Douglas. 49. Schindler's List. 50. Anthony Hopkins and Jodie Foster.

QUIZ 192 | Technology

HARD - LEVEL THREE

1 Who discovered radio waves?

2 Who gave his name to a unit of radioactivity?

3 Which scientist proposed that the Earth orbited the Sun?

4 Who is best known for his theory of black holes?

5 On what did Hahn, Meitner and Strassman work?

6 In which branch of mathematics was Hipparchus a pioneer?

7 Which Baron of Largs gave his name to the degrees on the absolute scale?

8 What does Hans Geiger's Geiger counter detect?

9 Whose process decarbonized iron?

10 Which tracking device did Sir Robert Watson-Watt develop?

11 Of what did Crick, Watson and Wilkins determine the structure?

12 Who formulated a law of electromagnetism ?

13 Which French philosopher created analytical geometry?

14 Which English chemist discovered the most elements?

15 Which virus was Robert Gallo one of the first to identify?

16 Which English physicist discovered the neutron?

17 What did Edward Teller develop?

18 What sort of tube did William Crookes invent?

19 Who gave his name to the law that states that the pressure of gas is proportional to its volume?

20 Which physicist gave his name to the law of induction?

21 In terms of Nobel prizes how did Marie Curie achieve two "firsts"?

22 Which physicist was also a civil rights campaigner?

23 Which German-born rocket engineer worked on the space programme?

24 Which aids to calculation did John Napier devise?

25 Which two elements did the Curies discover?

26 Leibnitz's calculating machine was the first to perform which function?

27 Which word was Candolle the first to use in plant classification?

28 For which measuring system did Joseph Louis Lagrange lay the foundations?

29 Which Islands inspired Darwin write "The Origin of Species"?

30 For which Soviet development was Igor Kurchatov team leader?

31 Which country was the first to legalize trade unions?

32 In which decade was British Petroleum privatized?

33 Which product did Proctor & Gamble launch in 1969?

34 Where did one of the worst industrial accidents take place in 1984?

388

35	Along with Corn Flakes which cereal did Kellogg's export to the UK in 1922?
36	What name is given to an alloy that joins surfaces together?
37	Which company's first computer, the 701, was produced in 1953?
38	Which company's red-triangle trademark was the first to be registered?
39	Which industrialist became first Lord Mayor of Dublin in 1851?
40	Who invented and marketed a vehicle powered by a washing-machine motor?
41	Which company did Israel Moses Sieff develop?
42	The jelly Vaseline was a bi-product from which industry?
43	Which convenience product was launched from its factory in St Andrews Road, Walthamstow?
44	Which London retailer sold the first Heinz products in the UK?
45	Who formed the Electric Suction Sweeper Co. in 1908?
46	How is a complex electronic circuit built on a small piece of silicon more commonly known?
47	Which two companies first developed the compact disc?
48	Who founded the British and North American Royal Mail Steam Packet Company which later bore his name?
49	Fred Dibnah was famous in which industry?
50	Which company introduced travellers' cheques?

Answers to Quiz 191, Pot Luck

1. Hinduism. 2. Eyrie. 3. Alloway. 4. Twelfth Night. 5. Hitler and Mussolini. 6. Lettuce. 7. Lilies. 8. Marston Moor. 9. Max Miller. 10. Motor car manufacturing. 11. Jacobean. 12. Quorum. 13. Johann Strauss the Younger. 14. Korean War. 15. Dog. 16. 1940. 17. Horst Jankowski. 18. Wind speed. 19. A hazelnut. 20. The Bosporus. 21. Dictionaries. 22. HMP Slade. 23. Otters. 24. York. 25. Lusitania. 26. Tennis. 27. Mothering Sunday. 28. Fred. 29. Rhodes. 30. The Avon Gorge. 31. Ways of ringing church bells. 32. Goat. 33. Nigeria. 34. Eye. 35. Its passion play (held every ten years). 36. Carlisle. 37. Ginger Rogers. 38. Forehead. 39. Palm Sunday. 40. Take My Breath Away. 41. Ivor Novello. 42. A watch. 43. Jerusalem. 44. Lemmings. 45. Tax collector. 46. Ring road. 47. Dr Samuel Johnson. 48. Hamlet. 49. Evening. 50. Sheep.

Q_{UIZ} 193 Pot Luck

HARD - LEVEL THREE

1. Of which country is Freetown the capital?
2. What is the term for a group of partridges?
3. What was the occupation of the legendary "Casey Jones"?
4. According to the proverb what is the mother of invention?
5. What is an area of water separated from the open sea by a coral reef?
6. In cricket how many balls are there in an over?
7. In the London theatre what is the longest-running play ever?
8. Which toilet roll ad features a Labrador puppy?
9. In astronomy what are falling stars properly called?
10. What are Hickling, Barton, and Breydon Water?
11. In 1989, which electronic giant bought Columbia Pictures?
12. What is meant by the Italian phrase "che sara sara"?
13. What does an American mean when he talks of a check in a restaurant?
14. Whom might you expect to see working in a dig?
15. If a ship runs up a yellow flag what does it mean?
16. Which is the smallest bird in the world?
17. Which Saint's day falls on 30 November?
18. In fiction who lived in the stables at Birtwick Hall?
19. Who was Oberon?
20. Can you name a hydrocarbon fuel?
21. In cookery, what is meant by coddling?
22. Which trade is especially likely to use an awl?
23. What was pioneered by the Austrian physician Dr Mesmer?
24. In World War II on what were we "going to hang out the washing"?
25. In which city was there formerly a parliament building called the Reichstag?
26. In which London building is the Whispering Gallery?
27. Which duo have produced songs for Tottenham Hotspur?
28. With which ceremony do we associate orange blossom?
29. What name was given to an airship that could be steered?
30. According to the ad, what couldn't Ian Botham eat three of?
31. If VAT is 17.5% what is the VAT on an item costing £2?
32. In which county are the Brecon Beacons?
33. Whose real name is Georgius Panayiotou?
34. Where would you find treads and risers close together?
35. As what did Henri Fabre achieve

fame?

36 Whose official residence is Lambeth Palace?

37 Who was advertised as the patron saint of pipe smokers?

38 What are woofers and tweeters?

39 Which former "Coronation Street" star is comedian Duggie Brown's sister?

40 What is meant by "sotto voce"?

41 In which ocean is the Sargasso Sea?

42 What are made by wainwrights?

43 What do Catholics call the string of beads they use when praying?

44 Who painted the most famous version of "The Last Supper"?

45 What is the subject matter covered by a Gibbons's catalogue?

46 What happens when red litmus paper is put in an alkaline solution?

47 Who wrote the novel "Gone with the Wind"?

48 Which naturalist is the author of "My Family and Other Animals"?

49 What word is used for the science dealing with the body structure?

50 What is a coup d'état?

A nswers to Quiz 192, TECHNOLOGY

1. Hertz. 2. Becquerel. 3. Copernicus. 4. Stephen Hawking. 5. Nuclear fission. 6. Trigonometry. 7. Kelvin. 8. Atomic particles. 9. Bessemer. 10. Radar. 11. DNA. 12. Ampère. 13. Descartes. 14. Davy 15. HIV 16. Chadwick. 17. Hydrogen bomb. 18. Cathode ray tube. 19. Boyle. 20. Faraday. 21. First woman. First person to receive it twice. 22. Andrei Sakharov. 23. Werner von Braun. 24. Logarithms. 25. Polonium, radium. 26. Multiply. 27. Taxonomy. 28 Metric. 29. Galapagos. 30. Explosion of the atomic bomb. 31. Britain. 32. 1950s. 33. Ariel. 34. Bhopal, India. 35. All Bran. 36. Solder. 37. IBM. 38. Bass brewery. 39. Guinness. 40. Clive Sinclair. 41. Marks and Spencer. 42. Petroleum. 43. Andrex toilet roll. 44. Fortnum & Mason. 45. William Hoover. 46. Microchip. 47. Philips and Sony. 48. Cunard. 49. Steeplejack. 50. American Express.

QUIZ 194 | Politics

HARD - LEVEL THREE

1   How long is a Member of Parliament elected for?

2   In which year in the 1970s were there two general elections?

3   How many general elections had the Liberal Democrats contested by 1995?

4   Who has been MP for Old Bexley-Sidcup (Bexley) since 1950?

5   Who became deputy prime minister after the 1995 Tory leadership election?

6   Who was Britain's first black woman MP?

7   Which MP starred in the film "Women in Love"?

8   Who became Labour leader after the 1992 election defeat?

9   Which future PM failed to win Dartford for the Tories in 1950 and 1951?

10   Which two Davids headed the Alliance party in 1983?

11   Which prime minister's father was a trapeze artist?

12   The House of Commons consists of how many members?

13   Which Essex seat was won by Tory David Amess against all predictions in 1992?

14   Who gave up the title of Viscount Stansgate to remain an MP?

15   Which MP is the son in law of Alf Garnett's son in law?

16   Which MP takes his dog into the House of Commons?

17   Which MP's father starred in the film classic "The Blue Lamp"?

18   Who wrote the novel "A Parliamentary Affair"?

19   Who resigned as a minister over the Sara Keays affair?

20   Which party won the general election in 1945?

21   Which former minister presented "Six O Six" on Radio 5 Live ?

22   Name the 1992 Tory party chairman who lost his Bath seat?

23   Which former deputy Labour leader, whose father was once a Catholic priest, stood down after the 1992 General Election?

24   What was Norman Tebbitt's job before entering Parliament?

25   Which party did Screaming Lord Sutch represent?

26   Who became deputy Labour leader after the 1992 General Election?

27   Who turned from blue to yellow in December 1995?

28   What did the Ecology party change its name to in 1985?

29   What was Dennis Skinner's job before he entered Parliament?

30   Which MP won gold medals at the 1980 and 1984 Olympics?

31   Who was the first Tory leader to have gone to a grammar school?

32   In the 70s who was the Minister for Drought?

33 In 1997 David Blunket won which constituency?

34 What was the name of Harold Wilson's wife?

35 Who published the white paper "In Place Of Strife"?

36 Mrs Thatcher became Baroness Thatcher of where?

37 Which Tory Scottish Secretary lost his seat in 1997?

38 Who was deputy prime minister when Harold Macmillan resigned?

39 Who threw herself under the king's horse at the 1913 Derby?

40 What was the Tory slogan on posters of a queue of the unemployed?

41 Who first became prime minister - Gladstone or Disraeli?

42 To two years, when did John Major first win Huntingdon?

43 Who lost the Labour leadership to Michael Foot in 1980?

44 What was the name of the male model in the Jeremy Thorpe affair?

45 Prime Minister Arthur James Balfour belonged to which party?

46 Dennis Skinner is known as the Beast of where?

47 Who followed Anthony Crossland as Labour's Foreign Secretary?

48 Who said that Gorbachev was "a man we can do business with"?

49 Who was Labour leader when the red rose appeared?

50 Which politician created the police force?

1. Sierra Leone. 2. A covey. 3. Railroad engineer. 4. Necessity. 5. Lagoon. 6. Six. 7. The Mousetrap. 8. Andrex. 9. Meteors. 10. Norfolk Broads. 11. Sony. 12. What ever will be, will be. 13. The bill. 14. Archaeologist. 15. No disease aboard, and it needs clearance. 16. Humming bird. 17. St Andrew. 18. Black Beauty. 19. King of the fairies. 20. Coal, gas, oil. 21. Simmering briefly. 22. Leather worker/shoemaker. 23. Hypnotism. 24. Siegfried Line. 25. Berlin. 26. St Paul's. 27. Chas & Dave. 28. Weddings. 29. Dirigible. 30. Shredded Wheat. 31. 35p. 32. Powys. 33. George Michael. 34. On a staircase. 35. Naturalist, entomologist. 36. Archbishop of Canterbury. 37. St Bruno. 38. Loudspeakers. 39. Lynne Perrie (Ivy Brennan). 40. In a low voice. 41. Atlantic. 42. Wagons, carts. 43. Rosary. 44. Leonardo. 45. Postage stamps. 46. It turns blue. 47. Margaret Mitchell. 48. Gerald Durrell. 49. Anatomy. 50. Seizure of power.

QUIZ 195 | Pot Luck

HARD - LEVEL THREE

1 According to the proverb, what is better than no bread?

2 What kind of animal is a Persian Blue?

3 Who composed the opera "Carmen"?

4 On a ship or boat what is a painter?

5 What kind of food is gazpacho?

6 Where in London is the statue of Peter Pan?

7 Who had a hit with "This Little Bird"?

8 In geometry, what is meant by concentric?

9 Which wooden puppet was first written about by Carlo Collodi?

10 In which of Dickens's novels does Sam Weller appear?

11 Which food, not rationed during World War II, was rationed after it?

12 In which year did Sir Winston Churchill die?

13 What is the name of the marmalade cat created by Kathleen Hale?

14 For what is the Médoc area of France famous?

15 What are Cheshire, Gouda and Gorgonzola?

16 How is Cherilyn La Pier better known?

17 As what did Beau Brummel achieve fame?

18 Which country used to have a coin called a bawbee?

19 Who was the first presenter of "Family Fortunes"?

20 What do we call what the Italians call pesce?

21 In London, the Cambridge, the Lyric and the Adelphi are all what?

22 Of which country was Field-Marshall Smuts prime minister?

23 Which religious writer was born in Elstow, near Bedford?

24 What word can go after salad and before gown?

25 In which year was the Gunpowder Plot?

26 Who wrote the novels "Sons and Lovers" and "The Rainbow"?

27 What does a chandler make?

28 Which metal do we make from bauxite?

29 Black, Whooper, and Bewick are all types of which bird?

30 What is a golden hello?

31 In which country did the poets Keats and Shelley both die?

32 How many tusks does a warthog have?

33 What is the nearest star to the solar system?

34 Who wrote "Porgy and Bess"?

35 Who was king of France at the time of the French Revolution?

36 Which card game has two forms, called auction and contract?

37 In which country does the Amazon rise?

394

38 Graphite is composed of which element?

39 In ads, which sign meant "happy motoring"?

40 What can be seen from Earth only once every 76 years?

41 Who was prime minister of Australia from 1983 to 1991?

42 Where was the Mount Pinatubo eruption?

43 Who burned his guitar at the Monterey Pop Festival in 1967?

44 What is brighter than a hundred million suns?

45 Who became potter to King George III in 1806?

46 What does "m" stand for in Einstein's equation $E=mc^2$?

47 Which sign of the zodiac is represented as a man pouring water from a jug?

48 Who preferred "50,000 rifles to 50,000 votes"?

49 Who devised the modern system for naming and classifying plants and animals?

50 Whose fan did Oscar Wilde write about?

A nswers to Quiz 194, POLITICS

1. Five years. 2. 1974. 3. Two. 4. Edward Heath. 5. Michael Heseltine. 6. Diane Abbott. 7. Glenda Jackson. 8. John Smith. 9. Margaret Roberts (later Thatcher). 10. Owen and Steel. 11. John Major's. 12. 651. 13. Basildon. 14. Tony Benn. 15. Tony Blair. 16. David Blunkett. 17. Jeremy Hanley. 18. Edwina Currie. 19. Cecil Parkinson. 20. Labour. 21. David Mellor. 22. Chris Patten. 23. Roy Hattersley. 24. Airline pilot. 25. Monster Raving Loony party. 26. Margaret Beckett. 27. Emma Nicholson. 28. Green party. 29. Miner. 30. Sebastian Coe. 31. Ted Heath. 32. Denis Howell. 33. Sheffield Brightside. 34. Mary. 35. Barbara Castle. 36. Kesteven. 37 Michael Forsyth. 38. Rab Butler. 39. Emily Davison. 40. Labour isn't working. 41. Disraeli. 42. 1983. 43. Denis Healey. 44. Norman Scott. 45. Conservative. 46 Bolsover. 47. David Owen. 48. Margaret Thatcher. 49. Neil Kinnock. 50. Robert Peel.

Q UIZ 196 | The Royals

HARD - LEVEL THREE

1 How many times had Wallis Simpson been married before she married Edward VIII?

2 When she married in 1973 who was Princess Anne's bridesmaid?

3 Which prince's last three names are Charles Albert David?

4 What colour was the suit Diana Spencer wore in her engagement photograph in 1981?

5 What is the name of the Princess Royal's second husband?

6 What was Prince Philip's father called?

7 Which Scottish school did Prince Charles go to?

8 What did the Queen agree to pay for the first time in 1992?

9 Who created Princess Elizabeth's wedding dress in 1947?

10 Who interviewed the Princess of Wales when on "Panorama"?

11 Who was the Duchess of York's financial adviser in 1992?

12 In what capacity was Mrs Susan Barrantes invited to the wedding of Prince Andrew and Sarah Ferguson?

13 Whom did Katharine Worsley marry in 1961?

14 Who is the former Serena Stanhope's mother-in-law?

15 Where is the Prince of Wales' home in Gloucestershire?

16 Which organization did Prince Charles set up in 1976?

17 Who is the Queen's second eldest grandchild?

18 Who is Mrs Frances Shand-Kydd?

19 Who is Earl of Chester?

20 Which opera singer sang at the wedding of Charles and Diana?

21 Who designed Diana Spencer's wedding dress?

22 Whose Christian names are Elizabeth Angela Marguerite?

23 Who is the Duke of Kent's sister?

24 Who was known as Uncle Dickie?

25 Which princess's first names are Marie Christine?

26 What is the Princess of Wales' brother's first name?

27 Royal wedding rings are made from gold from which country?

28 Which coloured stone was in Fergie's engagement ring?

29 Who as a child was known to her family as Lilibet?

30 Which branch of the armed forces did Prince Edward briefly join in 1986?

31 Who did Prince William invite to a parents' event at Eton in 1997?

32 Who is the first female in line to the throne?

33 Which King (name and number) was the subject of a 1995 film?

34 Who are the parents of Lady Helen Taylor?

35 Who played John Brown when